THE MOTHER OF GOD

Healing
and liberation
through fasting

Collaborators: **Sr. Emmanuel Maillard and Fr. Giuseppe Cionchi**

Translator: **Paula Wade-Muzic B.A.Th.**

© Shalom Editors - 24.06.2006 St. John the Baptist

ISBN   9 7 8 - 8 8 - 8 4 0 4 - 1 0 4 - 3
To order this book please cite the code 8355

TOTUS TUUS

For orders please contact:

Editrice Shalom

Via San Giuseppe, 57
60020 Camerata Picena (An)

Tel. 0039 071. 74 50 440 r.a.

Monday to Friday From 9 to 7pm

Mir Editors

d.o.o. Medjugorje bb 88260
Bosna i Hercegovina

Tel. 00387 36. 65 17 16

If you would like to take a souvenir from Medjugorje home
with you, you will find rosary beads, crosses, medals, holy
images, books and lots of other objects in our shop.

Index

Introduction

To fast means to accept an essential aspect of Christian life. For it is vital to enter into the corporal element of our faith. To abstain from food is one of these aspects. Without virginity and fasting, the church is no longer what it should be because it conforms to the world around it... Besides in this world where many die from hunger, we need to bear a collective loving witness of free renunciation from food.

Card. Joseph Ratzinger

We cannot begin to understand Blessed Cardinal Stepinac in his life of heroic sanctity and martyrdom without first knowing his mother, Barbara. This woman prayed the rosary daily and fasted three days a week, (Monday, Wednesday and Friday) so that Alojsije would become a priest. She never said it to her son however in order not to influence his choice. In July 1931, Fr. Alojsije returned to his village, Krasic, to celebrate his first Christmas Mass, after his ordination in Rome. The Parish Priest said to his mother that she could finally give up fasting. "Absolutely not", she replied. "Now I must fast and pray much more so that he will become a holy priest." This is the secret power of prayer and fasting, of the family and of the love of a Mother. This woman had completely understood the value and the meaning of fasting which is authentic only when it is sustained by prayer and love of the Lord. She can be a reference point for us who seek to understand fasting. We will look at its' foundations in Orthodox Catholicism and its presence in the lives of the saints. It will also lead us to offer our 'yes' to the experience of fasting.

It seems that in the world there is more and more talk of therapeutic fasting or dieting which will alter our state of obesity, prevent obesity or prevent various illnesses which are provoked precisely by overeating or over-drinking. There are also diets to improve our appearance and our physical well-being. Here however, we would like to present fasting as a way of healing souls.

Perhaps you will feel that this is all exaggerated, the idea that one should fast twice a week on bread and water, Wednesdays and Fridays, especially in these times when all trace of fasting seems to have disappeared from the Church. Only Ash Wednesday and Good Friday remain.

But even these two days have lost their true practice and significance.

Sometimes we will be convinced that it is actually impossible or unfeasible and yet the Mother of God has told us that only through fasting and prayer will we be assured of a better life, a peaceful life. Choose the experience of fasting as an act of love of God and you will discover how much good it does to fast, for the body as well as the soul.

We dedicate this first edition to Christine Zaums, a young American girl who as we write is fasting Monday Wednesday and Friday for a special intention of ours.

Healing and liberation through fasting

Teaching on Fasting

by Sr. Emmanuel Maillard

Would you dive?

Let's start with this question to test your reaction: suppose you were walking alongside a river on a freezing day in December.

Suddenly you hear screams - a small child two years old is drowning! If you don't go to his rescue, he will surely die. What do you do? Do you dive into the freezing cold water or remain motionless?

Of course you will dive into the river to save him. You cannot let the child die when you have the means to save his life; and it is so simple to just dive in! Fasting follows the same principle. It enables us to save lives by preventing young people from committing suicide, keeping children from dying and saving families from falling apart. Unfortunately, for the last half-century we have abandoned fasting in the West, (this is not the case in the East) generating terrible destruction to our bodily and spiritual health.

Have you noticed the correlation between giving

up fasting in the West and being infested with Satan and his demons?

Today, Satan can more easily penetrate various facets of society-even coming within the confines of the Church. Because when we do not fast, the protective doors are no longer locked!

Our Lady, in Medjugorje, issues a cry for help and a cry of distress; not for her sake but for ours. She says, "You have abandoned fasting!" Through the visionaries, the Blessed Mother has taught us five fundamental points to practice that are basic in our path towards God. Most often fasting is the one point people do not want to consider.

It is the "rejected message". I can go anywhere in the world and meet people who are fervent devotees of Medjugorje. I see that they live the other four points very well: attending Mass, reading the bible, going to confession, reciting the Rosary. However, when I question them about fasting, they look down and don't answer because they have given up fasting. We have not understood what fasting is! Combined with the other four points, it allows us to reach sainthood; with it, we can attain the fullness of God's love and defeat Satan. Our Lady discloses the meaning and beauty of fasting as the power of God working through us, a potent instrument in our hands that can work extraordinary wonders for us and obtain the things that we need.

Two days out of seven

Fasting is part of the Jewish tradition and the Christian tradition, as well as several other religious traditions. Today, Our Blessed Mother in Medjugorje asks us to fast Wednesdays and Fridays on bread and water. In the first Century, even Our Lady fasted two days a week with St. Joseph, Jesus and all the pious Jews. Isn't it incredible to think that the Blessed Mother is reinstating this dynamic tradition from the very early Church in which she herself lived!

Why on those specific two days? To unearth the roots of this practice we must turn to Jesus' first disciples who wrote about life and culture during the first Century.

The "Didache", an ancient Church document dating from approximately 90 A.D. (Christian Sources), was written by the first disciples and notes that: "The hypocrites (the Pharisees) fast on the 2nd and 5th days (Mondays and Thursdays), but we (Christians) fast on the 4th and 6th days (Wednesdays and Fridays)." Thus, in Medjugorje, Mary has us returning to the original days of fasting.

In the 80's, Mary selected young people from the village to form a prayer group whom she led and trained in the Faith. While Gospa has not fully explained the reason she asks us to fast specifically on Wednesday and Friday in Her messages to the world, members of the prayer group tell us that everything Our Lady asks has only one goal: to reveal Jesus. She comes because of Jesus, to help us love Jesus and to bring us closer to Jesus' heart.

How does fasting on Wednesday and Friday bring us closer to Jesus?

A few members of the prayer group disclosed to us Mary's request that every Thursday of the year we venerate the gift of the Eucharist and the Priesthood.

One way to live this veneration is by fasting with love on Wednesday and Friday. We remember in joy, in faith and in thanksgiving that Jesus gave His Body and His Blood to us as food and drink. Our Lady is so much in love with the Eucharist, (the Bread of Life), that she gives us all day Wednesday to prepare ourselves for this commemoration. It does not mean that we should attend Holy Mass only on Thursday! Starting on Wednesday, she wants to eliminate the distractions of food, grocery shopping, cooking and the worries related to food. That way, since Jesus chose bread to be transformed into His Body, we become immersed in the flavor of bread, the bread that will become the real Body of Jesus. On Wednesdays, we should not think, "I can't wait to eat." Rather, if we start to fast with joy and with the heart we begin enjoying the reality of bread. We prepare ourselves like the Hebrews in the desert during the Exodus. God gave them manna, the bread that came down from heaven. He was preparing His people to receive the mystery of the Eucharist. In the same manner, Our Blessed Mother is preparing us today. On Thursday we celebrate and commemorate the institution of the Bread of Life.

When I listen to the visionaries in Medjugorje I am always surprised to learn that Our Lady never mentioned fasting on Friday as a remembrance of Christ's death on the cross.

They never mention that! Instead, Friday is the day after Thursday. Our Blessed Mother doesn't want us to quickly return to the distractions of food. She wants us to remain focused and not go right back to lobster bisque, chicken a la king, prime rib and all those special dishes.

On Friday, she wants us to savor the taste of bread and remain immersed in His mystery as long as possible. It's the same attitude the Jews have towards the Sabbath day. It is their holiest feast day, and when the sun sets on Saturday evening at the end of the Sabbath, Jews continue to sing and recite hymns as if they could keep the Sabbath from ending. To the Jewish people, the Sabbath day is like a fiancé to his beloved - they just don't want to let it go! Similarly, when we fast on Fridays we do it to savor the taste of bread as long as possible, the bread that reminds us of the Bread of Life.

I always imagine the Virgin Mary remaining on earth after the Ascension among the apostles. When she entered into the kitchen, after the last supper, how could she look at bread as she had before the Last Supper? As soon as she saw bread, something must have made her motherly heart throb. No doubt she thought, "My Son lost Himself in bread. This is the substance that became my Son!"

When we look at a single grain of wheat from which bread is made, we have before us the whole story of Christ, the story of the Redeemer. When Jesus speaks about the grain of wheat in the Gospel, we see that the grain of wheat must fall on the ground, be buried and die. It is through this death that life will come again and produce fruit in abundance - thirty-fold, sixty-fold, or one-hundred-fold. This is the whole story of the death and resurrection of Christ, and of the fruit of His Redemption. For the grain of wheat to become bread, it has to be crushed to produce flour. Jesus also was crushed: His body, His heart, His soul, His whole Divine Being. The story of the grain embodies the story of Jesus' love for us. He let Himself be crushed so that we might be nourished by Him and sanctified through His food. When Jesus spoke about the Bread of Life He said, "He who eats this bread will have Eternal Life."

Loving the Eucharist

That's why we can welcome Wednesdays and Fridays with love for bread, with love for our Redemption. The Blessed Mother wishes to engross us in it, not only spiritually, but also in practice. As a very sensible Jewish woman, she immerses us in bread so that we almost have to be with Jesus. Through fasting, she focuses our attention on the loving presence of Jesus. She allows us to marvel at the fact that, in an utmost gesture of humility, Jesus transformed Himself into bread. Here, we have the real meaning of fasting: it is a matter of loving the Eucharist.

Everything that she says and directs us to is centered on Jesus. And if we fast in this way, with a love for the Bread of Life, our fasting changes. It becomes a joy! This is why Our Lady says, "Dear Children, fast; but fast with the heart." We'll gain a great love for the Eucharist. And this is an incredible grace because as a great French mystic, Marthe Robin, said: "Our glory in heaven will be proportional to the fervor we put into our Holy Communions on earth." The more we receive the Bread of Life with care, love and deep gratitude, the greater our glory will be in heaven.

The Body

The moment we offer God something related to our body, we can say that we are truly giving ourselves. It's easy to give money, time, a good word, or offer our services, but fasting affects something vital, food. Food is a matter of survival. It affects our profound ontological and metaphysical habits. As Father Slavko Barbaric advised during his fasting retreats, "Fasting reveals our dependencies, our addictions. When fasting on bread and water, there are flashing signals that light up: Coffee! Cigarettes! Wine! Chocolate!" But the Blessed Mother doesn't come to point out our attachments and make us feel bad. Rather, she wants us freed and liberated when we realize how dependent we are on our daily routine. An English lady founded a community at the request of Our Lady. One day I asked her if Our Lady had asked their members to fast.

"Yes," she answered. "Our Lady asked us to fast everyday."

"Everyday?" I gasped. "That's impossible"

"We fast everyday from 4:00 to 6:00 p.m."

I laughed to myself and seeing the smirk on my face she explained, "We British have grown up having our tea-time from 4:00 to 6:00 p.m. every day." If we take tea-time away from an Englishman, his identity is affected - he is detached from his child-hood traditions and his national identity.

When I started fasting on bread and water, my first discovery was the joy it gave me to have freedom from food. It didn't matter whether I ate or not. Giving of our bodies is a sign of having really given ourselves to God. Fasting creates a vacuum that liberates a space in our souls, in our bodies and in our hearts.

When we are not worried about eating, there is a free space where God comes to dwell as never before.

This is new tangible territory within ourselves that God can invest in. This is why those who fast have a special spiritual sensitivity and sharpness.

During their missions, it did not matter to the Apostles whether they had time to eat or not. Their utmost concern was working intensely for God.

A friend of mine from Mexico once told me that she stopped fasting for one year because she was pregnant. During that year she lost a certain "feeling" or ability to explain about life and the realities of life to her children.

Her words just didn't hit home! As soon as she started fasting again, she was suddenly inspired by the Holy Spirit to speak on their level, to their understanding. Words came to her spontaneously and the children listened to her with their hearts.

This is a nice example of how our fasting invites the Holy Spirit to occupy this new space in us and take over.

Through prayer and fasting we not only save one child, as we should by diving into a freezing river, even better.

By fasting on bread and water, we can save many lives without running the risk of catching pneumonia or getting sick.

In fact, studies have shown that in the West, we absorb one-third too many calories compared to what is necessary. Fasting can prevent many illnesses and premature deaths that are due to overeating.

Thus, fasting allows us to meaningfully consume fewer calories without dieting just to lose weight.

Two Weapons Against Satan: Prayer and Fasting

Why is Satan so weakened when we fast? Everything Our Lady teaches answers the struggles within our world today. The whole world needs our prayer and fasting because for millions of people, it is a matter of life and death. In her messages, Our Lady stresses that Satan wants to destroy families. Satan is enraged and aggressive, in Medjugorje especially, because he knows he has lost when we fast and pray.

Our Lady has shown us a few examples, locally, as if to illustrate the tremendous benefits of fasting on bread and water.

I remember during the war in 1992, we could hear the bombing all over Mostar, in Ljubuski, in Citluk and all around Medjugorje. We could see the bombs in the sky; we could hear the destruction and of course see on T.V. what was happening. By the pure grace of God, I remained in the village with my little community of the Beatitudes. On the 25th of April 1992, we received the first monthly message after the beginning of the war in Bosnia-Herzegovina. We were all expecting Our Lady to respond to the tragedy happening all around us. Everyone sought her nurturing words as a Mother. She said very clearly: *"Dear children! Only through prayer and fasting can wars be stopped"*. She could not have been clearer than that! She said, *"Only through prayer and fasting."* This means that if I have another approach, I must forget it!

This is especially important today because we are very often in the grips of evil. At the beginning of the apparitions, Mary was not talking about military wars, but wars within families. She says, "Today Satan is strong as never before." The culture of death has been implanted in the West. We don't have to look far to see the havoc that Satan causes in our families, in our children and especially in our young adults! Mary tells us that war starts in our hearts! If I feel hatred towards my brother, if I have closed my door to this or that person, if I have judged them harshly, if I have been jealous of them, if I've spoken ill of them, if I've harbored bitterness or resentment towards them, then there is a war inside my heart that comes through to the outside. These are the wars that Mary wants to remove from us. The only way to accomplish this is by fasting and praying! Many pilgrims come to Medjugorje, because their children are using drugs, have become prostitutes or are following a road leading to death. These parents ask me to intercede to the visionaries on their behalf. They ask that the visionaries pray so that their children stop taking drugs, stop becoming prostitutes, stop trying to fill the empty spaces in their hearts with distractions that are evil. After promising to pray for them, I ask them, "Have you fasted for your children?"

And they answer, "But I pray a lot, I do novenas, even to the precious blood of Christ, I recite the rosary..." Then I ask again, "But you are not answering my question, do you also fast?" They respond: "But I pray sister, I pray." I then remind them that Our Lady talked about wars that are being waged in their families and in the hearts of their children and these are the very wars that could destroy the life of their child. I then remind them that Mary has already given them the weapons to stop these wars - prayer and fasting.

Jesus also spoke in this manner: Do you remember when Jesus saw his disciples coming back from a mission? Normally they returned very happy and proud because the power of Christ was within them.

They said to the sick: "Be healed!" And the person was healed. They said to the crippled: "Get up!" and the cripple got up and ran. They said to the blind: "See!" And the blind saw. They were so happy to be with Christ. But one day it didn't work. So they came back to Jesus ashamed. And they said to Him: "Jesus, we tried to expel that unclean spirit, but we were unable. It just didn't work." And you know the answer of Jesus? "These demons can only be cast out by prayer and fasting." Now we have the key from Jesus himself.

Throughout the entire Bible we see the power of fasting. It is the same today. If you fast, Satan won't be able to harm you or your family. I do not say you won't suffer because the cross is a cross. But one thing is different- you can suffer without being harmed. Jesus did suffer, but Satan never got a hold of Him to harm Him.

In1992, the Blessed Mother said to Ivanka, "Dear children, I ask you to defeat Satan." One can't help but think, 'she is asking ME to defeat Satan. But who am I to defeat Satan?' We are children of God and she needs each one of us without exception. She says: *"Dear children, without you I cannot help the world. Each one is important."* And in the same message to Ivanka, Mary gives us the weapons to defeat Satan: "the weapons to defeat Satan are fasting and prayer. Pray for peace. Satan wants to destroy the little peace that you have."

During the first weeks of the apparitions, all the villagers listened attentively to each word of the Gospa. Then, about two months after the beginning of the apparitions, Our Lady said, "Satan has a plan of destruction for this parish. Dear children I ask for all the parishioners to fast on bread and water for three days and to say the rosary in order to defeat Satan". And everyone, united together, did what the Gospa asked. For three days, as if of one heart, they fasted and prayed that their Queen of Peace might crush the serpent's head. On the fourth day she said, *"Dear children, I thank you for your prayers and fasting. The plan of Satan has failed. We won!" She did not say, "I won."*

Rather, she said, "we won." She needed the people of the parish of Medjugorje to defeat Satan. The people made a very powerful sacrifice. Without it Satan's plan would have succeeded on that day and Medjugorje would have sunk. And today this river of blessings that is flowing from Medjugorje for 23 years would not exist. Without Medjugorje, how many lives might have perished? How many families might still be separated instead of now being united? How many young people might have committed suicide? Look at the good that Medjugorje has done for us because 500 people of that village, of that time, fought for three days to defeat Satan! God presented Medjugorje to the world and henceforth millions of pilgrims have come here to regain strength. Such is the impact of saying "YES" to fasting and prayer.

Through prayer, we are united to the soul of Jesus and the Holy Spirit creates an intimate dialogue between ourselves and God. We receive His words, His confidence and we listen to His voice. In confidence we speak our heart to Him, allowing an incredible unity between God and our soul. This union, received through fasting and dialogue, is of course the most powerful tool against Satan.

Parents who implore the healing of children, children who implore the reconciliation of parents, know that this powerful weapon is available, keeping in mind that none of the saints prayed without fasting and they certainly did not fast without praying.

Protection

Fasting also bears another fruit: protection. What parents do not want to protect their children and grandchildren? Today, people get life insurance, flood insurance, health insurance... but life insurance never stopped anyone from dying and accident insurance only goes into effect after the accident has taken place and only if it's not restricted by a random detail in fine print where coverage does not apply. Fasting insurance however, works before the "covered event" and prevents evil from harming a person. "Dear children I can do everything, and prevent Satan from attracting you to evil and draw him away from this place. Satan, dear children, is watching each one of you. It is particularly in the daily things that he wants to spread into each one of you."

I have to admit that I sometimes become angry when people say: "We shouldn't see Satan everywhere, we're not even sure that he exists. Our Lady's theology includes four statements: 1) he exists 2) he is stronger today than ever before 3) he is continually active and 4) his goal is to destroy us and to "destroy everything in us that is holy, to destroy nature and the planet on which we live." Our Lady also tells us: "Dear children see how with humble prayer we can disarm him". "We" here refers to Our Mother and us, her children.

If, as a mother, I have ten children at home and I know that there is a Satanist roaming outside trying to torture, rape and kill them, I need to warn them. If I don't and instead say, "Relax, feel good, go outside for a walk in the woods," then I am an accomplice to the murder of my children! We cannot hide from children the fact that spiritual combat exists. God is not the only actor, but there is also an enemy who lives in - yes, let's tell them - Hell.

Hell also exists. Jesus did not come to die on the

cross for the fun of it. He came to save us from evil and from Hell! Now it is no laughing matter that Jesus has sent His Mother to Medjugorje for so many years - to warn us that NOW is the time to convert! Because evil exists, because the enemy exists, because a sadistic murderer is indeed lurking around us, we must rely on Mary's messages for guidance and awareness. There is a reason why Mary tells us, "Dear children, Satan is watching out for each one of us, he wants to take you onto the road of sin and death." She is warning us for our lives today! The rate of suicides has never been so high. Even wars, illnesses and road accidents combined are responsible for fewer deaths than suicide. We steer clear of suicide when we protect ourselves with fasting insurance and prayer. It is through fasting and prayer that God can insure our protection. Because He is not a magician, He invites us to collaborate with Him. Aren't we one body with Him after all? "Pray as much as possible," she says. "Fast, persevere in prayer and sacrifices and I will protect you and I will answer your prayers." Our Lady sees how much we need to be protected! She tells us: "Dear children, with your help I can do everything." Imagine what that means! When we pray to Our Lady, do we really believe that anything is possible? We often believe like people who have a God that is neither powerful, nor really capable of helping us. If Mary tells us, "...with your help I can do everything," just imagine what can be accomplished through God's power!

After more than 24 years of protection, it is easy to take Our Lady's' messages for granted. We become cold to her exhortations. But in 2004, just as in 1988, she warned us again not to become lax in her messages. She said: "Dear children, Also today I call you to live my messages even more strongly in humility and love so that the Holy Spirit my fill you with His grace and strength. Only in this way will you be witnesses of peace and forgiveness. Thank you for having responded to my call." (April 25, 2004).

Purification of Evil

In Medjugorje, Mary invites us: "give to God all the evil that has accumulated within you, so that He may purify you from all the sins of your past. Only thus will you be able to recognize all the bad that is within you, and give it to the Lord so that he may purify you completely. So don't stop praying and prepare your hearts with sacrifices and fasting."

We have been committing sins since the time that we were able to choose and we have accumulated many of them over the years. Even after confessing our sins, we still suffer the consequences of those past sins. Through fasting, our hearts are being prepared so that she may heal us from the consequences of our sins. She is truly a mother to us! When a child falls and hurts himself, the mother takes care of him and relieves him of the consequences of his fall. Only the blood of Christ cleanses us from sin, but His Mother can repair the damages. By fasting we invite the Blessed Mother to heal us so that we may be purified more quickly.

Satan's suggestions

Jesus delivers us from past sins, and Our Lady restores our beauty. It makes the Evil One furious that we have made room for God in our bodies and souls and he is chased away by our fasting. Mary warned the prayer group in 1983, "Be careful because Satan tempts all those who have made the resolution to consecrate themselves to God. He will suggest to them that they are praying too much, they are fasting too much, that they must be like other young people and go in search of pleasures. Don't listen to him; don't obey him. When you are strengthened in your faith, the Devil will no longer be able to seduce you."

What will Satan do when we decide to fast?

He will suggest, "Fast two days a week? But you are doing too much! You will set yourself apart from the others! And on those days you look so glum; you look pale and drawn. Come on, have a hamburger! Even if it is Wednesday, it will do you good. God never asked anyone to be weak and if you fast, you'll become weak. Be like the others, you see, they don't worry about such things. Enjoy life, eat what you like. Be merry!" His seduction can be so subtle! But fasting strengthens our faith. Did Jesus ever direct us in the Gospel to behave like everybody else? When we hear this kind of voice we can be sure where the temptation comes from. One good way to put ourselves into the hands of Satan is precisely by acting like everyone else! Christian life does not consist of everyone else's idea of right and wrong. Rather, in imitating Jesus! It means being the disciple of the Master. Acting like Him, going wherever He goes and gazing at Him as our model.

When Satan tempts us, let's not be so foolish as to answer him. If he says, "You should eat. See how pale you look? Everybody else is eating." We must not answer him: "I want to fast. Besides, have you seen how ugly you are? Get lost!" No! We must never start a dialogue with Satan. If he bothers us, we must talk directly to God: "Lord, that other guy is bothering me, please do something." Satan will surely out-smart us and trick us if we engage him in a conversation. This is the way Eve was fooled. Rather than starting a dialogue with him if she would have told God, "Lord there is a serpent that is telling me the opposite of what you told me, what

I should do?" She would hot have eaten the fruit!

When Satan acts, Our Lady says that we have only one recourse - prayer. In prayer, we learn to trust the Lord's plans and the humility of Christ penetrates and influences our deepest self. When we act with trust and humility, Satan is bound. In 1982, one year after the apparitions began; Jelena delivered a message to father Tomislav Vlasic regarding the problems of his parish (that she could not have been aware of). Jelena said: "Do not have recourse to anyone. When you have a problem, you must remain smiling and praying. When God begins a work, no one will stop it." Our Lady said: "Pray, fast, and allow God to act," (Quoted from Words from Heaven, St. James Publishing 2000). If we stick closely to these words of advice, it is a great sign to our Creator of our dedication to Him and our trust in His love for us.

Suspending Natural Laws

In every school we have fire extinguishers to put fires out, and in every home we have aspirin for headaches. Fasting is like a fire extinguisher or an aspirin. We can use it to fight against the evil that is developing within us, within our family, within our society and within the Church. Our Lady said, "Through fasting and prayer you can stop wars and suspend NATURAL LAWS." We don't pay enough attention to this message. This means that disasters such as avalanches, earthquakes, land-slides can be avoided if someone in a threatened village would only fast.

This message also applies to the natural laws of our body. I know an American nurse. She was stuck in a very sinful life. She would go with any man that came across her path. Even though she was baptized, she had no faith. She went to Catechism as a child but forgot everything. There was no God in her life. In the hospital where she worked there was a doctor who came to Medjugorje and converted radically. When he returned home, he started to live the messages with his heart. He recognized that the poor woman needed his help. He decided to fast for her conversion. He fasted four years on her behalf!

One day, in deep despair, she decided to commit suicide. As a nurse she knew exactly the quantity of pills it would take to ensure her death. She swallowed the pills and went to bed expecting to die. But in the morning, she woke up in perfect health. She felt no negative effects from the pills! It was as if she drank milk before going to bed instead of eating poison. She was so shocked to still be alive that the thought immediately came to her: "Somebody wants me to live." She considered who it could be: "Maybe it's God who wants me to live?" So she reflected on God and wondered, "Why does God want me to live?" And then she came to the point, "Maybe he loves me."

She returned to work and felt compelled to tell this story to the doctor. Only then did the doctor realize the effect of his fasting.

Through his fasting, he allowed God to work miracles in the life of the nurse.

Before the incident, she rejected everything he said that was related to God. But after this event, her heart was open to hear about God's mercy. She immediately understood that the doctor's fasting had prevented the natural laws of chemical interactions from acting in her body.

The doctor asked her, "Now will you go to Medjugorje?"

She came and Our Lady showed immense love for her and even appeared to her! She couldn't believe the Mother of God would manifest herself to such an impure person.

The nurse fell deeply in love with Our Lady and went to confession. She confessed all of her sins and from that day forward changed her life. Now she is an apostle of Our Lady in America. She says, "I was born in Medjugorje."

Healings to Seize

Our Lady also spoke about HEALING. Many pilgrims seek the intercession of Mary and ask the visionaries to pray for the sick in their families. At almost every night-apparition on the mountain,

Ivan tells us that Our Lady (who is close to all who are sick in mind and body), prays especially for the sick and for those we carry in our hearts. She advises, "to obtain healing for the sick, it is important to recite the following prayers: The Creed followed by seven Our Father's, 7 Hail Mary's, and 7 Glory Be's, and to fast on bread and water." When someone is sick in the family, most of the time we go to a lot of trouble trying to find the best doctor, the best medicine, the most renowned specialist - we do everything possible to save the sick person's life. Especially when children are suffering, we are ready to move heaven and earth and spend fortunes to save that child's life! But things are so much easier than all that. Do we realize that we only need to pray and fast?! Of course, nothing is automatic but in many cases prayer and fasting will obtain a miraculous cure for someone who is sick.

What about the sacrament of the sick?

Even if a physical cure is not obtained, the sick often acquire peace of heart when they receive this sacrament. Of course it would not be prudent to wait until the eve of the sick person's death to go to his bedside with a priest wearing his stole and carrying holy oil. Such a sight might send fears of impending doom through a person and cause a premature death! Instead, as soon as someone falls seriously ill, the priest can be called and fasting may be started for the person. The sacrament of the sick can often be called "extreme unction", but this is a misleading title, as the illness doesn't have to be extreme at all.

One lady who had cancer came to see me. She said: "My problem is that no-one in my family believes, so I have no-one who will pray and fast for me". I told her that we would pray and fast for her family. This is a common problem in our world today that each one of us can address practically. Go and visit the sick of those families who are non-believers. Speak to them about the Lord, announce the Good News and tell them that you will pray and fast for them. When the visionaries asked Our Lady if she would heal this or that person, very often she would answer, "I myself cannot heal, only God can heal. But my children pray and I will pray with you; believe firmly, fast, do penance, God comes to help all. I am not God; I need your sacrifices and prayers."

Healers/Charlatans

Rather than visit specialist after specialist in the medical field spending much time and money searching for healing from another source wouldn't it be wiser to fast and pray?

Especially since fasting works more miracles than one would think!

It is very popular in the new age movement to go to healers, yoga-masters, reiki masters or healing touch therapists in order to alleviate symptoms of illness.

But where do these "healers" receive their abilities? Many receive them from an unknown source.

When, for example, someone visits a healer because of a bad knee, his left knee gets better; but his right one might begin to ache. The illness has simply been displaced. It has moved to another organ and will become more serious. The person then returns to the "healer", who may again recite several incantations or formulas and "heal" the second pain; but then a third illness will erupt, or perhaps worse - cause death. In short, people who visit healers are never healed.

Their problem only moves from the body to the heart, and then from the heart to the soul.

Starting from a physical illness, it suddenly develops into temptations of suicide, incredible hatred or deep depression.

Why are we finding so many of our youth today committing suicide when apparently nothing in his or her life could have motivated such an action?

In the most disparaging cases, parents with good intentions take their children to "healers" looking for a miracle and their children suffer the consequences of bad medicine in death.

The bad fruit of a charlatan can manifest itself not only as an illness but a lack of motivation as well. Suddenly a spouse becomes unbearable to his wife, every idiosyncrasy is an annoyance: his way of walking, of talking, of eating his doughnut.

All at once a devout person cannot pray. Or, for example, people with a zest for life can no longer enjoy it.

The Church and the different religious communities within Her have seen many bizarre cases of these "healings". She shoulders the burden of caring for the "after-sales service" of unauthentic healing cures.

The Church has found that the healer often recites incantations, pronounces strange words (sometimes mixed with Christian prayers), uses secret formulas, does massages and, as if by accident, mentions the name of the traitor, Judas. When a fake healer converts and renounces his job, I ask him to tell me his secret formulas of prayer.

They often say that their healing power came from someone who received it from someone else, who received it from someone else. By tracing the history of the healing power, it originated from Satan who gave it to a witch who then spread it!

Do not be mistaken, Satan pretends to heal by mimicking the healings that Jesus performed. In the Gospels, Jesus tells us that the false prophets of the latter days will perform spectacular signs and wonders, even to the point of seducing the chosen ones. This is reality! Satan doesn't give presents away for free.

He only deceives us in displacing the sickness, making it worse.

Several times Our Lady said to go and see doctors, but never to go and see healers. Why? Because she knows who is behind them! False healers have caused many deaths, many suicides and many mental illnesses. I beg anyone thinking of going to a healer: please don't go!!!

Even if you have a statue of Our Lady of Lourdes in your house, with a rosary in her hand, do not bargain your life for healing at any price. Chances are you will only end up sicker than before and quite probably penniless!

If you've been to see a false healer for yourself or for your child, find a priest and ask Jesus' forgiveness.

Also, ask the priest to pray so that all the bonds from darkness that might bind you (or your child) will be broken by God's Word and blessing.

Very often, a good confession is enough to break the chain of evil because there we renounce evil and all practices of darkness.

You can also renew you Baptismal vows.

This is an effective means to break all ties with evil, with Satan and his works.

The healings obtained through fasting and

prayers are real, unlike the false cures that Satan and his servants offer. The Lord gave us true healing, not only for our bodies, but also our hearts, our spirits and our souls. When He doesn't heal, he has another plan and blessing for the sick.

What about children?

It is not a question about making children fast on bread and water two days a week. But parents are their best example! When children see their parents fast they'll say, "And me! Dad I want to make a sacrifice too!" So they will give up a candy bar, an ice cream cone, a favorite dessert, or they'll turn off the T.V.

I often start talking to children about fasting by explaining what a sacrifice is. For example, I ask them to pay attention to their language and try to say only one foul word instead of ten. Then I tell them that Our Lady collects the sacrifices we have made throughout the day in a basket. I ask them to close their eyes and search for a sacrifice to offer when Our Lady makes a round of all the homes in the evening. They close their little eyes tightly, concentrate in prayer... and then, they tell which sacrifice they have chosen. It's incredible how generous and willing children are!

Children have bottomless goodwill to love and give! They teach us generosity! I know parents who have abandoned the thought of divorce thanks to their children's sacrifices and prayer. Let's be mindful of how much they do and how much we ask from them. They are quite smart and they understand which efforts to make. Sometimes they understand so well that they can be mischievous too. My six-year old nephew Francois-Joseph got a sneaky idea one evening. We all arrived at the dinner table and Francois Joseph realized that his least favorite meal was being spread out in front of him. After the blessing he announced: "Dad, tonight I'm fasting!" And his father replied, "Ok, for your fasting, you'll eat everything on your plate!"

Purgatory

Once again the Blessed Mother comes to our rescue. Of course, she speaks of the Mass as being the greatest and most powerful way to help souls get out of Purgatory, but she also speaks of fasting. Those souls who have preceded us over the veil and are now in Purgatory, suffer immensely. Through Mary we understand that fasting is a very powerful instrument. Fasting, among other sacrifices, creates a beautiful link between the living and the dead. Mary told us in Medjugorje, *"These people are waiting for your prayers and your sacrifices."*

After losing a close friend or relative, it is certainly nice to bring flowers to the cemetery, put their pictures on our dresser and remember all the good actions they did for us; but the reality is that these things are of no use to them.

If we want to help release them as quickly as possible from the terrible sufferings of Purgatory, we should fast for them. This will be an unconditional and perfect act of love that will put an end to their agony.

Preparing for God's great works

Fasting prepares us to work for God and to accomplish His will. Think of Jesus in the Gospel for example. Each scene of His life shows us the Father's careful preparation of His son for the Cross. Baptism by John in the river Jordan marked Jesus' public ministry. But instead of attending to the people right away, where did He go? He was driven into the desert by the Spirit where He remained for forty days fasting and living among wild beasts. At the end of this time, Satan tempted Him three times trying to compromise His obedience to the Will of His Father. But, unlike the temptations of Adam in Paradise; and of Israel in the desert traveling from Egypt to the Promised Land, Jesus was prepared through fasting and could carry out the plan of God for His life.

I was graced to meet Fr. Zdenko, a holy Franciscan priest who lived in Siroki Brijeg, near Medjugorje. He slept on the floor and fasted regularly. Through his ascetic ways and unending love for God, he obtained many favors from the Lord. He not only had the gift of healing, but he could read people's souls as well. In spite of his rustic ways, he became immensely popular, ministering to people all over ex- Yugoslavia who came to visit him. If someone had a problem they would need only his blessing to be better and sometimes even healed. He was so well loved that when he passed away, thousands came to his funeral mass. One of my Croatian friends from Medugorje, Ivica Dodig, told me the following story. She said it came from her grandmother, who was a childhood friend of Fr. Zdenko. One day the Lord spoke to this humble man and said:

"Zdenko, would you accept to fast on bread and water for seven years?" He answered, "Yes." He then fasted for seven years, and the last day of the seventh year, the Lord spoke to Him again,

"Zdenko, would you accept to add an eighth year to your fast?" Again he said,

"Yes". And guess what date was the last day of the 8th year? June 24th 1981-the date of the first apparition in Medjugorje! It's needless to give any more explanations. Who knows how the great works of God are prepared? Only in heaven we will find out these secrets.

Here is another event related to Fr. Zdenko: a very sick woman was brought to him who was drunk daily on hard liquor. Nothing had ever worked to get her off drinking. Fr. Zdenko saw her and said to her, "You mustn't drink. Do you promise not to drink any more?"

The woman promised and the priest blessed her in the name of the Father and the Son and the Holy Spirit; and off she went! The following day and the day after that she didn't drink. But on the third day it was hot and the temptation to drink was getting stronger and stronger. So she took a large bowl and filled it with wine. Just as her lips touched the bowl, she saw a finger over the bowl and she heard Fr. Zdenko's voice, "I told you not to drink anymore!" She was so shocked that she dropped the bowl on the floor. She was cured of her drinking for the rest of her life.

What was so special about this man? He just prayed and fasted with all his heart, listening to God's needs and working with Him! And how many lives were saved? This is only one of many examples. We too can do so much good through prayer and fasting! Our Mother warns us, "Dear children, peace is particularly threatened these days; I ask you to renew fasting and prayer in your families. Dear children I want you to realize the seriousness of the situation and that much of what will happen depends on your prayer." By teaching us to fast, Our Mother is giving us the key to God's mercy and His heart.

Until the Plan is Fulfilled

We all desire to fully live the vocation that God placed in us when He created us. We'd like everything to be accomplished before we leave this world. We'd like to hear the Lord say, "I am happy. You allowed me to accomplish all things that I planned for you!" In 1985 Our Lady said, "Dear children, be sure to fast. Through fasting you will be able to give me the joy of seeing the fulfillment of the plan God has designed for you here in Medjugorje." When she speaks about the plan in Medjugorje, she also means the plan for each one of our lives. Through fasting we allow God to fully accomplish the plan He has for us, for our families, for our cities. When He created us, He put such hope in us.

When we pray we hope that God will answer our prayers. The same goes for the Lord. When He looks at us, He hopes that all the seeds he has deposited in our hearts will grow and that until we die we will be like a flower opening with His grace, to fully live the potential that he has instilled in us - the potential to become a saint. Fasting gives us the means to carry out that plan to its fullest and to thank Him for His love for us. Do we want God to answer all our prayers? Here is the message that will open our horizons, "I desire to be constantly in heart with you. Prayer is the only road that leads to peace. If you pray and fast, you will obtain all that you want," the Blessed Mother tells us.

In the beginning of the apparitions when the visionaries were being scrutinized and Satan was causing division among the priests, some of Our Lady's plan was threatened by Communist pressure.

She needed the prayers and sacrifices of the visionaries then in order to fulfill even little pieces of the plan that is still unfolding today.

In July of 1983 when again there was a problem between Bishop Zanic and the parish over the apparitions, she said, "Fast two days a week for the intentions of the Bishop, who will bear a heavy responsibility. If there is a need to, I will ask for a third day. Pray each day for the Bishop." This message is just as powerful today as it was then and yet how many of us are fasting for the Bishop?

Practical questions

Why Bread?

Often we are asked, what's special about bread and water? Why not take potatoes lentils or rice? The answer is simple: Everything is related to the Eucharist, to the Bread of Life. Jesus did not say: "I am the potato of life" or "I am the rice of life" or "I am the banana of life..." He said, "I am the bread of Life." Further, when we open ourselves to Eternal Life, the peace that fulfills us will flow from us and irrigate the world. Our Lady says, "A river will spring forth from your hearts, dear children, and reach the whole world."

Which Bread to use?

It may be difficult to fast on the bread we buy in the grocery stores considering the preservatives and artificial additives. Often made of refined flours with little nutritional value, it's preferable to fast on richer bread, made from unrefined flour. For days of fasting, try to find whole wheat or cereal bread, or spelt - something that sticks to your bones. Bread is a basic necessity in our nutrition. Our Blessed Mother doesn't want us to go hungry on fast days (work days). If you want to bake your own bread, you will find recipes in the back of this booklet.

What time to start fasting?

Good question! According to Our Lady, "the whole day!" But the most important thing is to do it with love. Through prayer we'll know in our own conscience, how Mary asks us to start fasting. It is sometimes in stages. For example, as she directed us to say the Rosary, "Do not impose the Rosary on those who have never prayed.

Today let them say one Our Father with the heart, tomorrow one Hail Mary with the heart, the day after tomorrow one Glory be with the heart."

This way applies to fasting too. If we can

immediately start fasting on bread and water two days a week, praise God! But we can also do it progressively. It is better to start step by step and remain consistent rather than start too quickly only to give up two months later.

One could start on Friday at lunch, and then add Wednesday lunch, then Friday evening and little by little.

Our Lady did not specify the time, she only said two days a week, and our day starts at midnight and ends at midnight. Of course it can be adjusted to our schedule if we work nights or other shifts. French Grandmothers tell me that Wednesday is not convenient as there's no school in France on that day and they baby-sit for their grand-children. In that case fasting could be shifted to Tuesday (the Blessed Mother won't hold a grudge). Or, if Wednesday is a Holy day like the Annunciation or Christmas, we do not have to fast that day, but we fast the day before or the following Monday.

The important thing is to fast with the heart.

Vicka often says that Our Lady asks us to make a firm decision to fast with love in thanksgiving for her coming here. If we have a headache or nausea it is because we have not made a firm decision to fast with the heart.

How much bread?

Our Lady never gave any instructions as for the quantity of bread. She wants us to use our freedom and decide according to our heart. Let us not react by thinking "Since I'm fasting I'll eat a lot of bread". Rather, let's eat without fears and let's eat moderately. Also, Our Lady did not specify whether bread could be toasted or not. Some people prefer to choose toasted bread. Why not? The same is true of water. She didn't specify whether the water should be cold or hot. Here, as well, we decide according to our hearts (or the temperature of the season!)

I remember a conversation between Mirjana and an American lady. Upon hearing that we should fast two days a week on bread and water, the lady's eyes widened and she begged Mirjana, "When I get up in the morning, may I still drink just a little bit of coffee, with just a little bit of sugar, just so I can wake up?" And smiling Mirjana answered her: "this atmosphere of love that surrounds the Blessed Mother is tremendous. We can feel at ease with her, like children with their mother." This wonderful Mother gives us the means to have more love in our hearts and to bear more fruit; she gives us the means to grow in joy, in peace and in freedom. Experiencing that, we then receive fasting like a gift from heaven!

What about the sick?

Our Lady makes it clear that the sick are exempt from fasting. But those in good health are called to fast. She invites the sick to offer their suffering to God or to give up something they are attached to such as television, smoking, alcohol, or any other pleasure. The Virgin Mary says, "I will be happier if you renounce sin".

If we regularly read pornographic magazines, for instance, let fasting be an incentive to stop. When we have a bad habit, masturbation for example, what a reason to stop on a fasting day, and with the help of Our Lady never take it back. She advises, *"Dear children, the best fasting is fasting on bread and water."*

It's understandable that those who are sick are exempt from fasting; but let's not ignore that fasting actually heals a variety of illnesses. Certainly, medical treatment should not be stopped abruptly, nor should medicine suddenly be discarded. Consult your physician to see how to incorporate fasting into your diet.

One meal a day on bread is not necessarily bad for health. I know a man who never used to fast because of a severe stomach problem.

One day, while he was in prayer, he knew he had to start fasting. And fasting actually healed his stomach problem.

Each case is particular and requires wisdom.

People on strong medication should act with great care.

Fasting is a grace that we shouldn't take for granted. With humility, let's ask for it on the eve of a fast day.

Let me tell you a secret: For seven years, though living in Medjugorje, I wasn't able to fast. I had been sick as a child and that prevented me from altering my diet. I was part of the "feeble club" in our Beatitudes Community of Medjugorje. There were only two of us out of fifteen who ate on the days when the others fasted. I did not feel comfortable with this situation, but no matter how much I asked Our Lady to do something, nothing seemed to work. So one day I appealed to her feelings in a way that she could not possibly resist my plea: "Dearest Gospa" I said "You invite me to travel all over the world to share your messages, but you've noticed that I have passed over the subject of fasting rather quickly. I don't want to be a hypocrite and since I don't fast, I cannot speak at length about fasting that I haven't experienced for myself.

So, if you want me to be convincing about fasting, you will have to give me the grace for it!

Don't you wish that your children would grasp the importance of fasting? Don't you wish to use me for that?"

A short time later I met a man from Mexico.

His conversion in Medjugorje had been so radical that he created a large apostolate broadcasting the messages on Mexican T.V.

While we were talking about the ways to run our apostolates, and how to deal with specific struggles, I asked him what he did when he lacked material support for his work.

He answered: "Whatever you need, whatever you ask from Mary for your apostolate, be it money or health, material things or favors, whether it's for you or for others, Our Lady will always give it to you IF you do everything she says."

This IF challenged me!

Fasting immediately flashed to my mind!

Then I confronted my heavenly mother and said, "From tomorrow on I will do whatever you say, no matter what!"

It was as if the testimony of my Mexican friend held grace for me.

I declared to Mary: "*Tomorrow I'm going to fast on bread and water, please give me the grace for it! You know that I am not very brave so I am asking you for a sign: and that all day tomorrow which is Friday - I won't feel hungry.*" She answered my wish. I fasted all day and in the evening I felt fine. That's how I received the grace of fasting. Each of us can ask for that grace too!

How about my neighbor's plate?

If we fast we must never look at our neighbor's plate- this is so important! If fasting leads us to criticizing our neighbor who doesn't fast, then it is better not to fast. Let everyone's conscience guide him and help him respect the other's freedom; comparative criticism comes from the Devil.

Our neighbor might not fast for ten years while he is in good health. Let's close our eyes and humbly pray that he starts fasting one day and obtains many graces from God, like the workers in the eleventh hour.

This is being Christian. While fasting, keep hoping that more and more people will fast, but mostly we fast to answer the call that God addresses to us through Mary.

Looking at our neighbor's plate is not our job. Everyone has been given a special mission to fast by Our Lady, even priests. This act of mercy enlarges our hearts. Not only will we be fasting for our child, our husband, our wife or our parish priest, but we will also be enlarging our heart to the dimensions of God's heart because fasting urges us to grow in humility and forgive one another.

Our heart is already big enough to hold God, Himself, but fasting allows God to extend the boundaries of our heart and encompass all of the heavenly dimensions. Through prayer and fasting, the Lord strengthens His divine presence into us and His powerful spirit reaches all those who are in need throughout the world. Fasting is like invisibly taking people who are walking in darkness by the hand and communicating light and joy to them.

It helps them to bend down on their knees and say, "O Father, I thank you for the gift of life and for the joy of life that I have found again." We'll become the extended hands of God for the unbelievers who wander in darkness today. What a great mercy fasting on bread and water is! And what a joy!

Yes, fasting is an act of wonderful mercy, especially when it is practiced in secret. Only then does it become praiseworthy in its humility. "By all means let your fasting remains secret and unknown to others," says Mary. We can't fast in secret if we are with our family or in a community.

But if we work in an office no one needs to know that instead of going to the corner restaurant, we eat a morsel of bread somewhere. Our Lady constantly pushes us to humility in fasting. She said: "Pray and fast! I desire humility from you; but you can become humble only through prayer and fasting," (Prayer Group, Feb 10, 1984).

Let's thank the Lord for this gift of fasting! Let's start! Once we have started we become witnesses of its power. In fact, some are now tempted to tell Our Lady, "Dearest Gospa, only two days a week? You could have asked for more!" Let us strive to make Our Lady happy by fasting for her intentions. On Our Lady's 2000th birthday, august 5th 1984, she said: "I am very happy! Continue, continue. Continue to pray and to fast.

Continue and make me happy each day." Isn't this a beautiful mission that Medjugorje compels us to take up, making our Mother happy??

Where does fasting come from?

Let's establish Scriptural origins for fasting

In biblical revelation, fasting is closely linked to the invitation to prayer and conversion. The prophets fasted before receiving special revelations or new prophetic missions while other biblical characters fasted out of joy, gratitude, in times of sadness, or in reparation for offenses they had committed. The whole nation, at times fasted in preparation for various solemnities. They also fasted to be delivered from imminent catastrophes, or to supplicate for a way out of troublesome circumstances. The following extracts have been taken directly from the Bible (The New American Bible) to better illustrate the relationship between a man who fasts and God.

Fasting is an encounter with the Divine

"Then the LORD said to Moses, 'Write down these words, for in accordance with them I have made a covenant with you and with Israel.' So Moses stayed there with the LORD for forty days and forty nights, without eating any food or drinking any water, and he wrote on the tablets the words of the covenant, the Ten Commandments." (Ex 34:27-28)

For forty days and forty nights, two friends meet and talk: God and Moses. This is a deep experience with the Divine. Fasting facilitates man to enter into a communion with the Lord. Moses chose to ignore hunger, desiring to receive the commandments of God, to sculpt them into the plates of rock and to offer them to the people of God. The people of God however, while awaiting the message of the Lord down in the pastures, became impatient and distanced themselves from the ways of the Lord. In anger against his own people, who had erected a golden calf to adore as their God, Moses cast down the plates of rock. In order to win back the Lord's favor for his people Moses offered his fasting for another 40 days, a fast totaling eighty days.

It is most likely one of the longest fasts ever recorded. God accepts the sacrifice of Moses and gives him The Law engraved in rock once again to be placed in the arc of the covenant as a sign of God's friendship with His people.

Fasting opens our hearts to prayer. It helps us feel lighter and freer to implore favors from the Lord and to intercede for others in a closer way. God invites man to fast in difficult moments, regardless of whether they are personal or communal. God puts Himself beside those who fast, not only those who fast from food, but also from any form of injustice or iniquity.

Fasting, as an expiation for sin

"*The word of the LORD came to Jonah a second time. 'Set out for the great city of Nineveh, and announce to it the message that I will tell you'. So Jonah made ready and went to Nineveh, according to the LORD'S bidding. Now Nineveh was an enormously large city; it took three days to go through it. Jonah began his journey through the city, and had gone but a single days walk announcing, 'Forty days more and Nineveh shall be destroyed,' when the people of Nineveh believed God, they proclaimed a fast and all of them, great and small, put on sack-cloth.*

When the news reached the king of Nineveh, he

rose from his throne, laid aside his robe, covered himself with sackcloth and sat in the ashes. Then he had this proclaimed throughout Nineveh, by decree of the king and his nobles: 'Neither man nor beast, neither cattle nor sheep, they shall not eat, nor shall they drink water. Man and beast shall be covered with sackcloth and call loudly to God; every man shall turn from his evil way and from the violence he has in hand. Who knows, God may relent and forgive, and withhold His blazing wrath, so that we shall not perish. When God saw by their actions how they turned from their evil ways, He repented of the evil that He had threatened to do to them; he did not carry it out." (Gn 3,1-10)

Jonah is a prophet who rebels. He runs from his responsibilities to the point of wanting to hide from God. While on the run, he gains a victory over his own fears in the stomach of the whale. He comprehends the reality of his sinfulness and utters a prayer of trust and asks to be forgiven for not listening to God's call. Secure from all danger, he decided to place himself in the service of God, and, he convinced the King to assemble the people of Nineveh and request a collective fast.

The Lord responded to the fast by suspending the chastisement that He had intended for the city. Fasting and prayer profoundly touched the heart of God.

Prayer and fasting

"There was a certain man from Rama-thaim, Elkanah by name, and a Zuphite from the hill country of Ephraim. He was the son of Jeroham, son of Elihu, son of Tohu, son of Zuph, an Ephraimite. He had two wives, one named Hannah, the other Peninnah; Peninnah had children, but Hannah was childless. This man regularly went on pilgrimage from his city to worship the LORD of hosts and to sacrifice to him at Shiloh, where the two sons of Eli, Hophni and Phinehas, were ministering as priests of the LORD. When the day came for Elkanah to offer sacrifice, he used to give a portion each to his wife Peninnah and to all her sons and daughters, but a double portion to Hannah because he loved her, though the LORD had made her barren.

Her rival, to upset her, turned it into a constant reproach to her that the LORD had left her barren. This went on year after year; each time they made their pilgrimage to the sanctuary of the LORD, Peninnah would approach her, and Hannah would weep and refuse to eat. Her husband Elkanah used to ask her: "Hannah, why do you weep, and why do you refuse to eat? Why do you grieve? Am I not more to you than ten sons?" Hannah rose after one such meal at Shiloh, and presented herself before the LORD; at the time, Eli the priest was sitting on a chair near the doorpost of the LORD'S temple. In her bitterness she prayed to the LORD, weeping copiously, and she made a vow, promising: 'O LORD of hosts, if you look with pity on the misery of your handmaid, if you remember me and do not forget me, if you give your handmaid a male child, I will give him to the LORD for as long as he lives; neither wine nor liquor shall he drink, and no razor shall ever touch his head.' As she remained long at prayer before the LORD, Eli watched her mouth, for Hannah was praying silently; though her lips were moving, her voice could not be heard. Eli, thinking her drunk, said to her, 'How long will you make a drunken show of yourself? Sober up from your wine!' 'It isn't that, my lord,' Hannah answered. 'I am an unhappy woman. I have had neither wine nor liquor; I was only pouring out my troubles to the LORD. Do not think your handmaid a ne'er-do-well; my prayer has been prompted by my deep sorrow and misery.' Eli said, 'Go in peace, and may the God of Israel grant you what you have asked of him.' She replied, 'Think kindly of your maidservant,' and left. She went to her quarters, ate and drank with her husband, and no longer appeared downcast." (1 Sam 1:1-18)

Anna desired to have a son, but was sterile. Sterility at the time was considered to be a punishment of God and the result of sin. Anna went up to the Temple every year, accompanied by her husband, Elkana, to implore God to relieve her of the shame of not having children. God heard the prayers and accepted her fasts and granted her a son whom she called Samuel: He will be the prophet to unveil the mystery of God to his people.

Fasting in difficulty

"The message was brought to Jehoshaphat: 'A great multitude is coming against you from across the sea, from Edom; they are already in Hazazontamar. Jehoshaphat was frightened, and he hastened to consult the LORD. He proclaimed a fast for all Judah." (2 Chr 20: 2-4)

"Then I proclaimed a fast, there by the river of Ahava, that we might humble ourselves before our God to petition from him a safe journey for ourselves, our children, and all our possessions." (Ezra 8: 21)

In the face of obstacles, in personal crises, political or community, almost spontaneously a desire emerges to cry out to God to help us. Undoubtedly, the Israelites were a people privileged and chosen by the Lord, but at the same time they were tried and tested by so many difficulties. At the most difficult times, God intervened reminding the people that it is not possible to win their enemies without His protection, which could be obtained through fasting and prayer. For this reason, when confronted with their enemies, Jehosephat and Ezra didn't hesitate to proclaim a fast on behalf of the whole nation.

Fasting as an outward sign of penance

"Then they took their bones and buried them under the tamarisk tree in Jabesh, and fasted for seven days". (1 Sam 31: 13)

"Then they went to console David with food while it was still day. But David swore, 'May God do thus and so to me if I eat bread or anything else before sunset'.". (2 Sam 3:35)

"Likewise in each of the provinces, wherever the king's legal enactment reached, the Jews went into deep mourning, with fasting, weeping, and lament; they all slept on sackcloth and ashes". (Est 4:3)

"Yet I, when they were ill, put on sackcloth, afflicted myself with fasting, sobbed my prayers upon my bosom". (Ps 35:13)

Fasting in order to obtain healing

"Then David said to Nathan, 'I have sinned against the LORD'. Nathan answered David: 'The LORD on his part has forgiven your sin: you shall not die. But since you have utterly spurned the LORD by this deed, the child born to you must

surely die'. Then Nathan returned to his house. The LORD struck the child that the wife of Uriah had borne to David, and it became desperately ill. David besought God for the child. He kept a fast, retiring for the night to lie on the ground clothed in sackcloth. The elders of his house stood beside him urging him to rise from the ground; but he would not, nor would he take food with them." (2 Sam 12:13-17)

Fasting in suffering and sickness

Awareness of our sinfulness and sufferings weighs us down and leaves us needing to unburden ourselves. In these moments, the heart takes refuge in the Lord humbly asking his help. The best way to show God that we love Him is to let ourselves be led by the Spirit and to dedicate more time to prayer and to fasting. When Nehemiah was touched by the suffering of the people, before turning to the Lord in prayer, he dedicated himself to fasting.

"They answered me: 'The survivors of the captivity there in the province are in great distress and under reproach. Also, the wall of Jerusalem lies breached, and its gates have been gutted with fire.' When I heard this report, I began to weep and continued mourning for several days; I fasted and prayed before the God of heaven. I prayed: 'O LORD, God of heaven, great and awesome God,

you who preserve your covenant of mercy toward those who love you and keep your commandments, may your ear be attentive, and your eyes open, to heed the prayer which I, your servant, now offer in your presence day and night for your servants the Israelites, confessing the sins which we of Israel have committed against you, I and my father's house included. Grievously have we offended you, not keeping the commandments, the statutes, and the ordinances which you committed to your servant Moses. But remember, I pray, the promise which you gave through Moses, your servant, when you said: 'Should you prove faithless, I will scatter you among the nations; but should you return to me and carefully keep my commandments, even though your outcasts have been driven to the farthest corner of the world, I will gather them from there, and bring them back to the place which I have chosen as the dwelling place for my name'. They are your servants, your people, whom you freed by your great might and your strong hand0". (Neh 1:1-10)

Ezra therefore, as a sign of sorrow and mournfulness for the infidelity of his people who were deported, fasted and invoked the mercy of God.

"Then Ezra retired from his place before the house of God and entered the chamber of Johanan, son of Eliashib, where he spent the night neither eating food nor drinking water, for he was in

mourning over the betrayal by the exiles." *(Ez 10:6)*

We can obtain many benefits by fasting during sickness and interior sufferings. Elihu, Job's friend, tells how, when man is severely suffering, he hasn't the will to eat, but rather, prefers to manifest his pain by fasting.

He withholds his soul from the pit and his life from passing to the grave. Or a man is chastened on his bed by pain and unceasing suffering within his frame. So that to his appetite food becomes repulsive, and his senses reject the choicest nourishment. His flesh is wasted so that it cannot be seen, and his bones, once invisible, appear. (Job 33:18-21).

Fasting to obtain blessings and peace

"Then I proclaimed a fast, there by the river of Ahava, that we might humble ourselves before our God to petition from him a safe journey for ourselves, our children, and all our possessions. For I would have been ashamed to ask the king for troops and horsemen to protect us against enemies along the way, since we had said to the king, 'The favoring hand of our God is upon all who seek him, but his mighty wrath is against all who forsake him'. So we fasted, and prayed to our God for this, and our petition was granted". (Ez 8:21-23)

Fasting after a return to the true God

"On the twenty-fourth day of this month, the Israelites gathered together fasting and in sackcloth, their heads covered with dust. Those of Israelite descent separated themselves from all who were of foreign extraction, then stood forward and confessed their sins and the guilty deeds of their fathers." (Neh 9:1-2)

Fasting in the Psalms

"I have wept and fasted, but this led only to scorn. I clothed myself in sackcloth; I became a byword for them." (Ps 69:11-12)

"My knees totter from fasting; my flesh has wasted away. I have become a mockery to them; when they see me, they shake their heads." (Ps 109: 24-25)

Fasting as preparation for, or in reply to the Word of God

"Then Jeremiah charged Baruch: I cannot go to the house of the LORD; I am prevented from doing so. Do you go on the fast day and read publicly in the LORD'S house the LORD'S words from the scroll you wrote at my dictation; read them also to all the men of Judah who come up from their cities.

Perhaps they will lay their supplication before the LORD and will all turn back from their evil way; for great is the fury of anger with which the LORD has threatened this people. (Jer 36:5-7)

And Baruch read the words of this scroll for Jeconiah, son of Jehoiakim, king of Judah, to hear it, as well as all the people who came to the reading: the nobles, the kings' sons, the elders, and the whole people, small and great alike-all who lived in Babylon by the river Sud. 5They wept and fasted and prayed before the LORD, and collected such funds as each could furnish. (Bar 1: 3-6)

In the New Testament

The fasting that Jesus did

Jesus did not ignore the Jewish observance of fasting, but rather both practiced it Himself and taught his disciples to do so. Jesus fasts in the important moments of His life. For example, before starting His public ministry, He is led into the desert in order to be tempted and remains there for forty days without eating.

"Then Jesus was led by the Spirit into the desert to be tempted by the devil. He fasted for forty days and forty nights, and afterwards he was hungry. The tempter approached and said to him, 'If you are the Son of God, command that these stones become loaves of bread.'

He said in reply, 'It is written: One does not live by bread alone, but by every word that comes forth from the mouth of God. Then the devil took him to the holy city, and made him stand on the parapet of the temple, and said to him, "If you are the Son of God, throw yourself down. For it is written: He will command his angels concerning you and with their hands they will support you, lest you dash your foot against a stone.' Jesus answered him, 'Again it is written, 'You shall not put the Lord, your God, to the test.' Then the devil took him up to a very high mountain, and showed him all the kingdoms of the world in their magnificence, and he said to him, 'All these I shall give to you, if you will prostrate yourself and worship me.'

At this, Jesus said to him, "Get away, Satan! It is written: 'The Lord, your God, shall you worship and him alone shall you serve'.". Then the devil left him and, behold, angels came and ministered to him.' (Mt 4: 1-11)

Jesus, now liberated from every material reality: food, success, power, breaks into a new world, the world of the reign of God, and opens up to mankind, a new road: the road of redemption. Whoever fasts, enters into his own desert, and recognizes in a clearer way what is evil and what comes from the evil one. Whoever fasts struggles successfully in order to arrive at the sum of all goodness, the prime good, who is God Himself. Having decided for God, the way is open to a new world; the reign of God.

The words of Jesus concerning fasting

Jesus emphasizes that it is not an exercise of personal strength to see if our ability to remain without eating is greater or lesser than that of other people. It's more about opening up a new relationship with God, the God of love and mercy.

When you fast, do not look gloomy like the hypocrites. They neglect their appearance, so that they may appear to others to be fasting. Amen, I say to you, they have received their reward. But when you fast, anoint your head and wash your face, so that you may not appear to be fasting, except to your Father who is hidden. And your Father who sees what is hidden will repay you." *(Mt 6: 16-18)*

"Two people went up to the temple area to pray; one was a Pharisee and the other was a tax collector. The Pharisee took up his position and spoke this prayer to himself, 'O God, I thank you that I am not like the rest of humanity-greedy, dishonest, adulterous-or even like this tax collector. I fast twice a week, and I pay tithes on my whole income'. But the tax collector stood off at a distance and would not even raise his eyes to heaven but beat his breast and prayed, 'God, be merciful to me a sinner'. I tell you, the latter went home justified, not the former; for everyone who exalts himself will be humbled, and the one who humbles himself will be exalted." *(Luke 18: 10-14)*

The disciples of Jesus will fast

The behavior of Jesus and His disciples is one that disturbs the doctors of the law and the Pharisees. Jesus was considered someone who ate and drank often. He was even found sitting, several times, at the table of sinners. We seldom see Him fasting. He couldn't be considered an ascetic model, like St. John the Baptist and his disciples who spent long periods in the desert observing all the fasts that the Jewish law prescribed. In fact the writers of the Gospels never mention that the disciples of Jesus were fasting.

"The disciples of John and of the Pharisees were accustomed to fast. People came to him and objected, "Why do the disciples of John and the disciples of the Pharisees fast, but your disciples do not fast?". Jesus answered them, "Can the wedding guests fast while the bridegroom is with them? As long as they have the bridegroom with them they cannot fast. But the days will come when the bridegroom is taken away from them, and then they will fast on that day." (Mark 2: 18-20)

The first thing that Jesus points out to the Pharisees, who are worried about appearance, is that it is not possible to assume penitential attitudes in times of feasting and in the presence of friends.

Jesus is our friend and spouse. Now He is absent and has gone back to the house of His Father. Fasting after His ascension into Heaven takes on a new meaning, and is of great value. Whoever is awaiting a guest must remain awake and cannot over-indulge in the feast when the tempter comes to take him by surprise in a moment of weakness.

Jesus recommends fasting to us in order to be more open to the mystery of prayer and to have the interior strength necessary to face the struggle against evil that is all around us.

Fasting as a power against evil

"Then the disciples approached Jesus in private and said, "Why could we not drive it out?" He said to them, "Because of your little faith. Amen, I say to you, if you have faith the size of a mustard seed, you will say to this mountain, 'Move from here to there,' and it will move. Nothing will be impossible for you. But this kind does not come out except by prayer and fasting." (Mt 17: 19-21)

Fasting and prayer in preparation for service

The New Testament shows us how when proclaiming the Word, or in moments of extreme danger, the apostles fast and pray in order to obtain a grace. The Book of the Acts of the Apostles, is the chronicle of the first Christian community who proclaimed Jesus as the Messiah and announced the Good News.

The followers of Jesus, for the first time, are referred to as, "the community of Antioch". In this city, the Apostles, the prophets and doctors, decide to lay their hands on Barnabas and Paul before sending them out as missionaries. First of all, however, they unite in prayer and fasting.

"Now there were in the church at Antioch prophets and teachers: Barnabas, Symeon who was called Niger, Lucius of Cyrene, Manaen who was a

close friend of Herod the tetrarch, and Saul. While they were worshiping the Lord and fasting, the Holy Spirit said, "Set apart for me Barnabas and Saul for the work to which I have called them". Then, completing their fasting and prayer, they laid hands on them and sent them off." (Acts 13: 1-3)

The consecration of the Presbyters, deacons and all those responsible for the community was also preceded by fasting and prayer:

"They appointed presbyters for them in each church and, with prayer and fasting, commended them to the Lord in whom they had put their faith. Then they traveled through Pisidia and reached Pamphylia. After proclaiming the word at Perga they went down to Attalia." (Acts14: 23-25)

Fasting forgotten

For the pious Jew, it was necessary to have serious motives for not fasting twice a week and only a Levite could give the dispensation not to fast.

It is from this Jewish tradition that the two days fast was carried over into the early church: the two days, Wednesday and Friday were chosen with particular motives. Wednesday, for the expiation of sins, because it was exactly on Wednesday of Holy week that Judas went to the Pharisees to see how, where and for how much he would hand Jesus over to them. Friday was chosen in remembrance of Jesus passion and death on the cross.

Over the centuries however, the Church lost sight of the teachings of Jesus, and slackened into a numeric, formal ritualism concerning the days and the ways of fasting. {The parable about the publican and the Pharisee in Luke's Gospel 18: 10-14, warns against fasting as a mere observance of the law. Fasting in an attitude of repentance is looked on favorably by God.}

The concern was to establish rules and boundaries to safeguard the practice of fasting: they were to be every Wednesday and Friday during Lent and on the eve of the more important feasts of the Church. Slowly, however fast days were reduced to a minimum; Ash Wednesday and Good Friday. At one time, Friday was a day in which Christians abstained from meat.

Today, it has become a matter of choice. Much has been lost though, not only on a spiritual level, but also for physical well-being. The fasts in preparation for the solemnities of the Church have also been lost.

Originally the Eucharistic fast began at midnight on the day one was to receive the host and lasted for three hours after. Today it has been reduced to an hour before Holy Communion. The saints received great help from communion, because before approaching the altar, they would spend much time preparing to worthily receive the

Holy Body of Christ. St. Luigi Gonzaga spent three days preparing for Holy Communion and three days in thanksgiving to the Lord.

Can fasting be replaced by other sacrifices? The Blessed Mother says, *"Dear children, I ask you above all, to renounce the sin which is within you"*. This is the prime and absolute fast that we all should do. Then there are other forms of fasting: from television, from alcohol, from cigarettes, from vices, from drugs, from greed, from selfishness etc. The Blessed Mother in Medjugorje also says: "Dear children, the best fast is that of bread and water".

Fasting and prayer are the main instruments of purification, interior liberation and are the essential requirements for healthy spiritual growth. They help us to relate to ourselves, to others, to nature around us and to God in the right way.

Fasting as a change in our way of life

Fasting is intended to be a way of bringing us to a conversion and a transformation in our way of feeling and understanding life. It obliges us to come out of our small and restricted world of egoism to better serve and perceive those around us with love.

Fasting is uncomfortable because it requires coherence. Isaiah, the prophet of hope, who contemplates beyond narrow mindedness.

He aspires to go beyond the pettiness of Israelite legalism and it is no coincidence that he is at the same time the prophet of true interior fasting.

He condemns all practices that are sterile; which are not accompanied by an interior change bearing a practical reflection in our everyday life.

The love of God, which is always accompanied by His justice, must bloom outside of us toward those around us. In the book of Isaiah, we find the statutes of biblical fasting:

"Cry out full-throated and unsparingly, lift up your voice like a trumpet blast; Tell my people their wickedness, and the house of Jacob their sins. They seek me day after day, and desire to know my ways, Like a nation that has done what is just and not abandoned the law of their God; They ask me to declare what is due them, pleased to gain access to God. "Why do we fast, and you do not see it? We afflict ourselves, and you take no note of it". Lo, on your fast day you carry out your own pursuits, and drive all your laborers. Yes, your fast ends in quarreling and fighting, striking with wicked claw. Would that today you might fast so as to make your voice heard on high! Is this the manner of fasting I wish, of keeping a day of penance: That a man bow his head like a reed, and lie in sackcloth and ashes? Do you call this a fast, a day acceptable to the LORD? This, rather, is the fasting that I wish:

releasing those bound unjustly, untying the thongs of the yoke; Setting free the oppressed, breaking every yoke; Sharing your bread with the hungry, sheltering the oppressed and the homeless; Clothing the naked when you see them, and not turning your back on your own.

Then your light shall break forth like the dawn, and your wound shall quickly be healed; your vindication shall go before you, and the glory of the LORD shall be your rear guard. Then you shall call, and the LORD will answer; you shall cry for help, and he will say: Here I am! If you remove from your midst oppression, false accusation and malicious speech; If you bestow your bread on the hungry and satisfy the afflicted; then light shall rise for you in the darkness, and the gloom shall become for you like midday; Then the LORD will guide you always and give you plenty even on the parched land. He will renew your strength, and you shall be like a watered garden, like a spring whose water never fails. The ancient ruins shall be rebuilt for your sake, and the foundations from ages past you shall rise up; "Repairer of the breach," they shall call you, "Restorer of ruined homesteads".

If you hold back your foot on the Sabbath from following your own pursuits on my holy day; If you call the Sabbath a delight, and the LORD'S holy day honorable; If you honor it by not following your ways, seeking your own interests, or speaking *with malice*

Then you shall delight in the LORD, and I will make you ride on the heights of the earth; I will nourish you with the heritage of Jacob, your father, for the mouth of the LORD has spoken. (Is 58:1-14)

Paul the Apostle fasts within his body and points out that there are more important things than food:

"For the kingdom of God is not a matter of food and drink, but of righteousness, peace, and joy in the holy Spirit." (Rom 14: 17)

In this way, Paul, just like the prophet Isaiah, *(Is 58:1-14)* leads his listeners beyond the normal of the rules of fasting which already established among the early Christians. He does this by putting forward a more demanding and more authentic form of mortification, which in essence, is an interior removal of all evil from within and abandonment. In doing so, we become more like Jesus, and so we are a live presence of the Risen One, free from the enslavement of our passions.

"For you were called for freedom, brothers. But do not use this freedom as an opportunity for the flesh; rather, serve one another through love. For the whole law is fulfilled in one statement, namely, "You shall love your neighbor as yourself". But if you go on biting and devouring one another, beware that you are not consumed by one another. I say, then: live by the Spirit and you will certainly not gratify the desire of the flesh. For the flesh has

desires against the Spirit, and the Spirit against the flesh; these are opposed to each other, so that you may not do what you want. But if you are guided by the Spirit, you are not under the law. Now the works of the flesh are obvious: immorality, impurity, licentiousness, idolatry, sorcery, hatreds, rivalry, jealousy, outbursts of fury, acts of selfishness, dissensions, factions, occasions of envy, drinking bouts, orgies, and the like. I warn you, as I warned you before, that those who do such things will not inherit the kingdom of God. In contrast, the fruit of the Spirit is love, joy, peace, patience, kindness, generosity, faithfulness, gentleness, self-control. Against such there is no law. Now those who belong to Christ (Jesus) have crucified their flesh with its passions and desires. If we live in the Spirit, let us also follow the Spirit." (Gal 5:13-25)

Paul rejects the idea that some foods are impure, and must therefore be avoided.

"For the sake of food, do not destroy the work of God. Everything is indeed clean, but it is wrong for anyone to become a stumbling block by eating; it is good not to eat meat or drink wine or do anything that causes your brother to stumble.

Keep the faith (that) you have to yourself in the presence of God; blessed is the one who does not condemn himself for what he approves". (Rom 14:20-22)

Our life is a hymn of praise, our bodies a sacrament of the love of Our Lord. Hence we have a duty to reveal the image of God, in whose image we are created.

"So whether you eat or drink, or whatever you do, do everything for the glory of God." (1Cor 10:31)

God promises eternal life to those who are seeking to overcome the deepest rationale of evil, in order to live an intense goodness, producing fruits of goodness and love. Fasting purifies our earthly human feelings and renders us capable of contemplating and sensing the subtle desire to live according to the Spirit, to live the fruits of the Spirit.

Fasting now in order to participate later at the Eternal Banquet

Man, is a pilgrim seeking God in everything, constantly threatened by the danger of losing himself, of wandering or of stopping somewhere along the way. To fast means to free oneself from what is earthly and not to give in to earthly passions that cloud over the vision of eternal life with God.

Earthly fasting prepares us for the Eternal Banquet. In the Bible we find over eighty references to banquets in different situations. Among these, we find the Passover from the Israelite slavery in Egypt, referred to as "the memorial of our freedom". Fasting makes us free and Eucharist is the memorial of that freedom.

"On the tenth of this month every one of your families must procure for itself a lamb, one apiece for each household. If a family is too small for a whole lamb, it shall join the nearest household in procuring one and shall share in the lamb in proportion to the number of persons who partake of it. The lamb must be a year-old male and without blemish." (Ex 12: 3b-5a)

Even the way in which it is to be eaten is clearly stated:

"This is how you are to eat it: with your loins girt, sandals on your feet and your staff in hand, you shall eat like those who are in flight. It is the Passover of the LORD." (Ex 12: 11)

This banquet also has an eschatological significance, because it is a symbol of the Eucharistic banquet. Before His Passion Jesus blesses the Passover celebration with His Apostles and presents Himself as Eucharist. He is the Lamb of God who offers himself, not only for the Israelites but for the peoples of the whole world. So the Old Testament Passover prefigures the institution of the Eucharist.

"When the day of the Feast of Unleavened Bread arrived, the day for sacrificing the Passover lamb, he sent out Peter and John, instructing them, "Go and make preparations for us to eat the

Passover". They asked him, "Where do you want us to make the preparations?" And he answered them, "When you go into the city, a man will meet you carrying a jar of water. Follow him into the house that he enters and say to the master of the house, 'The teacher says to you, "Where is the guest room where I may eat the Passover with my disciples?'.". He will show you a large upper room that is furnished. Make the preparations there".

Then they went off and found everything exactly as he had told them, and there they prepared the Passover. When the hour came, he took his place at table with the apostles. He said to them, 'I have eagerly desired to eat this Passover with you before I suffer; or, I tell you, I shall not eat it (again) until there is fulfillment in the kingdom of God.' Then he took a cup, gave thanks, and said, 'Take this and share it among yourselves; for I tell you (that) from this time on I shall not drink of the fruit of the vine until the kingdom of God comes. *(Luke 22: 7-18)*

Isaiah too speaks of an eschatological banquet:

"On this mountain the LORD of hosts will provide for all peoples a feast of rich food and choice wines, juicy, rich food and pure, choice wines. On this mountain he will destroy the veil that veils all peoples, the web that is woven over all nations;

He will destroy death forever. The Lord GOD will wipe away the tears from all faces; the *reproach of his people he will remove from the whole earth; for the LORD has spoken. On that day it will be said: "Behold our God, to whom we looked to save us! This is the LORD for whom we looked; let us rejoice and be glad that he has saved us!" For the hand of the LORD will rest on this mountain, but Moab will be trodden down as a straw is trodden down in the mire." (Is 25: 6-10)*

Jesus spoke of the kingdom of God in images often referring to banquets. He also speaks of the eternal banquet of the Kingdom of Heaven. St Luke quotes the words of Jesus:

"It is you who have stood by me in my trials; and I confer a kingdom on you, just as my Father has conferred one on me, that you may eat and drink at my table in my kingdom; and you will sit on thrones judging the twelve tribes of Israel." (Luke 22: 28-30)

"After the institution of the Eucharist, Jesus says: 'I tell you; from now on I shall not drink this fruit of the vine until the day when I drink it with you new in the kingdom of my Father'.". (Mt 26: 29)

But there are conditions necessary in order to be able to participate at the banquet:

"The kingdom of heaven may be likened to a king who gave a wedding feast for his son. He dispatched his servants to summon the invited guests to the feast, but they refused to come". (Mt

22: 2-3)

It is not enough to be invited. One must respond to the invitation and one must participate in the Eucharistic Mass. There are various ways of behaving and modes of participating.

"The virgins are waiting for the spouse in order to go to the banquet with him. When he doesn't arrive, they fall asleep. Five of them are taken to the wedding with the oil in their lamps, while the other five are really foolish, because they are without oil." [See Mt 25:1-12]

"We have to be wary in our wait. If the servant concludes that the benefactor will be late, then he will only think about himself, about food and drink and as a result, there will be misunderstandings, fights and wars." (Mt24: 45-51)

Fasting teaches us to wait, and not to tire in waiting, and at the same time, to testify to the great wait for the eternal banquet in the Reign of God. Everything that is written in the book of the Apocalypse will come about in this way:

"Behold, I stand at the door and knock. If anyone hears my voice and opens the door, (then) I will enter his house and dine with him, and he with me." (Ap 3:20)

What does the Catechism of the Catholic Church say about fasting?

In the *Catechism of the Catholic Church*, fasting is mentioned for the first time in article n.575. It is to be found between brackets referring to forms of devotion, "charity, fasting and prayer":

Many of Jesus' deeds and words constituted a "sign of contradiction", but more so for the religious authorities in Jerusalem, whom the Gospel according to John often calls simply "the Jews", than for the ordinary People of God. To be sure, Christ's relations with the Pharisees were not exclusively polemical. Some Pharisees warn him of the danger he was courting; Jesus praises some of them, like the scribe of Mark 12:34, and dines several times at their homes. Jesus endorses some of the teachings imparted by these religious elite of God's people: the resurrection of the dead, certain forms of piety (almsgiving, fasting and prayer), the custom of addressing God as Father, and the centrality of the commandment to love God and neighbor.

In article n.1430, it is stated that Jesus' invitation to conversion and penance does not refer exclusively to the exterior works of, 'sack cloth, ashes and fasting':

"To prepare for worthy reception of this sacrament, the faithful should observe the fast required in their Church. Bodily demeanor (gestures, clothing) ought to convey the respect, solemnity, and joy of this moment when Christ becomes our guest."

It is more about the conversion of the heart and interior humiliation. Penitential acts are shown to be fruitless and useless without the interior conversion of the heart. The link between exterior practices and interior conditions of the heart and soul are fundamental.

Jesus' call to conversion and penance, like that of the prophets before him, does not aim first at outward works, "sackcloth and ashes," fasting and mortification, but at the conversion of the heart, interior conversion. Without this, such penances remain sterile and false; however, interior conversion urges expression in visible signs, gestures and works of penance."

In article n. 1434, interior repentance is underlined as 'having different expressions' i.e. fasting prayer and charity. These find expression in the way we relate to ourselves, to God and to our neighbor. Fasting, prayer and charity are instruments through which the remission of sins, reconciliation with our brethren and a concrete love with regard to others can be obtained.

"The interior penance of the Christian can be

expressed in many and various ways. Scripture and the Fathers insist above all on three forms, fasting, prayer, and almsgiving, which express conversion in relation to oneself, to God, and to others. Alongside the radical purification brought about by Baptism or martyrdom they cite as means of obtaining forgiveness of sins: effort at reconciliation with one's neighbor, tears of repentance, concern for the salvation of one's neighbor, the intercession of the saints, and the practice of charity "which covers a multitude of sins. "Above all let your love for one another be intense, because love covers a multitude of sins" (1 Pt 4,8)

In article n.1438, the times of repentance are referred to: Lent and Fridays. In these periods more spiritual exercises and retreats, penitential services, pilgrimages etc. should be organized Fasting is presented as a spontaneous renouncement which we make in favor of those around us.

"The seasons and days of penance in the course of the liturgical year (Lent, and each Friday in memory of the death of the Lord) are intense moments of the Church's penitential practice. These times are particularly appropriate for spiritual exercises, penitential liturgies, and pilgrimages as signs of penance, voluntary self-denial such as fasting and almsgiving, and fraternal sharing (charitable and missionary works).

Article n. 1755, fasting once again is referred to as one of those practices which have no value if carried out with the wrong intentions, as for example, when we fast to show others what we are doing.

"A morally good act requires the goodness of the object, of the end, and of the circumstances together. An evil end corrupts the action, even if the object is good in itself (such as praying and fasting "in order to be seen by men").

The object of the choice can by itself vitiate an act in its entirety. There are some concrete acts - such as fornication - that it is always wrong to choose, because choosing them entails a disorder of the will, that is, a moral evil."

In article n.1969, the new law should be lived out through religious acts: charity, prayer and fasting, referring all things to a God who sees the very intentions of our hearts.

"The New Law practices the acts of religion: almsgiving, prayer and fasting, directing them to the 'Father who sees in secret,' in contrast with the desire to 'be seen by men.' Its prayer is the Our Father."

Article 2043 says that with fasting we should prepare for liturgical solemnities, because through it we obtain freedom of heart and we overcome our impulses.

"The fourth precept ('You shall observe the days of fasting and abstinence established by the Church') ensures the times of ascetics and penance which prepare us for the liturgical feasts and help us acquire mastery over our instincts and freedom of heart.

The fifth precept ('You shall help to provide for the needs of the Church') means that the faithful are obliged to assist with the material needs of the Church, each according to his own ability.

The faithful also have the duty of providing for the material needs of the Church, each according to his own abilities."

With fasting and prayer therefore, we can arrive at a true liberty of heart. Man is then delivered from what ties him and with greater ease affronts the evil which he encounters both in and around himself. For this reason, fasting is so important.

What have the pontiffs said about fasting?

Pope Paul VI: "Paenitemini"

It is important to refer to the Apostolic Letter of Pope Paul VI on fasting and penance. At the beginning of this document, the Pope describes the motives for this publication: Jesus himself linked the announcement of the Good News to penitential practices. He begins his preaching with an invitation to penance, conversion and trust in the Gospel. We also see in the Gospels that St. John the Baptist prepared for his own missions with severe penance, fasting and renouncements. *(See Mark 1:1ff)* St Paul sees in coming of Jesus, a forfeiture: He who is God renounces the Divine and His God-likeness, thereby becoming a servant who is man-like. *(See Phil 2:6-7)*. The Christian is called to participate in the work of Christ and therefore must takes on himself all that Jesus Himself did.

He prayed, taught, fasted and made renouncements through these practices, the passion and death of |Jesus on the cross can also be seen.

One of the principal tasks of the Church as teacher, is to convey the importance of penance, to teach mankind how to deliver itself from the attachments to material things so that along his earthly journey which leads to our heavenly home, we don't give up, or wander off course. We have to be careful not to hinder the work of the Divine within us, and collaborate with the grace that God is giving us.

Penance is necessary for interior purification and the remission of our sins *(see Acts 2:38)* and this is the necessary condition for an interior life united to God. Pope Paul VI points to biblical situations in which penance and fasting are activated. The Church appoints various penitential acts at a general level. Bishops are responsible for these practices in their own diocese, and the parish priests are responsible at a local level. While remaining open to the norms and directives of the Church, a space must also be left open for the everyday life penances of the faithful.

The most important penitential exercise is a conscious applying of one's self to the various obligations which each of the faithful has in their own lives. For example situations which require daily patience and arduous faith. Those believers who are afflicted with sicknesses, poverty, exile, etc are called to unite their pain to Christ's suffering. This is their daily penitential exercise.

The precept of penitence must be satisfied in a more perfect way by priests, who are more closely linked to Christ through sacred character, as well as by those who in order to follow more closely the abnegation of the Lord and to find an easier and more efficacious path to the perfection of charity practice the evangelical counsels.

The Church, however, invites all Christians, without distinction, to respond to the divine precept of penitence by some voluntary act, apart from the renunciation imposed by the burdens of everyday life. "I. 1. By Divine Law, the faithful are required to do penance.

2. The prescriptions of ecclesiastical law regarding penitence are totally reorganized according to the following norms:

"II The time of Lent has preserved its penitential character. The days of penitence to be observed under obligation throughout the Church are all Fridays during Lent and Ash Wednesday, that is to say the first days of "Grande Quaresima" (Great Lent), according to the diversity of the rite. Their attentive observance is gravely binding".

Abstinence means to not eat meat in those days. This rule obliges all believers from age 14 and upwards. Fasting means to eat once to the fill, and to have two smaller meals throughout the day, according to the customs of the area in which we live. This rule obliges all believers from 21 to 60 of age. Bishops and priests have the power to make alterations according to the customs of the area. Basically, fasting and abstinence remain a fundamental duty of the faithful.

Pope John Paul II:
"The Gospel of Life"

Pope John Paul II both fasts himself and invites us to fast with him. In the document, The Gospel of Life, he speaks about fasting and exhorts us to fast and pray, emphasizing that with fasting and prayer we are stronger for the battle against Satan and his reign. In paragraph 100 of this document, he says:

"In this great Endeavour to create a new culture of life we are inspired and sustained by the confidence that comes from knowing that the Gospel of life, like the Kingdom of God itself, is growing and producing abundant fruit (cf. Mk 4:26-29). There is certainly an enormous disparity between the powerful resources available to the forces promoting the "culture of death" and the means at the disposal of those working for a "culture of life and love". But we know that we can rely on the help of God, for whom nothing is impossible (cf. Mt 19:26).

Filled with this certainty, and moved by profound concern for the destiny of every man and woman, I repeat what I said to those families who carry out their challenging mission amid so many difficulties: 135 a great prayer for life is urgently needed, a prayer which will rise up throughout the world. Through special initiatives and in daily prayer, may an impassioned plea rise to God, the Creator and lover of life, from every Christian community, from every group and association, from every family and from the heart of every believer. Jesus himself has shown us by his own example that prayer and fasting are the first and most effective weapons against the forces of evil (cf. Mt 4:1-11). As he taught his disciples, "some demons cannot be driven out except in this way" (cf. Mk 9:29). Let us therefore discover anew the humility and the courage to pray and fast so that power from on high will break down the walls of lies and deceit. The walls that hide the evil practices and laws, which are hostile to life from our brothers and sisters. May these same powers turn their hearts to resolutions and goals inspired by the civilization of life and love.

One day on bread and water:
a request from Pope John Paul II

On the 18th of November 2001, having finished praying the Angelus, John Paul II asked all Catholics to spend one day fasting in order to pray with fervor that God would grant the world peace which is stable, founded upon justice. The Pope suggested the 14th of December which coincided with the end of the Islamic Ramadan. He said:

"My dear brothers and sisters, the international situation continues to be disturbed by worrying anxieties (...) in such dramatic circumstances, we feel the need to cry out to God. However insurmountable the differences seem, however obscure the prospective, this is all the more reason why we should insist in prayer to implore the gift of reciprocal understanding, of concordance and of peace from God.

We know that prayer has a special strength when it is accompanied by fasting and almsgiving. (...) In this suitable time (advent), I would ask Catholics that on December 14th following, we would live it as a fast day during which, we will pray that God grants us peace which is stable and founded upon justice. We ask that He grant us adequate solutions to the conflicts which are distressing the world. We can put whatever we deny ourselves during our fast at the disposition of the poor, especially those who, at the present time, are the victims of terrorism and of war.

I also want to make known that it is my intention to invite the leaders of the other world religions (...) to pray to be able to overcome these contra-positions for the promotion of true peace. We have to come together, in particular Christians and Muslims, to proclaim to the world that religion should never become a motive for conflict, for hatred or for violence. (...)

Again after the Angelus on the 9th of December, 2001, he said:

"My dear brothers and sisters, both peace and violence emerge from the heart of man, which only God has power over. Convinced of this, the faithful have always adopted the weapons of prayer and fasting against the gravest difficulties, accompanying them with acts of charity. Fasting is an expression of regret for serious error, but it also expresses the will to accept some responsibility. (...) When one fasts, he accepts with a humility that is hopeful, that an authentic personal and social renewal can only come from God, upon who we all radically depend. Fasting also permits us to share our daily bread with those who are without, in a way that goes above and beyond all piety or illusions of assistance.(...)

The date, 14th of December also coincides with the end of the Ramadan, during which the followers of Islam express their submission to the one God through fasting. I earnestly hope that the communal attitude of religious penance develops reciprocal comprehension between Christians and Muslims, who are called as never before, to be together actual constructors of justice and peace, in this time(...)".

Fr. Divo Barsotti, founder of the Community, the Children of God:

"The reasoning behind the choice of this date had significance in that the two positions which are most in conflict today would find themselves united. The unity which God wants to stabilize among men ought first of all to be realized in a unity of mankind in God, of all mankind in this humble prayer but a prayer which is full of hope in recognizing that only god can overcome the conflicts and the aspiration of all mankind for a peace which is long-lasting and given by God himself".

A few reflections on fasting from the Holy Father, Pope John Paul II

Conversion: "Fasting means repentance, a turning towards God, in so far as it purifies the heart from the many traces of evil, it beautifies the soul in virtue, it turns the will in the direction of good, and it broadens the heart so that it can receive the abundance of divine grace". *(To the young people on St. Peters Square, 21st of March 1979)*

Sobriety: "Penitential fasting, amongst other things, has a purpose of reviving our inner self. The effort to moderate our eating extends into other fields, and is of great support in the spiritual life. Sobriety, self containment and prayer go hand in hand." *(Angelus, March 10, 1996)*

Renunciation: "Fasting is a symbol and a sign, it is an invitation that is both serious and stimulating to accept or carry out renouncements. What renouncements? Renouncements of myself, or moreover renouncements to my many tantrums or sick aspirations, renouncements to my own weaknesses, to my destructive passions to illicit desires. Fasting means knowing how to say no, short and sweet, to the suggestions posed by my own pride, my own egoism and vices." *(To the young people, St.Peters Square, 21st March, 1979).*

Prayer: "Fasting must go hand in hand with prayer, because it directs us towards a discourse with God. On the other hand fasting, or the mortification of the senses and self dominion, gives prayer a greater strength."

Solidarity: "The practices of fasting and almsgiving, other than expressing a personal ascent, also have an important social value for the community. They remind us of the need to convert from our model of 'social development' towards a more just distribution of earthly goods, so that all men can live with dignity." *(The celebration in the Basilica of Saint Sabina, on the Wednesday of Holy Week, 17th of February 1999).*

Let's imitate the lives of the Saints

It's well known that the Saints fasted and prayed. In the rules of most religious orders, both male and female, Wednesday and Fridays were traditionally reserved as fast days along with prolonged periods of fasting such as lent. However, according to collected reports, fasting has practically disappeared even in the more rigid religious orders.

Within the Church, many cases are noted of Saints who have lived exclusively on the Eucharist such as St. Nicholas Flue, Theresa Neumann, and more recently Marthe Robin. Here the Lord concedes a special grace directly to the Saint who lives solely on the bread that comes from heaven. The Father tells us this in the Words of His Son: "I am the bread of life. Whoever comes to me will no longer be hungry and who believes in me will not thirst" *(John 6:35)*.

The following Saints illustrate this special grace:

Alexandrina Maria Da Costa

This Salesian helper was born in Balasar, Portugal on the 30th of March 1904. At the age of twenty she became paralyzed and bed-ridden because of an injury to her spine caused by jumping from the window of her house while trying to escape an attack on her purity by three men of ill-will. In the solitude of her room, Alexandrina became an angel of consolation to Jesus in all the tabernacles of the world. She was a hostess of the Divine Host and would be a victim soul offered together with Jesus for the salvation of souls. In her soul and body, she mystically lived the Passion of Our Lord Jesus Christ, from the agony in the Gethsemane to the crucifixion on Calvary in reparation for the outrages, sacrileges and profanations of the Eucharist.

Tabernacles and sinners were her mission entrusted to her by Our Lord in 1934:

Let devotion to the tabernacles be well practiced and well preached, because days and days pass by and no one visits me, souls do not love me, and make no reparation to me. They do not believe that I reside there. I desire that hearts would be lit up with devotion to this prison of love....there are so many who enter churches, who do not even greet me or remain a moment in adoration. I would like so many faithful guards prostrate in front of the tabernacles, so that many faults would not take place.

During the last thirteen years of her life, Alexandrina lived exclusively on the Eucharist, with no other form of nourishment. This was the last mission that Jesus entrusted to her in 1954: "Live from me alone to show the world the importance of the Eucharist, and what my life within souls can mean: light and salvation for humanity".

Young Saint Maccario

Young Saint Maccario of the fourteenth century lived almost all his live in a desert cell. At that time were many desert cell hermits who went to the desert from all over the world to live in abstinence and solitude. Among all the cell hermits of the desert, St Maccario became the most austere.

There is a story told of the basket of grapes received by the Saint that is significant. He decided to give the basket of grapes to another hermit who was sick. The sick one thought it better to give it to an elderly one; the elderly one passed it on to a younger one and so on and so on.

The appetizing basket of fresh grapes went around and around the cells and came back completely intact to St Maccario without any one of the hermits injuring either abstinence or charity.

He was ordained a priest and for a while lived in a very strict monastery. Once there however, the monks, who were used to a life of harsh penances, were shocked by the Saint's austerity and desired that he leave the monastery. They said, "It is as if he has no body at all". Effectively the Saint had become pure spirit, ignoring the need to eat or drink. He was on his feet from morning to night, without eating, ever sleeping, not sensing either heat or cold or the stings or bites of insects.

He would be motionless in prayer.

All excepting his hands which as if they were on 'automatic' would weave palm leaves into baskets and other objects.

Often in order to resist temptation he would heave a sack of sand onto his back, and with this he would hurry here and there in the desert.

This was his way of making the body which he referred to as "that old white-haired glutton" submit. To anyone who tried to help, he would say: "Leave me alone; this is my way of tormenting the one who torments me".

Saint Syncletia

Saint Syncletia was a rich Egyptian who, having understood at the age of thirty that she was afflicted with a cancer which gave her very little hope of surviving, distributed her riches to the poor and went to live in a tomb to be ready to accept death when it came. When it did arrive, the saint was 84 years of age Fifty years had passed by during which the woman had conducted a life of total self-deprivation, nourishing herself exclusively on bread and water.

Saint Verdiana

Saint Verdiana was a virgin and a recluse. She remained closed up in a hermitage on the sea-shore of Elsa devoting herself to prayer and penance, limiting herself to communicating with the outside world through a tiny window, that opened into a prayer room. She ate only once a day, usually bread and water, to which she sometimes added some vegetable.

Usually she slept on the bare floor, though when winter became rigid, she would use a plank of wood to lie on. She distributed almost all of what she received through the charity of her visitors to the poor who often came to receive a word of consolation from her. It is said that one day, two snakes entered her cell through the small window and remained a long time in the cell with her tormenting her. She kept silence about their presence so that she could offer up some extra suffering.

Saint Simeon Stylites, the elder

His fasts were interrupted on Sundays only. He wore a hair shirt that reduced him to the state of a foul-smelling hound.

He had a chain around his feet that restricted his movements and caused his flesh to be consumed by worms.

He spent two years and a half buried in the convent garden and carried out so many other tremendous mortifications and austerities that he was considered insane by his severe monk brethren and his superiors.

It is told that he wanted to be walled up in a monk cell for the whole duration of lent. This was permitted after he accepted to bring with him ten loaves of bread and a vessel of water. At the end of lent he was taken out, almost out of his senses, on the ground not having touched the provisions at all. But after receiving the Eucharist the saint gained consciousness. He renewed this Lenten "total fast" another forty three times, on his feet in the beginning, then sitting and finally lying on the ground. Later on, he succeeded in remaining on his feet for the duration of the forty days. However, it was the choice of an even more unusual form of penance which made him famous: He lived for forty years on top of a column which was thirty meters high (For this reason, he was noted in history as St. Simeon, the stylite). On top of this column, exposed to the elements, harsh sunshine, rainstorms and cruel winds, with the protection of the hood of his habit only, he prayed continuously with his arms extended and raised. Hundreds of times he would bow so low as to touch his toes with his forehead (this position in fact acquired him a wound on the base of his feet and other wounds which were healed subsequently quite miraculously.

Twice a day he preached to the people, giving them advice. Blinded by the sun, folded over himself, on his knees, occupying the tiny tip of the column, with humility, simplicity and tenderness, he healed the people and freed them from possession. As for food, he ate the small provisions that were extended up to him on a stick from time to time.

St. Paul of Tebe, the Hermit

After the outbreak of the revolution at Decio against the Christians, Paul, who was both Christian and rich, in order to escape the attention of the authorities, wandered in search of a remote and secure refuge. He eventually came to an open hallow that was open at the base of a rocky mountain. When he moved the rock that was blocking the entrance, he found himself looking at a grotto in which a date tree stood reaching out in the sky and offered its fruits to nourish him. There was also a spring of water which, after a short flow on the surface, re-entered the earth. From this he was able to drink. In this lonely and secure place, apt for living without the need to go out for supplies, this saint decided to spend the rest of his life, in the most perfect silence and in the most perfect union with God.

A miraculous and mysterious daily visitation by a crow that dropped him a ration of bread confirmed his vocation and way of life. It is told that the evening, in which the meeting between St. Paul and St. Anthony took place, the crow brought not one, but two rations of bread.

(St. Anthony had been informed in a dream of the existence of a man who embraced the monastic life in an even more perfect way in the desert. He decided at ninety years of age to begin to walk in search of him, without knowing the way beforehand. He wanted to see with his own eyes this model of angelic life.)

St Benedict

St Benedict the Father of Western Monasticism as we know it. In the rule of his order, and for his spiritual children, fasting took a principal part. These words became a golden rule in St. Benedict "Love fasting! Love purity!".

For St. Benedict there is a profound link between fasting and purity. Purity in the religious sense means to abstain from sexual desire and to rise above it.

This is possible if when we renounce the pleasure of food through fasting.

For this reason, often the religious loves fasting and purity, because thanks to these offerings, they renounce themselves and establish a profound communion with God. In this way they are predisposed to love God and one's neighbor just as Christ asks. Fasting purifies the heart and soul, while giving joy and freedom to the person entirely.

In chapter thirty nine of his rule, St. Benedict of Norcia, set down how much it is possible to eat on a fast day:

Up to one kilo of bread with no limit to how much water can be drunk. The hours of eating regarding the seasons was also set down with great wisdom.

From Easter to Pentecost, the brothers had lunch and a meal in the evening time.

After Pentecost and for the duration of the summer, if the monks do not have any heavy work in the fields, or tormented by excessive heat, they fast on Wednesdays and Fridays from about three in the afternoon onwards.

On the other days they have lunch at about midday but this hour could be changed if work in the fields necessitated it (subject to the Abbots discretion).

The Abbot must discern wisely since the salvation of the monks souls was in his hands. He should avoid causing the brothers to complain about the arrangements.

From the 14th of September until the beginning of Lent, Lunch was always after three. During Lent right up to Easter, Lunch was served after evening prayer. *(Rule XLI)*

St. Francis of Assisi

St. Francis of Assisi spent long periods fasting and tasted its great fruits. In the rule of his order, the saint instructed the brethren to: "fast from the feast of 'All Saints' up until Christmas and until the Epiphany, when Our Lord Jesus Christ began to fast, up until Easter." At all other times fasting was not obligatory except on Fridays. After this period, they were allowed to eat all foods that were set before them, as the Gospel says, *(Lk 10: 8)*. In him, we see the example of someone who fasted with no sadness, he is decisive and generous, his heart and countenance were full of joy.

St. Francis often fasted for long periods, as related in the account, The little Flowers of St. Francis, tells us, *(chapter VII, ff 1835)* where the saint fasted for forty days and forty nights on an island in the lake of Perugia. He ate nothing more than half a loaf of bread during that time.

To St. Francis, fasting meant at least one meal a day. As for the quantity of food allowed, it seems that the saint had recourse to the teaching of St. Benedict who had already thought it out with discretion and precision.

As for the Franciscans travelling around the world, and lay Franciscans (the third order), fasting was not easy. The discourse on fasting, on foods and on lent risked causing confusion in various ways throughout the kingdom of God. The brethren came face to face with heretics of every shape and form, in particular with the Catars who were very fond of fasting and indoctrinated the crowds demanding special ways to fast according to the moral value of Manichaeism.

(Some of them were strict vegetarians; others allowed milk and its by-products. Some of them divided the milk products into what was good and what was bad. But the bottom line was Manicheistic which professed, from the time of St. Augustine, that the world was created with two co-eternal and co-equal principles, saying that they should fast 'like this and like that', and that certain foods were permitted. From the principle of good for example, the soul was created. From the principle of evil, the body was created, in which the soul has fallen, as if into a prison. It follows that this good soul needs to be liberated from the evil body. Some foods come from the principal of good and others from the principle of bad and therefore are evil. The evil and sinful foods were those of the Old Testament and those of the Eastern Tradition and were considered impure. And so pork and other meats were considered to be impure, but some Catars were also forbidden milk products, because milk comes from the teat, and this has associations with the breast and therefore is connected to sexuality which comes from the principle of evil.

Not even an egg could be eaten, because it too had sexual associations.)

So it happened that the brethren, who were travelling for the purpose of evangelization, often came in contact with those heretics and let themselves be indoctrinated by these theories. On the other hand, the people offered them whatever they had: sometimes meat, sometimes eggs, sometimes milk-products and sometimes vegetables. What should they eat?

St. Francis in the first place watches over the minds of his disciples and wants them to remain Catholic. It is significant that when Francis is confronting the whole area of fasting and food, he always adds the comment: "And let them be Catholics". The same orientation he gives to his lay-members (the third order), who live in the world. Francis wants to see what mentality is hidden behind so much fasting and so much penance: "If I know that something is doing me harm, do I let it continue? In this case we can be at peace. But if there is an oriental mentality hidden behind the fasting and not a Catholic one, then we have to be more severe: "All the brethren are Catholic and live as Catholics and speak as Catholics. If one of them by their words or by their behavior distances themselves from the faith or from the Catholic life, they are to be expelled totally from our fraternity." (Rule non bollata 19, 1 FF 1)

Even today, if you dig in a little deeper to the mentality of many vegetarians, it is easy to see that the roots have come from the East and we have gone beyond the Jordan and have almost arrived at the river Ganges.

Francis insistently repeats though, for love of God's providence, and for those who offer us hospitality, the line from the Gospel: "Eat what is set before you" *(Lk 10: 8)*. Francis's soul really was of rare nobility. If he happened to be at table with people of the world, and they offered him food that he liked, he barely tasted them offering some excuse, so that no-one realized that he was doing penance. But when alone, he discovered ways of doing even more rigid penances which as time went on, he exercised and deepened. He was, at almost all times, "a principle of the way of perfection", always looking for new ways to chastise human concupiscence.

When he went out into the world to preach the Word, he ate the same foods as those with whom he stayed; when returning home however he practiced rigorous abstinences and parchezza.

He did however avoid putting penances on the shoulders of the brethren which he feared would not be able to withstand it.

Saint Basil

St. Basil was born into a noble family in the third century in the country which we today call Turkey. His mother and brothers were also saints, but his own natural genius singled him out as a doctor of the church and as one of the more important of the patriarchs. His contributions to Church culture meant that eastern monasticism was placed on a more organized basis. The following are some thoughts about fasting from his writings:

You think that I believe that fasting has its origins in the Mosaic Law? For me fasting is even older than the law itself! It's so old it began with the creation of man itself. It was a decree as far back as the garden of Paradise. The first precept received by Adam was, "to not eat of the tree of the knowledge of good and evil". This "Do not eat" is the law of fasting and abstinence. Lazarus entered paradise through fasting. Noah never tasted wine.

Moses would never have arrived at the peak of the mountain if he hadn't gone through the cloud and he hadn't equipped himself with the armor of fasting *(Ex 24: 18)*; and it was through fasting that he was able to receive the Commandments, God's own handwork. At the top of the mountain it was fasting which would make the breakthrough to the commandments, while at the foot of the mountain many regressed into idolatry. In fact, the people sat, feasted and drank and afterwards sought to divert themselves. And so that which the servant Moses had gained with forty days of fasting and intense communication with God, was rendered fruitless because of the orgy which the people held. Exactly at the time that the people were about to receive the knowledge of God, this breakthrough was impeded through the sin of gluttony and the foolish idolatry which had more in common with Egyptian ways than Jewish traditions. And what was it that ruined Esau and made him into the slave of his brother? Was it not for a plateful of lentils that he sold his birthright? *(Gen 25: 30-34)* And was it not fasting united with prayer which gave Anna their son Samuel? *(1 Sam 1: 13-16)* What was it that made Samson such a strong and invincible man, if not the fasting that his Mother practiced when she conceived him? *(Jgs 13: 4-14).* He was conceived during a fast, nourished by the same fast, as if in a cocoon and grew precisely because of the fasting which the angel had prescribed to his mother: "She must not eat anything which comes from the vine, nor eat unclean things."

Fasting motivates the prophets, strengthens the weak, fasting administers wisdom to legislators. It is the custodian of the soul, and the secure defense of the body. It is like armor for those who are in battle, or like training for athletes.

Fasting distances us from temptations, it makes

us tend towards piety, and it is the friend and intimate companion of sobriety and the artifice of chastity. In times of grave problems, it reacts with strength, in times of peace, it aids our tranquility. It sanctifies and perfects priests. Elijah, when fasting for forty days, purified his own soul, and in the end, in the cave in Mt. Oreb, he was able to see God is so far as it is possible for a man. *(1Kings 19: 8-13)* Strengthened against death through fasting, he handed his son over to the widow. The voice which came from a mouth which fasted closed the heavens for three years and six months on a wicked people and indicated with famine, that the people should fast. *(1 Kings 17:1)*

To put it briefly, we can find Saints from East to West and from age to age, and these were brought to a life which was worthy of God through the practice of fasting and renunciation.

Fasting is like the dew laden breeze which protected the young people in the furnace of Babylon *(Dan 1:8-16, 3:24-50)*. Through their fast they obtained this dew-laden breeze.

Daniel, who was a man of desires, having fasted for three weeks, in a den even taught the lions to fast! *(Dan 10:2, 6:16-22)* It was as if his fasting had created an iron barrier that the lions could not overcome. Fasting holds back the force of fire and closes the mouths of lions.

Fasting is the airwave that transmits our prayers

to heaven and he who fasts is like one whose footsteps are aided by ethereal wings in the direction of heaven.

Fasting is to the advantage of the whole household. It is a stronghold for wedded life. It benefits the health of the mother, it is the teacher for the young, it is the jewel and treasure of the elderly and it is the good friend of whoever carries it on their journey. The husband who watches his wife fasting is sure that no corruption or entrapment is corroding their relationship. A wife who sees that her husband has embraced fasting will not suffer from jealousy.

Whoever heard of fasting being the cause of household bankruptcy? Examine your household accounts today and then re-examine tomorrow after fasting, you will find that you have only been enriched.

Can you not see that the sun is more joyful after the night? Just as waking is more playful after repose. Just as good health is so desirable when one has had an experience of hardship- in the same way, the storehouse, (or as we would say today: 'the refrigerator'), looks so much more gratifying after a fast, for those who have in abundance.

Does the story of the rich man who flittered through his luxuries and was then sent to the fires frighten you? Well to extinguish this fire that is raging there is a need of water.

No one ever became a glutton by drinking water. No one ever got a headache from drinking water. No one who was familiar with water ever finished up begging at his neighbors' door. Contrarily, the vices with which many live comfortably generate painful suffering even within the human body. The countenance of the one who fasts is not flushed with an unhealthy red, but rather is adorned with a pallor that is modest, the eyes are placid and serene, and their walk is very composed. Their faces are not creased by worries and anguish, neither are they given to raucous laughter, their conversation is simple, their hearts are pure.

Why was Lazarus able to rest tranquilly in the bosom of Abraham? Because he fasted.

And wasn't the life of John the Baptist a continuous fast? He had no table, no bed, no fields, and no livestock: and these were among the reasons why "among those born of woman, there is no-one greater than St. John the Baptist".

More importantly though, Our Lord Jesus Christ in his flesh, would not have conquered the devil if he hadn't first strengthened that body which he assumed for love of us, through fasting. In doing so he also taught us and prepared us for the battle against temptation, as well as offering us a reference point for defeating the adversary by hunger. Satan wouldn't have been able to tempt because of the sublimity of Jesus' Divine nature if he hadn't subjected him to experience human weakness through hunger. And he also tasted food before he returned to heaven to prove to us that it was a human body that he had re-taken.

If you wish to make the mind strong, then dominate the flesh by fasting. This is also what the Apostle says: "although our outer self is wasting away, our inner self is being renewed day by day." *(2 Cor 4: 16)* So why do we not have less craving for these nutrients which decay. Why shouldn't we be enveloped by the desire for the heavenly banquet that you can begin to prepare for now by fasting?

Was there ever anyone who feasted and banqueted splendidly and also procured the perpetual delicacies, or was allowed to partake in spiritual gifts? In order for Moses to receive the Law a second time it was necessary to fast a second time. For as long as the people of Israel were content with the desert manna, and the water from the rock, they could overpower the Egyptian army, cross the Red Sea and none of their tribe were ill. But when they started to crave their meat dishes and regret the loss of their luxuries in Egypt, they could no longer see the promise land.

Not even Daniel, the great wise-man would have had his visions if he had not made his soul pure through fasting.

Fasting is armor against demons: As Jesus himself said "This kind can only come out through fasting and prayer". While many good things come from fasting, all wantonness originates in bodily satisfaction. Infact, when raptures and intoxication are caused by the sweetness of a sumptuous food or fruit, there is an immediate correspondence in lechery and lustfulness.

Do not think that fasting consists only in the abstinence from food- because true fasting means opposing all vices. It breaks the chains of iniquity, it makes allowances for the bother caused by our neighbor, and opens the way to forgiveness. We cannot fast while fighting or arguing: can we abstain from meat but devour our brother? Can we abstain from wine and indulge in insult and injury? We await sun-down so that we can eat but we attack our brother the whole day long? Woe to those who are intoxicated not by wine, but in their thoughts. Anger is the intoxication of the mind. The athlete before the race must train. And whoever fasts prepares for the battle through abstinence. To gain victory over our vices and passions, we must assume the crown of fast and abstinence". *(From St. Basil's homily on fasting.)*

Some brief thoughts on fasting:

• **Aristide** wrote to the emperor Adriano with regard to the first Christians saying, "And then there are also some poor people who are in need, the community fasts two or three days and send them the food that they otherwise would have used".

• **St. Augustine:** "Will your fast be pleasing to God if you forget a brother? Fast and take action: Prayer flies up to heaven when transported by these wings. Therefore fast: in this way, others can eat instead of you and you should rejoice in being deprived of your meal. For whoever is without food would like to be helped in their poverty. Be careful not to ignore the poverty of our God, he is starving and waiting for your help".

• **St. Leon Magno:** "Prayer and fasting are what pleases God and frightens Satan. It contributes both to our own and to the salvation of others. There is nothing more effective than fasting to bring us closer to God! Let us not ignore this great means, this effective therapy for our wounds. Let us be thankful for our well-being: why can't the fasting of the community of the faithful, become the food of the poor".

- **Gandhi:** "My religion teaches me that in whatever trouble I might find myself, we need to pray and fast!"

- All religions, beginning with the most ancient, knew of and practiced fasting. The periods and the situations in which they fasted vary, but the objective is always the same, to create the conditions for a better relationship with God and with all Divine things. In one ancient proverb it says: "Fasting is the food of the soul, it keeps the brakes held on the carelessness of the tongue, it shuts the mouth, it reduces the desire for pleasure and calms a cantankerous temperament. It aids us in decision making, it fortifies our bodies, liberates us from nightmares, cures headaches and strengthens our sight!"

- **Buddha:** "The more my body retreats, the brighter my soul becomes, the spirit is vigilant and the wisdom and ability to delve into myself is available!"

- **St Francis de Sales:** "Here are a few pointers, if you know how to fast, it would be good to fast even more often than the Church recommends. Apart from the ordinary effects of fasting, (which would be the liberation of the Spirit and domination over the body to practice virtue and to increase the reward which awaits us in eternity), fasting helps us to dominate our appetites and keeps bodily desires in second place to that of the spirit. Even if we do not fast often, the enemy when he realizes that we know how to fast, will fear us more. Wednesdays, Fridays and Saturdays were the days that the Christian community fasted. Choose one among them, according to your own spirituality and the discretion of your own Spiritual Director."

We must greatly respect the words which Our Lord, Savior and Redeemer said to His Disciples: "Eat whatever is set before you". I'm of the opinion that it is more virtuous to eat, without being fastidious whatever is put in front of you, and in whatever order, and ignoring what is to your greater liking, even choosing more of whatever is not. Because even if this latter way of fasting seems more austere, the former requires more mortification, for you must renounce not only your own taste, but also your own personal choice, and it seems to me a greater penance to surrender our preferences to whatever the situation offers. As well as this, these mortifications go unnoticed and therefore cause no annoyances. In this indifference to what we shall eat and what we shall drink, we find our perfection in the Word of God. (from Filothea- available at Shalom bookstores)

• **The Imitation of Christ:** "My son, what do you

do when you fast?" Faithful soul: "In the mornings I plait the palm branches, and while I work, I meditate on the psalms. When I finish one basket I pray for a while. In the afternoons, I have a short sleep. Then I get up, I go into my room and I work some more, until I have completed three baskets. In the evenings I pray, and after bowing one hundred times, I get up to go and recite my office. The following day, I cook until nine and then I eat until I am no longer hungry."

The elder responds:

My son, this is not fasting. If you renounce food, but say hateful things and make judgements, then you are vindictive with regards to others. If you are allowing hateful thoughts to enter you, or in your soul you wish to be in someone else's shoes, it would have been better had you spent the day eating and avoided everything, other than filling yourself. What advantage is it to a soul, if he renounces food, but lets himself feast in every other way? Do you not know that whoever satisfies their own desires in their thoughts, eats and drinks without swallowing anything? If you want to practice moderation, and if you want to fast in the manner that God requires, then abstain from jeers and scoffing, don't slander or defame, don't condemn and close your ears to those conversations which do likewise. Purify your heart of every bodily or spiritual stain. Eat in moderation and it will be easier to restrain the other inclinations of the flesh".

• **St. Thomas Aquinas:** "When Satan is defeated in tempting you in your eating habits, he moves on to tempting you in indecency and impropriety."

• **St. Alphonsis Maria de Ligouri:** "Whoever is weak in sins of gluttony, and doesn't try to rectify it, will never make any notable progress in the ways of the spirit."

• **St. Peter Chrisologo:** "Ours is a fast of simplicity, be holy in an innocent way, be clean with purity, be genuine with sincerity. Be hidden to mankind, unknown to the devil, but acknowledged by God.
  Fasting washes the defects from our senses, cancels the sins from our souls, dissipates the guilt of the heart, making the blemishes of that very heart disappear and leads the soul, to candor and chastity with an extraordinary splendor."

• **Fr. Thomas Spidlik:** (A Jesuit and a teacher of spiritual theology): In the history of religions, fasting not only entails the abstinence from meat or of food. Ther are also fasts of work or of words, of joys or of the sexual life. One of the most ancient motives for fasting was the sadness that surrounds death: When a family lost a loved one, they fasted to show that life was so sad that it was almost not worth living. Fasting was also linked to the idea of preparation: for example the spouse who had to go to a new family fasted, precisely in view of the new life she was about to start. With regard to how prayer is related to fasting, we can say that to combine these two elements is at the heart of the Christian fast. Perhaps the majority of us understand this in a very common way: We say "I pray and until God grants me my request, I will fast too". But the Fathers of the Church teach us exactly the opposite: "If you do not fast, you cannot pray well: if you are not capable of renouncing something, how can you say that your conversation with God is sincere? Saint Basilio says, "fat ducks cannot fly up to the rooftops" Perhaps this expression makes us want to laugh. But within there is a profound truth about prayer. Fasting is the prayer of the body, which, in this manner, participates in my whole spiritual outlook.

• **Lucia from Fatima:** It was Francesco who thought up a good sacrifice: "Let us give our breakfast to the sheep and we will make the sacrifice of not eating." In a few minutes, all our provisions were eaten up by the flock. This is how we ended up doing our first day of fasting, which wouldn't have been the most austere acts of the

Carthusians. These were not the only fasts we did. We decided to give our lunches to the poor whenever we met up with them, and those poor children, who were so happy with our offerings, deliberately would try to meet us, by waiting on the roadside."

Let us pray together with the Church

Here are some prayers and songs of the Church, from the period of Lent, in which we see what fasting represented and what it should represent for Christians today.

"Grant O Lord, that by our fast and abstinence we may enter into a conversion which is authentic, so that with the weapons of penance we may be victorious in the battle over the spirit of evil." *(Ash Wednesday, the Collect of the Mass)*

Fasting, prayer and good works are the instruments thanks to which we can become strong against the spirit of evil, and persevere in doing good. Fasting is the means which gives us the strength to change our life and to discover the love of God and his mercy. For this reason in the antiphon of the benediction rite of the ashes on Ash Wednesday, the prayer goes as follows:

"Let us renew our lives in a spirit of humility and penance. Let us fast and cry out with tears to the Lord so that He who is merciful, will be willing to forgive all our offenses". *(Ash Wednesday, antiphon)*

O God who has mercy on he who repents and gives peace to whoever converts, receive with paternal goodness the prayers of your people and bless, these your children, who will receive the austere symbol of ashes so that through this spiritual journey of fasting, we may arrive completely renewed to celebrate the Paschal Mystery of your Son, who is the Christ. *(Ash Wednesday, prayer during the imposition of ashes)*

In the Mass prayers of Ash Wednesday, fasting is seen as an atonement for greed and a purification from sin; and this medicine is pleasing to God.

"Grant Lord, that through works of charity and penance, we overcome our vices and, free from sin, we can celebrate the Paschal Mystery of your Son." *(Ash Wednesday, prayer over the gifts)* "May this sacrifice that we have received , sustain us on our journey, sanctify us and make effective the healing of our spirit". *(Ash Wednesday, prayer after Communion)*

Inspire our actions Lord, and accompany them with your aid, so that all our actions have their beginning and end in You. *(Thursday after Ash Wednesday)*

May the bread from heaven which you have given us, Father, nourish us in our faith, increase our hope, strenthen our love, and teach us to be hungry for the Lord, the true and living bread, and to lie by every word which comes from the mouth of God. *(Eucharistic prayer from the first Sunday of Lent)*

This means that we must have an ardent desire for Christ, the bread come down from heaven and the living Word of the Father; the fast to which we are called by our blessed Mother will help us to live through Jesus and by every word that comes from his mouth.

Fasting means discipline for the body and freedom for the spirit, to the point that they burn for God.

"O merciful Father, turn you gaze to this family, and grant that we may oercome all forms of egoism, reflects a great desire for you" *(Tuesday of the Ist week of Lent, Collect)*

"O God the eternal Father, grant that our hearts conert to You, so that while seeking the only necessary good and in our works of fraternal charity, we are always seeking Your glory" *(Saturday of the 1st week of Lent, collect).*

The Church also prays that our physical renouncements will give birth to spiritual fruits, showing in this way the links between fasting and spiritual fruits.

"O God who makes it possible for bodily penance to heal the soul, grant that we may abstain from all sin in order to have the strength to observe Your commandments of love." *(collect from Monday of the nd week of Lent)*

"O Lord sanctify our efforts of conversion and grant that our outer Lenten practices correspond to a true transformation of Spirit". *(Offertory prayer from the second Thursday of Lent)*

These prayers face us with a big problem, a problem which caused Jesus to discuss hotly withthe Pharisees and accused them of fasting and praying for prestige without harmonising their hearts with what they were doing. Whoever prays and fast must do so to the point that the interior journey follows the outward acts. If this doesn't happen then our prayer and fasting is dubious. Prayer and fasting must prepare the human heart for the celebration of the Resurrection. This is the principle significance.

The Church also recognises the intensity with which God looks on us men when it prays:

"O merciful God and fount of all goodness, you have given us a remedy for sin, fasting prayer and fraternal charity; look favorably on us who recognize our own misery and grant us remorse tor our transgressions and your mercy which soothes us." *(3rd Sunday of Lent, Collect)*

Fasting, like renunciation, give strength, disposes us toward prayer and leads to joy.

"O Lord our God, grant that your faithful, helped by our efforts to do good and listening to your Word, may serve You generously free from all egoism, and in communion pray to You". *(Collect from the 3rd Wednesday of Lent)*

"O God our Father, who in Lenten celebrations give us a taste of the joy of Easter, let us come to a deeper understanding of the mystery of redemption to reap the fullness of its' fruit". *(Collect, Saturday from the third week of Lent)*

Lenten devotion, (fasting, prayer and fraternal

charity included) predispose man to be a witness and a messenger of the salvation of the world, to live conversion to do good deeds and tobecome holy.

"Faithful and merciful God, in this time of prayer and penance, grant that you children worthily live this paschal mystery and bring to our brothers the good news of salvation" *(Collect, fourth Tuesday of Lent).*

"O Father who has given us the grace to purify ourselves with penance and to make ourselves holy by good deeds, grant that we walk faithfully on the way of your precepts, to arrie fully renewed and the Easter feast. *(Collect from the 4th week of Lent)*

During the Easter Week, the Church celebrate the importance of Jesus' fasts, which must be equal for us Christians:

"He consecrated the institution of a time of penance with his fast for forty days, and gaining victory over the snares of the ancient tempter, we are thought to dominate the seduction to sin" *(Preface from the 1st Sunday of Lent)*

"Every year you let Your faithful prepare with joy, purified in the spirit, at the Easter celebration, so that intent on prayer and charitable works..." *(First foreword of Lent).*

"You have established a time of spiritual renewal for them to convert with all their hearts, and free from sin live their lives in this life, alway directed towards the eternal good. And for this gift of you goodness, united to the angels..." *(Second foreword of Lent)*

"You wish that with the penitential works of Lent, so that gaining victory over our selfishness, we are more open to the needs of the poor, in imitation of Christ your Son our saviour..." *(3rd foreword of Lent)*

With the Lenten fast, you gain victory over our passions, elevate our spirits, grant us strength, and grant us our reward..." *(4th intro of Lent)*

The worthiness and the call to fasting

Fasting, the health of mind and body

It's clear that fasting positively influences the health of the body in maintaining equilibrium so it has a direct or indirect influence on psycho-physical state of the human being. When bodily equilibrium is lost, the psychological equilibrium is also threatened. And a psychological lack of equilibrium then has an implication on the physical condition of the person. Situations of the soul in which this most clearly can be seen are in ailments such as anorexia and bullemia.

Bulemia consists in an irregular consumption of food followed by self induced vomiting, while anorexia is a refusal of food. Surrounding these states of mind, there are always problems of the soul which induce deterioration in our relationship with the body. Healing can begin when we free the soul from a negative way of relating to the self and those around us. At this level prayer and fasting constitute a true 'spring-cleaning' of the soul. The root of all illnesses of the soul is the loss of interior freedom. Putting it simpler man becomes his own prisoner;a slave of his own ego. This enslavement can be to material things or certain satisfactions and so the soul becomes completely enslaved to themselves or to others or to material goods. In this way the process of autodestruction begins: leading sometimes to depression and sometimes to a loss of the sense of reality.

Thanks to fasting and prayer, the human soul can easily remain sane and can preserve some degree of peace.

It is very important for us to understand that we must defend ourselves from all forms of enslavement. We must maintain interior freedom, right from the beginning of our lives. If asked whether children should fast, we should answer in the affirmative.

When children live surrounded by abundance, when they get whatever they want whenever they want and without any effort then they cannot sufficiently develop some spiritual abilities and this will surface in the phases to come in their lives. If in a family, where there are only one or two children, these grow in an atmosphere which can make them egocentric and they cannot develop a correct relationship with others.

Life is really complicated and brings its own difficulties and problems. These represent battles that we can either win or lose. We have to know at the outset that we cannot always obtain what we want, and if we do; it won't be effortless. Children who, right from the beginning, were in the habit of getting whatever they wanted, and who never learned to look out for the interests of others but indifferently and sometimes even callously sought their own ends undergo an annulment of their own spirit. This is why there are always more and more people who, at the first failure at school, in work or in love, they lose sight of the meaning of life: They cannot experience joy anymore in living, and driven by their own ego-centrism, they embark on the road of destruction of those around them and ultimately of themselves.

When man loses his own interior liberty, either because he is too 'caught up in himself, or too tied to material goods or too close to other people, he actually loses sight of the true meaning of life. He gets too involved in relationships. For him, it is like observing a work of art from too closely to be able to see it properly. He can only see a black dot or a crooked line or a nice color. But he can never take in the meaning that that particular thing has in its totality. Hence he can never appreciate the beauty of the whole picture.

We have to teach children, right from the outset, to look at life and all that is in it, with a heart and a mind that is free. This can happen only if the family fast just as the Blessed Virgin asks us, two days a week. It's important to explain to children that none of these renouncements are without value. Therefore, if on Wednesdays or Fridays, the child gets a bar of chocolate, the child should be taught to put it away for the following day. The chocolate is his, but he can make use of it the following day. The waiting for tomorrow becomes part of a spiritual exercise. The child learns to resist whatever he desires, and in this way learns not to be greedy. An interior freedom is developed that, later on in life, will help him to behave as an man with equilibrium in his relationships with others and with himself.

Silence is the first step

For the duration of the period of fasting and prayer, silence is recommended. Often a constant babble of words is characteristic of an interior emptiness that is seeking its fulfilment, the greater the emptiness, and then greater again is the need for chatter and complications. Wherever this silence and tranquility is lacking, the right words cannot emerge. In fact, in these circumstances, often the only words that emerge are words of "violence". Here the idea is not a prohibition of speaking, or even of an invitation to renounce the gift of the word, but rather an exhortation to be men and women who are really capable of using the gift of words.

We enter into this silence with two questions in our hearts:

1. Where do my words come from?
2. How do my words come into existence?

If my words are born out of anger, fury, out of hatred or jealousy, out of envy or sadness, out of depression or interest, in selfishness or pride, or whatever other negative circumstance, then they are words that offend. My words in these circumstances are words which humiliate, words which disturb the peace, which bring about an altered state of soul in others, and carry out an attack on the heart of others.

When the soul is in silence, then it feels the sense of its own words. It feels the need to say: "Excuse my behavior, that's not what I meant...." and so on. Hidden behind words that are born in a disordered heart and soul, is the a degeneration of man. On the other hand, when words are conceived in peace, in trust, in hope and in joy, in friendship and goodness, then they edify and affirm man. These words are like a diffusion of all good feelings. Man doesn't need to excuse himself for these words, because they need to remain with us.

With regard to our words, Jesus said *"let 'yes' be 'yes', and your 'no' be 'no'"* (Mt 5:37). This is not a prohibition to speak, or a command to reduce our discussion to two words but rather stresses the need to know what we are saying and to remain faithful to it.

In the same way we can say that a man is his word and that words make the man. A man is his words, and words constitute his being a man in so far as his words are born out of peace and love, out of friendship and trust. That is why, from time to time, it is important to remain in silence and in silence to analyze our relationship with our own words, because I am what I speak and my words remain in me. In so far as a man is tranquil and self-collected, this is how much his words will be simple, peace-giving and edifying because words not only express a man, but also actually constitute the man. In the same way, in so far as a man is sliding backwards or has lost his peace, so too will his words be unable to help anyone to become more in touch with himself.

Our words need to be restored to their former strength in which they were able to represent the person, not by confusion or loudness, but rather through an activity which takes place at the level of the soul. In the light of all that is written above, we can interpret what St. James says with regards to the tongue and our words:

"Not many of you should become teachers my brothers, for you realize that we shall be judged more strictly, for we fall short in many respects. If anyone does not fall short in speech, he is a perfect man, able to bridle his whole body also. If we put bits into the mouths of horses to make them obey us, we also guide their whole bodies. It is the same with ships: even though they are so large, and driven by fierce winds, they are steered by a very small rudder wherever the pilot's inclination wishes. In the same way the tongue is a small member and yet has great pretensions.

Consider how small a fire can set a great forest ablaze. The tongue is also a fire. It exists among our members as a world of malice, defiling the whole body and setting the entire course of our lives on fire, itself set on fire by Gehenna. For every kind of beast and bird, of reptile and sea creature, can be tamed and has been tamed by the human species, but no human being can tame the tongue. It is a restless evil, full of deadly poison. With it we bless God our Father, and with it we curse human beings who are made in the image of God. From the same mouth come blessing and cursing. This need not be so my brothers. Does a spring gush forth from the same opening both pure and brackish water? Can a fig tree my brothers, produce olives, or grapevine figs? Neither can salt water cultivate fresh. (James 3:1-12).

We have to ask of ourselves to enter into silence and not to say anything that is not strictly necessary. This is one of the conditions through which man can re-enter himself, and through fasting and prayer can establish the conditions of interior processes. If 'not speaking' is difficult, then consenting to interior silence is even more difficult - to shut-down the imagination with its memories and feelings, so that a new space is created for an encounter with the Lord. Really, when one determines an interior silence, he or she can say that a part of ones purification has begun and a new relationship with God, with ourselves and with others has been activated.

The second step:
putting God in the first place

To fully understand what place God occupies in our lives, it is enough to ask ourselves who or what influences our most concrete decisions. We can establish that God is in the first place when He becomes the reference point for all of our decisions and actions.

We can say that in the life of Jesus this is how He worked. He did all and exactly as much as conformed with the will of the Father. When, during his fast in the desert, he had to battle against the Tempter, he did everything to ensure that glory was given to the Father, and His Father was adored, that His Word was lived and was not put to the test.

Even when He found Hmself facing the lethal battle in the Garden of Getsemane, He entrusted Himself totally to the Father; and on the cross he commended His Spirit into the hands of the Father. God awaits the first place in the hearts of man, in whatever circumstances life offers us.

If man is only in prayer, then selfishness and pride can easily enter into the spirit of prayer and into the very intentions that we pray for. This is why sometimes the way we pray can be superficial and we tend to measure the love and mercy and goodness of God in relation to what we have or have not obtained through prayer. Tragically, in these circumstances, the prayers of a lifetime are reduced to a battle between the will of God and our own will: hence we are not seeking God or His love or His reign, but rather whatever He can give us. For this reason Jesus wishes to put us on our guard telling us to seek the reign of God and His justice and then all else will be given to us in abundance, *(see Mt 6:26-34)*. If we do not listen to Jesus, we are in danger of praying only out of our own necessities, which if unanswered, we will distance ourselves from Him, disillusioned because we didn't get what we wanted.

On the other hand, whoever accepts the invitation to pray and to live on bread alone leaving all else behind enters into a process of liberating the heart from its' selfishness and pride, attached to its' own desires. We liberate ourselves from an afflicted dependence on others, upon material things and we open up a space for God. In this way He can come to occupy the first place in our hearts, not to imprison us, but rather to liberate, illuminate and to give us the way, the truth and the life, peace, love and being.

The third step:
a growing yearning for God

There are numerous prayer-texts in Sacred Scripture, both in the new and the old testaments, in which the Saints express a profound yearning for God, peace, joy, light, truth, love and all that comes from God. To understand the essence of prayer and its first and foremost condition, let's look at psalm 63.

The psalmist writes: *"O God, you are my God for you I long! For you my body yearns; for you my soul thirsts like a land parched, lifeless, and without water my soul clings fast to you your right hand upholds me…"*

Whoever yearns for Christ will have time for prayer, they will seek out God and they will find Him. But where these yearnings are non-existent, there will neither be prayer, nor the joyful awaiting of God nor an encounter with Him. In psalm 42, the psalmist expresses, in the simplest possible way, his profound yearning for God comparing his soul to a deer who seeks out a water-spring:

As the deer longs for streams of water, so my soul longs for you, o God. My being thirsts for God, the living God. When can I go and see the face of God? My tears have been my food day and night, as they ask daily, "where is your God?" Those times I recall as I pour out my soul, when I went in procession with the crowd, I went with them to the house of God, amid loud cries of thanksgiving, with the multitude keeping festival.

The question must be asked: How can we maintain that yearning which pushes the soul towards God like the deer that yearns for running water? Once again the answer should be sought out in prayer and fasting. Whoever prays and fasts will see their own soul become always freer and in this freedom will ceaselessly seek out God.

In the beatitudes Jesus says: *"Blessed are the poor in spirit, because theirs is the kingdom of heaven blessed are those who hunger and thirst for justice, for they shall have their fill. Blessed are the pure in heart for they shall see God. (Mt 5:3,6,and 8)*

We are speaking of the same problem, the poor in spirit are those who know that nothing can make them rich except God. This is why they will seek Him out and theirs will be the kingdom of heaven. Blessed are the pure in heart because they are aware of what they are most in need of, and they will not be blinded by the things of this world.

In this growing yearning for God, the believer is drawn ever-nearer to the heavenly banquet table which confers eschatalogical significance on his search, making him vigilant, capable of waiting, of seeking and finding, of going back to the start over and over again without ever giving up. This is love! The essence if love is exactly this; that he who loves is both close to and far away from the one he loves. He is near because physical and spatial distances do not present and obstacle. But he is also far in the sense that he is always seeking out this person that he loves.

Hence the spiritual dilemma of mankind today can be easily understood: His heart is often drawn towards material goods and often this blocks his road towards God. This is the major illusion that a man can experience today. Thanks to prayer and fasting however, these traps can be identified and easily overcome. And so the heart of man, on this earthly journey, ends up always facing the only One who really wishes his well-being, who really loves Him, God. This is the mystery of all the mystics and all the saints. They continually sought God out, and readily left all else to be able to follow Him, to fulfil their own yearnings for Him, the final fulfillment being in eternity.

Mary incessantly invites us to fast and pray in order to liberate heart so that we can seek out God at ever deeper levels.

The first goal: peace

Peace is a fruit of the spirit.

The deepest desire of the heart of man is peace. In everything that we do, good or bad, we are looking for peace. When we love, we are seeking peace, when we hate or seek revenge, we are seeking peace. When we battle against an addiction we are seeking peace, when we say unkind things, we are seeking peace. When we fight for our lives or for the life of a loved one, we are seeking peace and when we lay hands on ourselves in an effort to commit suicide or when we kill another, we are seeking peace.

In the end, all human decisions are efforts to attain peace.

It's obvious that when we behave well, we are seeking and to a certain extent, attaining personal peace and the peace of those around us.

On the other hand, when we commit an evil, we are looking only for our own peace, without taking account of the upset we could cause to others.

Analyzing the theme from another point of view, all those times when we obscured peace, it was because we were proud, selfish, envious, jealous, greedy, or dependant on power or glory. Experience teaches us that thanks to fasting and prayer, evil can be won over.

Pride and selfishness can be conquered.

The heart can open and love can grow. Humility, generosity and goodness can come into being and become the foundations of peace.

Whoever has peace, it is because he loves and forgives, and both his physical and spiritual health enables him to organize his life in such a way as to give glory to God. He lives life in a way that is worthy of man, who is the pinnacle of creation.

With fasting and prayer the needs of man are reduced to a just dimension, and here too, conditions for peace are set up and proper relationship with others and their material needs.

It is incomprehensible therefore, that fasting can be experienced negatively as a renunciation or that its spiritual benefits are irrecognizable. It's not possible therefore to substitute fasting with good deeds or with something else.

Thanks to fasting, man recognizes the things that he has to fight against within himself. In this way, our subconscious too is liberated from whatever brings us agitation and confusion.

The soul is tranquilized and the ground for interior peace is established.

The following text makes the interior battle easier to visualize: "If a king wants to conquer a neighboring town, he first cuts their water and their supplies, and in this way the starving enemies surrender. It's the same for the passions of the flesh: if a man fights with fasting and hunger, the enemies of the soul get weaker." (from John, the dwarf)

Experience clearly confirms that, without the battle against the interior enemies of peace, it is not possible to obtain peace, and fasting is really an efficacious and experienced method. It's not coincidental that all the prophets, Jesus, and the whole ecclesiastical tradition, invite us to fast and pray, so that man can open to true peace. The problem is though, that man seems to prefer the way of the false prophets who promise a comfortable peace, which in reality does not exist.

The second goal:
gratitude and humility

Gratitude is an interior state of the soul whereby one is deeply aware of being a creature of God, of not being the director of one's own life and that everything that one has and is, has been given by God. In such a condition, another attitude develops: one of responsibility towards the One who has given or entrusted to us. Whoever knows that everything he has is a gift, will know to put everything he has at the service of others and will be ready to give account for the gifts he has received.

Do you remember the talent that the servant restituted to the owner after having buried it? He hadn't lost his gift, he wasted it: He gave back exactly what he had received and this was his mistake, *(see Mt 24: 14-30)*. Reflecting on the above we can conclude that gratitude is a consequence of faith, because faith teaches us that we are created and that everything has been entrusted to us. But, if we do not use our gifts and talents for the service of others, they have no significance.

Gratitude cannot exist without humility. Without humility it is not possible to speak of a condition of gratitude. Pride and selfishness are lethal for the soul, because thanks to them the soul begins to illude himself that he is in charge of everything that he has and will not use them for the service of others. On the contrary, he will think that others are created to serve him. This is the essence of ingratitude.

When man fasts and prays, his heart is liberated from all slavery to himself and his own gifts, but also from all human and worldly slavery. Thanks to fasting and prayer, man is liberated from himself and finds an interior space. He manages to see the truth clearly and to live it. In this freedom, man begins to see everything that God has done for him and does not forget it: As well as this, he is aware of what all mankind is doing for him, the big things and the little things.

Fasting helps man to live anew as a creature who has received very much. H e sacrifices his primary needs and creates in prayer a time and place for God.

The thankful man therefore is a man of peace, who has joy in his heart. He will never be deluded because he never expects anything from others, but rather it is he who does things for others. When there is a state of ingratitude in the soul, peace and joy are also absent. The pride and selfishness present in the soul make it impossible for them to be at the service of others. This has a bearing both on their relationship with God and on their relationship with others. More and more will be expected of others, and when it is not received, the sufferer remains deluded. Violence, tension and all types of evil are born out of this delusion.

In reality, all sins are born out of this ingratitude, selfishness and pride. When man doesn't realize what God has done for him, and what the needs of his neighbors are, he is over-focused on himself. The ungrateful man easily forgets. He forgets all the good he has received when a situation arrives that is not to his liking.

When we reflect on the original sin of Adam and Eve, the ingratitude and forgetfulness are easily recognized. God had created every possible condition for man to be happy. There was only one prohibition; that of not forgetting that they belonged to God and that He was their Lord. The Tempter distracted Eve from what she has received and all she possessed. He urged her to focus on what she didn't have (and what wouldn't be good for her). The dialogue between Eve and the serpent is classical of the situation in which sin occurs most: "The Lord told us not to touch it."

The Tempter uses the same question in every sin: "Did God really tell you not to?" Eve, forgetting everything that she has, reaches out to take that which she doesn't have and hence the first sin takes place. If Eve had said, First of all I am going to touch what is allowed then I will move on to what is not allowed, the tempter wouldn't have waited for the moment of transgression, because the things that were allowed were so numerous. *(See Gen 3:1-7)*

Let us compare it with the situation in our homes. Returning home, we find our mother who has worked all day, and appreciating that which she has done, we feel in our hearts the wish to thank her.

Then there is a moment of joy.

But if instead, we only see what hasn't been done, and we start to criticize and complain, then a fight begins, there are accusations, defences, arguments, lack of peace and general pain.

A short while before Fr. Slavko died, he celebrated a mass in Cenacolo. He addressed the young ex-drug addicts saying:

Do you know how you lose your peace?

It's when you begin to see only one aspect of a person, an aspect that we don't like without looking at the whole person.

You see only that side of the person and the spirit of criticism take hold of us. We forget all the other aspects.

We lose sight of the beauty of the life of that person, all that he has done, all that he has suffered and all that he has given.

We then enter into a vision of that person which

is totally out of focus and we become prisoners of this false vision. We lose our gratitude and without this gratitude we cannot have peace, because it is gratitude that prepares the way of peace. (Sr. Emmanuel)

When man conquers interior freedom, he is ready to do good and to share his material goods with others, because he will see all that he has, and whoever is in need, and what can be given to them.

That is why whoever fasts; good deeds are also expected of him. Good deeds are the fruit of fasting and prayer: this is why it isn't possible to substitute prayer and fasting with good deeds as many tend to think.

The third goal:
good deeds

It is not enough to fast and pray; through fasting and prayer the believer must prepare himself to do good acts.

Whoever prays and fasts will be ready to realize what he needs and what can be put at the disposition of others.

If man does not pray and does not fast, his demands will continue to grow and he will not be able to keep them under control.

The more his needs grow, the less he is able to put himself at the disposition of others.

There are many things that we think we cannot do without and if we do not have them we become tense, violent, envious greedy and unjust because others have convinced us that these things are necessary.

Especially in the times we live, we are constantly under the suggestive power of the media, magazines and television in particular, that these new things are necessary.

Man is forced to work in order to follow the rhythm of the world, to make his life secure. In doing this he ignores the spiritual aspect of his being and his spiritual needs which ultimately will lead to his destruction.

Under these circumstances, man becomes blind

to all that he has, to those who are in need, or to that which could be put at the disposition of others.

Through fasting, man is freer and easily disposed to seeing and in this way will change his way of relating to material goods.

The value of fasting and prayer can be measured in how we keep up with the material world, and by the stop that we put to the race after material well-being.

The principle for judging the value of our fasting is the sensibility we develop to the needs of others and our readiness to help.

Whoever fasts and prays without developing this sensibility must ask themselves if their fasting and prayer is of any value at all. Whoever fasts and prays therefore ultimately becomes generous, merciful, and sensitive to others.

They are disposed to help the poorer and less fortunate.

They must be able to recognize Christ in the suffering and the needy because Christ sacrificed himself particularly for the outcast and the needy.

The fourth goal:
fortification in the face of evil

It is not coincidental that the decline in fasting has gone hand in hand with a lessened awareness of the battle that exists against evil. Nobody speaks anymore about fasting as a Church, and nobody speaks anymore about the battle we must fight against Satan and his reign.

In recent decades, the work of Satan is a theme which is avoided, and the practice of exorcisms and liberation from evil spirits which was entrusted to the apostles by Jesus, has been practically abandoned, *(see Mt 7: 22, 10: 8ff)*.

However, where Mary has been welcomed as Mother and Teacher of the Church, this battle has not been forgotten. It still continues.

In the book of the Apocalypse, a woman is prefigured who must give birth: Satan wishes to ambush the fruit of her womb; she flees into the desert and saves the child, *(see Apoc 12:1-6)*.

During an exorcism, there are always many insults against Jesus, against the cross, against the Blessed Sacrament and against Mary the Mother of Jesus. She will be the one to crush the head of Satan and will defeat him. It is normal that he will always clash with her. In the whole of the history of the Church, the priest-exorcists prayed and fasted in preparation for this work.

The same thing happens today, the priest surrounds himself with people who will pray and are willing to fast together with him and they support him, not only in the preparation, but also during the prayer. All of this is very useful and positive for the proptection of the priest, for the person who is possessed, and for the circumstantial situation itself.

In order to understand all of this, we have to think of the words of St. Peter: "Be sober and vigilant. Your opponent, the devil is prowling around like a roaring lion waiting for someone to devour" *(1 Pet5:8)*.

Fasting is for everyone

It might seem absurd in the consumer age in which we live to speak of fasting, when the media are constantly inviting us to spend, to have, to change, to avoid 'not having'. This egotistical culture urges us to satisfy our own well-being and not to waste a thought for those who are not as fortunate. Our solidarity, unfortunately, usually develops only in retrospect. Only after the tragedy has occured, after the deaths, after the waves created by calamities, there is a revolt and a hunt is begun to find out who is guilty. We don't try to stop these tragedies beforehand. The awareness of having to battle against evil has disappeared.

Fasting not only combats evil but also prevents it! Why should we fast? So that others don't live in difficulty and can have what is necessary! So that justice and goodness will triumph and there will be a reign of peace among us! So that we are prepared for the battle against all manifestations of evil and to train us to be ready for such events! So that we don't get sucked into a vision of life which is fundamentally destructive, where we disregard basic human values and seek the well-being of only a privileged few!

This is why all of us are called to fast: the healthy, the sick, the young, the old, the rich and the poor, the saintly and the sinners.

With fasting and prayer, the healthy will have more mercy on the sick. The sick will tolerate their cross with less difficulty, and there is evidence to suggest that some may even be healed of their sickness.

With fasting and prayer, young people will have the strength to preserve their interior freedom and won't enter into bad habits. It will be easier for them to discern good from evil and to abstain from what is not good. With fasting and prayer, the elderly will have more patience in their condition to live out their days serenely and in gratitude for the gift of life.

Fasting will help the rich not to become proud of their wealth and will preserve them from unjust behavior. It will teach them to be grateful to God for what they have and be better disposed to our less fortunate brethren. Through fasting too, the poor will manage to carry the cross of poverty with less bitterness and it will save them from temptations. It can often happen too that in the priesthood or the religious life, renunciations are made but the 'hundred times more,' which is promised in the scriptures, is not obtained. As a result, the meaning of their work and their lives is diminished and sometimes only bitterness and tension can be felt in them. Life becomes empty for them and more and more tragedies happen in the lives of those who have been called to announce the good news. How can this be so? The answer is that priests and Religious must also fast and pray, because through these practices, we are capable of entering the mystery of the reign of God and the love of God. When sharing this mystery; when 'in this communion', a person becomes the image of Christ, and is ready to give up his life for others.

Fasting and prayer will help the sinner to better understand his own condition. He will be able to understand his own responsibility, to repent sincerely and to find the strength to free himself from whatever evil threatens his soul.

Fasting and prayer will help all holy souls to grow in love and faith, in hope, devotion and in trust in God. Prayer and fasting will make us sensitive too to protect the world in which we live: less pollution, less destruction; we will be in a condition to overcome the danger of excessive despoiling of the earth's resources, as if we were the last generation that had to live on the earth.

To go back to prayer and fasting, in its' biblical significance means to create the conditions for a whole new life; fasting and prayer should be given adequate importance, for the benefit of the world of nature surrounding us, for others, for our own well-being, and most importantly, for our own relationship with God.

But does bread and water take hunger away?

Absolutely! We will try to demonstrate that this is absolutely true, and not only from a physical point of view. All the doubts that can possibly trouble us, either before or during a fast, when examined, are coming from a source divided from God. For this reason, let us trust him that fasting will satisfy our every need, hunger or thirst.

The components which make up bread

Bread is an essential source of nutrition and a basic component in the everyday diet. If we choose brown bread, or full grain or corn bread, we add a lot to the quality of our nutrition and of our own health. The darker the color of the bread, the healthier it is.

The quality of bread depends on the type of bread used. Whole-grains can be combined with white flour. So it is possible to use the breads that are available from our bakeries choosing, if possible, the darker varieties; because when baked well, these contain between three and ten per cent more minerals and vitamins. They also contain 2-3 percent more calcium and vitamin B than white breads. The protein value of brown bread is also superior to that of white bread because it contains germ and sprouts of the grain and bran. The basic daily need of vitamin B can be satisfied by an intake of 250gr of brown bread alone! To obtain the same amount of vitamin B from white bread, we would have to eat two and a half kilos! White bread satisfies our hunger, but it is very poor in protein vitamins and minerals. (50gr of white bread contains 130 calories, 50gr of brown contains 108, 50gr of toast contains 100gr, 50gr of rye-bread contains 120, and 50gr of soya bread contains 101 calories!)

Many people have given up fasting because of the poor quality of bread. Most bread on sale in fact is made with flour that is so refined that it is void of its nutritional value.

When we do not feel that our hunger has been satisfied, or other problems occur at the level of digestion, we forget the possibility of making our own bread is also open to us. The important thing though is not to let ourselves be convinced that we have an alibi for not fasting because bread doesn't satisfy our hunger or that it causes us digestive problems, or we don't have time, or we are not able to make bread at home!

A few pointers for making bread:

Making your own bread is very simple. It is not very expensive to make, but there are a few rules and components that are essential.

Flour: the best flour for making bread is wheat-meal. However, from a nutritional point of view, a composition using 100% wheat-meal is not the best; in fact the ideal combination would be a major percentage of wheat-meal with the addition of other cereals, seeds and grain-sprouts.

Yeast: to make the bread rise and to make it more digestible, either dried or fresh yeast is used. The fungi contained within the yeast in conditions of humidity and heat, begin to grow and increase the size of the dough up to four times its' original size. Because of this property, bread must be well cooked to avoid its 're-expanding' in the intestines. When the temperature rises above 49 degrees Centigrade, the fungi ceases to act. It is always better to mix the yeast with a spoonful of sugar and some flour so that the yeast, together with this sugar, can accelerate its' growth and you can be sure that the dough will grow.

Substitutes for yeast: if you do not have yeast, it is possible to substitute it with some left-over dough, or with 150gr of sugar, 50gr of white flour and half a litre of water, and cooked at a medium temperature for half an hour mixing from time to time. This yeast can be used the following day.

Water and heat: the temperature of the water has a fundamental role because it should be around 45 degrees Centigrade

Salt: improves the taste of the bread, but it can of course be eliminated for health reasons, if one cannot have salt in their diet. It is better to mix the salt with some water and then add the water to the flour. (The salt water has the opposite action of the yeast)

Oil: oil is not strictly necessary but, if added, the bread is softer and doesn't dry up. The dough is usually mixed for ten minutes until it has the same consistency and is soft.

The bread of Medjugorje:

In Medjugorje, the families bake their own bread. It is excellent and very easy to fast with. To bake your own bread is a plus from many points of view. It permits us to enter better into the spirit of fasting. It is a good opportunity to meditate concretely on the words of Jesus about the grain that fell to the ground, about the wheat and the darnel, about the yeast which the woman uses to three measures of flour and naturally the splendid gospel on the bread of life. In a simple way too we approach Mary-a Hebrew woman, who was careful to carry out her tasks under Gods watchful eye and to keep harmony within the home. Who can better prepare us for the Eucharist and help us to live the Bread of Life as she received Him on earth, after the ascension of her Son?

Fasting is easier when one asks God this grace prior to fasting, because to be able to fast properly is a grace that we must not take for granted.

We should ask the Father for our daily bread, and humbly ask him to be able to fast on bread and water. To fast willingly increases the power of fasting against the forces of evil, against division and wars.

The following is a recipe for approx. 1 kilo of flour:

Add in this order, to the flour, three quaters of a litre of warm water (about 37 degrees C), a little spoonful of sugar, and a large spoonful of dried yeast or confectioners yeast in a bowl.

Mix well and then add, two large spoonfuls of oil, a large spoonful of salt, a bowl of oat flakes or some other cereal (a 1/4 litre bowl). Mix all the ingredients and if the dough seems too sticky, add some more flour.

Let the dough rest for at least two hours (or else overnight) in a place that is well heated at a constant heat (not less than 25 degrees Centigrade). The bowl should be covered with a damp cloth. Spread out the dough to a height of not more than 4cm on a well oiled baking sheet. Let it rest for a further 30 minutes. Put into a hot oven at 160 degrees for 50-60 minutes.

Other recipes

Sifted flour bread: Mix a kilo and a half of sieved flour with some warm water, 30 gr of yeast and a large spoonful of salt. Mix the dough on a tabletop until it becomes sticky and not hard and elastic. After leaving it to rise, mix again and cook in a hot oven for 45minutes.

Mixed rye bread: Mix the dough with 600gr of rye-flour and 400gr of wheat flour, an envelope of dried yeast, some salt and three glasses of warm water. Keep the mixture in the heat with a damp cloth covering it and let rise for half an hour. Cook for 70minutes at 200 degrees.

Bran bread (refined): Mix a dough with 500gr of flour, a large spoonful of dried yeast, some salt 75gr of oat flakes and 75gr of linseeds, I egg, 50gr of butter or margerine 350 mili litres of warm milk. Keep in a heated space, covered with a damp cloth and allow to rise. Cook in a hot oven for 45 minutes at 180 degrees.

Vegetable Bread: Prepare a dough using 500gr of flour, a tablespoonful of dried yeast, 125gr of oat flakes, an egg, 50gr of butter or margerine, a glass and a half of lukewarm water and some salt. Add to this mixture a glassful of finely chopped herbs and seeds (parsley, celery, onion, unrefined wheat grains and some medicinal herbs if desired). Leave the dough to rise for about half an hour. Before baking add oat flakes. Bake at 180 degrees for 40 minutes.

Corn-bread: Mix 250gr of corn-meal, a kilo of flour, yeast, oil and salt. Knead into desired shape and put in a heated space to let rise. Bake covered in foil for one hour at 150 degrees.

Yeast-less bread: Mix a dough using a cupful of full-grain flour, half a cupful of buck-wheat, 1/5 of a cupful of salt. Divide the mixture into three portions and bake on a baking sheet at 150 degrees.

The Importance of Water

Water makes up 70-75% of our bodies and is a fundamental element in its make-up. This fact alone is indicative of its importance for the human organism.

Water penetrates nutritious matter, and through the bloodstream in the digestive system, reaches all other organs of the body and can eliminate the substances which are potentially dangerous to the body. For this reason it is absolutely necessary to supply the body with at least two litres of water a day. We can establish that, through other food substances there is an intake of about one litre, the rest can only come into the body through drinking. The average adult should drink between 6 and 8 glasses of water a day.

In fact, this is the basic requirement for the proper functioning of the kidneys and the removal of toxic substances from the body. In circumstances of heavy physical effort and when it becomes hotter, it may be necessary to increase this to ten litres (with the addition of salt in situations of abundant perspiration). On fast days it is necessary to drink a lot, either hot or cold beverages. The Queen of Peace didn't make specifications so it is up to the individual to fast freely in whatever way is apt to his spiritual needs and intentions, and also according to his health.

The best is pure water; if possible spring water, but fruit juices and milk are also good. Water that is low in mineral content, and is not effervescent, can be useful also for the correction of metabolic and digestive disturbances, as they regularize the intestinal functions and allow the body to purify itself.

Even when not fasting, drinking water should be a daily habit. Above all this is important for small children whose body is in the most sensitive phase of development and is also sensitive to disturbances in hydro-equilibrium.

Natural water is a source of nourishment because of its mineral content and can even be medicinal. These minerals are easily assimilated and do not have undesirable side effects. Coffee, tea (Russian or Chinese) and the various soda drinks cannot substitute water because they contain caffeine and can cause problems to the liver and the bladder.

We can conclude therefore that fasting, apart from its infinite spiritual benefits, also has enormous benefits for the body. So, going back to the question whether it is possible to live only on bread and water Wednesdays and Fridays the answer is "definitely yes" which we said in the beginning. This is so because bread, and especially brown bread, contains fats and vitamins from the A,B,E and D groups. This is sufficient to not let the system suffer too much and it guarantees correct digestion. The water brings another series of substances necessary for survival but also necessary for purification. With this nourishment, we have nothing to lose.

It is however important not to give-up after fasting, being careful to realize that its goal is not to lose weight. If we feel weak after fasting it is a suggestion to us that perhaps on the other five days, we do not eat in a way that compensates. We must eat a varied and balanced diet so that nothing is lacking in our body.

The Eucharistic Fast

Since the beginning of Ecclesiastical Tradition, the have faithful always prepared for the encounter with the Eucharistic Christ by fasting.

In the original Ecclesiastical Tradition (which is still recognized and practiced in the Oriental Church that geographically, is closer to the original Church) we have a good look at the initial spirit that reigned. This method of preparation can also be seen in the practice of the Orthodox Church today: Those who are preparing to receive communion, have a weekly fasting program which becomes increasingly intense as the day of communion draws near.

We must bear in mind that daily communion was not always allowed in our Church. According to Church precepts, confession should take place at least once a year and one should receive communion at least once, annually, at Easter. When the permission was granted to receive communion more often, the rule was that we should remain fasting from midnight until the moment of communion, we shouldn't even drink water. Eventually medicines were permitted.

After the liturgical renewals, introduced by Pope Pius XII, the afternoon celebration of the mass was introduced and Eucharistic fasting, for practical reasons, was reduced to three hours. After the Second Vatican Council, Eucharistic fasting was ulteriorly reduced to an hour before Holy Communion. In this way, preparation for the Eucharist through fasting was practically revoked. The problem is not really that Eucharistic fasting has been reduced, but moreover that an adequate preparation for the Eucharistic encounter with Christ is not made. We run the risk of losing the profound respect due to Christ in the Eucharist. St. Paul, speaking to the Corinthians, among other things writes:

"A person should examine himself, and so eat the bread and drink the cup. For anyone who eats and drinks without discerning the body, eats and drinks judgement on himself" *(1 Cor 11: 28-29)*

Eucharistic fasting is the door through which we enter with profound respect the great mystery of the presence of Christ; and this bread which is His body. First communion for children is an experience of awaiting Christ. In this encounter we prepare with a rigorous fast from midnight until the moment of communion. Thanks to this fast, the soul of the faithful can enter this mysterious and marvelous presence of Christ in the Eucharist. When the believer meets Christ in the Eucharist and is not properly prepared, a relationship of loving appreciation is less likely to be attained with the God who has remained with His people in this bread, and man can be in communion with Him.

The fact that the Blessed Virgin exhorts us to fast twice a week, Wednesdays and Fridays, is evidence of the necessity to prepare for this encounter with the Eucharistic Christ. Thursday always marks the day of Eucharist and Holiness. This is why fasting on Wednesdays, from a Eucharistic point of view, is a preparation for Thursday, the day of the Eucharist. Man, denying himself other foods and living on bread alone, prepares for the encounter with the heavenly bread: Friday becomes a day of thanksgiving for the Eucharist. This is one aspect of making the Eucharistic Christ everything in our lives. When we prepare ourselves properly for this meeting with the Eucharistic Christ, in this Eucharistic banquet, man prepares himself for the eternal banquet in Heaven. The Eucharist is a preparation and a possibility to pre-taste the eternal banquet in the Kindom of God.

Bread and water: food for the pilgrim

The invitation to live on bread and water is above all an invitation to prepare one's self for the encounter with Christ in the Eucharist. All in all, this invitation wants to make us aware of our pilgrim journey here on earth. Man, by his nature and in his essence searches for God. This tendency in itself presents many questions about Eternal Life, happiness and peace.

God Himself is the answer to all these questions. In this journey towards fullness and towards Eternal Truth (which can only be fully realized in God), man is no longer like a wandering beggar. Instead he is on a pilgrimage, abandoning everyday life more and more: his work, his security and his joys, as he directs himself ever-increasingly towards the people and the places where he can meet God.

In ancient times, there were no modern means to allow easy passage from one place to another and pilgrimages lasted weeks, months, even years. The pilgrim brought with him everything that he needed to survive i.e. bread and water.

He would leave behind him the things of everyday and he would set out with a bundle over his shoulder constantly liberating himself from every thing that weighed him down and everything that was unnecessary. In this way, he could freely follow and reach people and places where he could meet God.

In most cases though, these places were just simple places to temporarily pass through, or places that helped them to return to the mundane. For this reason not even the return to the everyday lent itself to this situation of always seeking God.

Pilgrimage is constant because man in this world doesn't have a fixed place. He is always journeying towards the eternal homeland, filled with peace and joy of eternal life and of communion.

Fasting on bread and water, today's humanity manages to preserve their liberty, and doesn't become a slave to material goods, or a victim to false promises. In this liberty, he is ready to love and forgive, to get over the conflicts and to live in peace.

If man loses sight of his pilgrim journey, then he stops along the way and plunges himself into the worries of this world.

God has granted the Bread of Heaven to mankind, and His Son as a companion along this journey.

This is why the name of the Messiah is Emmanuel, meaning God with us. When a child of God forgets that God, in the form of bread that signifies life for the world, is journeying with him, he turns to the world, but in the world he cannot feel good, because the only 'good' for man is God. In this frame of mind, we discover the last meaning of fasting. Fasting is not only an instrument of healing, but rather, when joined with prayer and charity, it is also an essential means of religious experience.

The invitation
of the Queen of Peace

The Queen of Peace invites us all to peace, fasting, prayer and conversion and to a solid faith. Many are surprised by this invitation to fast, but especially by the invitation to fast twice a week.

Many feel that this is too much, that it is impossible, and that it cannot be put into action. However, even a superficial glance, the past has shown us that the Jews were already fasting twice a week. The Pharisee who, back in his times, thanks God because he prays, helps the poor and fasts twice a week, returns home without the remission of his sins, because he condemns the sinner who is praying in a corner of the temple, *(see Luke 18: 9-14)*. Jesus didn't deny the value of fasting, neither did he prohibit fasting twice weekly, but he forbids us to judge others.

Mary is the Queen of Prophets. We know that all Prophets call us to conversion, fasting and prayer which are the pre-suppositions of peace. She has no other nor no better means of calling us to peace than the means which were preached by the Prophets ie: conversion, prayer, fasting and strong faith.

Exhorting us to fast two days a week, the Queen of Peace is not asking us something new from us. On the contrary, remaining in the traditions of the people of Israel, She brings us into the secular traditions of the Eastern Church. Mary speaks of fasting in various messages:

August 14, 1984 (Tuesday)

"I would like the people to pray along with me these days. And to pray as much as possible! And to fast strictly on Wednesdays and Fridays, and every day to pray at least one Rosary: the joyful, sorrowful and glorious mysteries".

The Blessed Virgin asked us to accept with conviction this message which puts the practice dear to all Holy Israelites-fasting twice a week (Wednesdays and Fridays) back into the center of our lives.

September 20, 1984

"Dear children! Today I call on you to begin fasting with the heart. There are many people who are fasting, but only because everyone else is fasting. It has become a custom which no one wants to stop. I ask the parish to fast out of gratitude because God has allowed me to stay this long in this parish. Dear children, fast and pray with the heart. Thank you for having responded to my call".

Mary asks us to pray and fast with our hearts. This means to pray and fast with love. Love towards God and mankind is the only true motivation for praying and fasting. From a biblical point of view, no other motive is sufficient.

September 26, 1985

"Dear children! I thank you for all the prayers. Thank you for all the sacrifices. I wish to tell you, dear children, to renew the messages which I am giving you. Especially live thefast, because by fasting you will achieve and cause me the joy of the whole plan, which God is planning here in Medjugorje, being fulfilled. Thank you for having responded to my call".

Fasting and prayer is the road that leads to joy, but also the conditions for establishing what God has promised. Without prayer and fasting it will not be possible to realize Divine plans. Our collaboration is very important. The Queen of Peace repeated many times that we are indispensable in the realisation of the plan which God has entrusted to her.

September 4, 1986

"Dear children! Today again I am calling you to prayer and fasting. You know, dear children, that with your help I am able to accomplish everything and force Satan not to be seducing to evil and to remove himself from this place. Dear children, Satan is lurking around each individual. Especially in everyday affairs he wants to spread confusion

among each one of you. Therefore, dear
children, my call to you is that your day would
be only prayer and complete surrender to God.
Thank you for having responded to my call".

Fasting and prayer are the best weapons against
Satan. Only with prayer and fasting can we force
Satan to cease with his evil plans and to distance
himself from the faithful. Jesus said to His
disciples that some evil spirits can only be cast out
by fasting and prayer.

December 4, 1986

"Dear children! Today I call you to prepare
your hearts for these days when the Lord
particularly desires to purify you from all the sins
of your past. You, dear children, are not able by
yourselves, therefore I am here to help you. You
pray, dear children! Only that way shall you be
able to recognize all the evil that is in you and
surrender it to the Lord so the Lord may completely
purify your hearts. Therefore, dear children, pray
without ceasing and prepare your hearts in
penance and fasting. Thank you for having
responded to my call".

Fasting and prayer are the means through which
we open up to God, who purifies us from all the sins
of our past. This is something that we can neither do
alone nor can we recognize the evil within us which

is waiting to destroy us. In prayer and fasting, the heart prepares to collaborate with God.

July 25, 1991

"Dear Children! Today I invite you to pray for peace. At this time peace is being threatened in a special way, and I am seeking from you to renew fasting and prayer in your families. Dear children, I desire you to grasp the seriousness of the situation and that much of what will happen depends on your prayers and you are only praying a little bit. Dear children, I am with you and I am inviting you to begin to pray and fast seriously as in the first days of my coming. Thank you for having responded to my call".

Fasting and prayer are the means through which peace is protected. Mary exhorts, not only individuals, but also families to pray and fast to arrest this evil. Here we are speaking about a very serious invitation because the future of the world will depend on us. The prophet Jonah, exhorted Ninevah to fast and pray so that the city would not be destroyed. Everyone fasted and prayed and the city was saved.

August 25, 1991

"Dear Children! Today also I invite you to prayer, now as never before when my plan has begun to be realized. Satan is strong and wants to

sweep away plans of peace and joy and make you think that my Son is not strong in his decisions. Therefore, I call all of you, dear children to pray and fast still more firmly. I invite you to realize the secrets I began in Fatima. I call you, dear children, to grasp the importance of my coming and the seriousness of the situation. I want to save all souls and present them to God. Therefore, let us pray that everything I have begun can be fully realized. Thank you for having responded to my call."

When Satan threatens the plans of God, then the Queen of Prophets, like all other prophets, invites us to fasting and prayer in order to obstruct Satan in his plans of destruction and annulment of divine plans, which in a particular way were revealed in Fatima. We really are dealing with the realization of everything that God has entrusted to Mary, Queen of Peace and Queen of Prophets.

March 25, 1992

"Dear children! Today as never before I invite you to live my messages and to put them into practice in your life. I have come to you to help you and, therefore, I invite you to change your life because you have taken a path of misery, a path of ruin. When I told you: convert, pray, fast, and be reconciled, you took these messages superficially. You started to live them and then you stopped, because it was difficult for you. No, dear children,

when something is good, you have to persevere in the good and not think: God does not see me, He is not listening, He is not helping. And so you have gone away from God and from me because of your miserable interest. I wanted to create of you an oasis of peace, love and goodness. God wanted you, with your love and with His help, to do miracles, and thus, give an example. Therefore, here is what I say to you: Satan is playing with you and with your souls and I cannot help you because you are far away from my heart. Therefore, pray, live my messages and then you will see the miracles of God's love in your everyday life. Thank you for having responded to my call".

We have received the message of fasting and prayer in a very superfical and immature way. For this reason, Mary warns us that Satan is threatening the well-being of our very souls. He is an enemy who can only be won through fasting and prayer. Mary is saddened by the fact that we are far away from her and her messages. Her desire is to create an oasis of peace, but whatever happens depends solely upon us.

April 25, 1992

"Dear children! Today also I invite you to prayer. Only by prayer and fasting can war be stopped. Therefore, my dear little children, pray and by your life give witness that you are mine and

that you belong to me, because Satan wishes in these turbulent days to seduce as many souls as possible. Therefore, I invite you to decide for God and He will protect you and show you what you should do and which path to take. I invite all those who have said "yes" to me to renew their consecration to my Son, Jesus, and to His Heart and to me so we can use you more intensely as instruments of peace in this unpeaceful world. Medjugorje is a sign to all of you and a call to pray and live the days of grace that God is giving you. Therefore, dear children, accept the call to prayer with seriousness. I am with you and your suffering is also mine. Thank you for having responded to my call".

With fasting and prayer, even wars can be stopped." This is one of the first messages which the Blessed Mother gave. With prayer and fasting, even natural catastrophies can be prevented. Peace depends on fasting and prayer. We must accept this with seriousness. Mary is with us and suffers with us.

December 25, 1996

"Dear children! Today I am with you in a special way, holding little Jesus in my lap and I invite you, little children, to open yourselves to His call. He calls you to joy. Little children, joyfully live the messages of the Gospel, which I am repeating

during the time since I am with you. Little children, I am your Mother and I desire to reveal to you the God of love and the God of peace. I do not desire for your life to be in sadness but that it be realized in joy for eternity, according to the Gospel. Only in this way will your life have meaning. Thank you for having responded to my call".

Fasting and prayer are the means through which we prepare for the coming of Jesus. This message was actually given at Christmas. Only with prayer and fasting can we purify our hearts and open them fully to the coming of Jesus. Prayer and fasting liberate man from the wrong relationship with himself, with others and above all with the material world around us.

March 25, 1998

"Dear children! Also today I call you to fasting and renunciation. Little children, renounce that which hinders you from being closer to Jesus. In a special way I call you: Pray, because only through prayer will you be able to overcome your will and discover the will of God even in the smallest things. By your daily life, little children, you will become an example and witness that you live for Jesus and not against Him and His will. Little children, I desire that you become apostles of love. By loving, little children, it will be recognized that you are mine. Thank you for having responded to my call".

Prayer and fasting can liberate us from whatever is stopping us from coming closer to Jesus. We have to conquer our own wills and open up to the will of God. In this way, we become witnesses of Jesus, and Apostles of love and we can recognise the signs of God's presence in this world. Through prayer and fasting, we carry out a battle for our interior freedom so that we can overcome whatever it is that is separating us from Jesus.

October 25, 1998

"Dear children! Today I call you to come closer to my Immaculate Heart. I call you to renew in your families the fervor of the first days when I called you to fasting, prayer and conversion. Little children, you accepted my messages with open hearts, although you did not know what prayer was. Today, I call you to open yourselves completely to me so that I may transform you and lead you to the heart of my Son Jesus, so that He can fill you with His love. Only in this way, little children, will you find true peace - the peace that only God gives you. Thank you for having responded to my call".

April 25, 1999

"Dear children! Also today I call you to prayer. Little children, be joyful carriers of peace and love in this peaceless world. By fasting and prayer,

witness that you are mine and that you live my messages. Pray and seek! I am praying and interceding for you, before God, that you convert; that your life and behavior always be Christian. Thank you for having responded to my call".

January 25, 2001

"Dear children! Today I call you to renew prayerand fasting with even greater enthusiasm until prayer becomes a joy for you. Little children, the one who prays is not afraid of the future and the one who fasts is not afraid of evil. Once again, I repeat to you: only through prayer and fasting also wars can be stopped - wars of your unbelief and fear for the future. I am with you and am teaching you little children: your peace and hope are in God. That is why you must draw closer to God and put Him in the first place in your life. Thank you for having responded to my call".

September 25, 2001

"Dear children! Also today I call you to prayer, especially today when Satan wants war and hatred. I call you anew, little children: pray and fast that God may give you peace. Witness peace in every heart and be carriers of peace in this world without peace. I am with you and intercede before God for each of you. Do not be afraid because the one who prays is not afraid of evil and has no hatred in the

heart. Thank you for having responded to my call".

"Dear children! Also today I call you to pray and fast for peace. As I have already said and now repeat to you, little children, only with prayer and fasting can wars also be stopped. Peace is a precious gift from God. Seek, pray and you will receive it. Speak about peace and carry peace in your hearts. Nurture it like a flower which is in need of water, tenderness and light. Be those who carry peace to others. I am with you and intercede for all of you. Thank you for having responded to my call".

At the beginning of the apparitions, many fasted and prayed. As time went on we became bored and tired. Mary invites us to return to our initial enthusiasm and to embrace once again the practices of fasting and prayer, so that our hearts may be renewed so that we can continue our transformation. We are called to become similar to the hearts of Jesus and Mary. Prayer and fasting are the conditions necessary to open us up to the peace that only God can give.

"Dear children! Also today, as never up to now, I call you to open your hearts to my messages. Little children, be those who draw souls to God and

not those who distance them. I am with you and love you all with a special love. This is a time of penance and conversion. From the bottom of my heart, I call you to be mine with all your heart and then you will see that your God is great, because He will give you an abundance of blessings and peace. Thank you for having responded to my call".

July 25, 2005

"Dear children! Also today, I call you to fill your day with short and ardent prayers. When you pray, your heart is open and God loves you with a special love and gives you special graces. Therefore, make good use of this time of grace and devote it to God more than ever up to now. Do novenas of fasting and renunciation so that Satan be far from you and grace be around you. I am near you and intercede before God for each of you. Thank you for having responded to my call".

Our "Yes"

The Holy Sacrifice of the Mass

It has already been said that fasting without prayer is empty and sterile because it loses its starting point, its substance and its end. For this reason it is fundamental to pray, but especially when we are fasting to "pump ourselves up with prayer". Just as a stable diet doesn" only include sweets and snacks because they do not supply adequate nourishment, so too with the spiritual life: We cannot grow properly with simple devotions or holy exercises, we have to go deeper and have a true encounter with Jesus in the Holy Mass. For this reason, the prime invitation to prayer on fast days is to participate in the Holy Mass.

We can attend the Mass at whatever hour is convenient for us, and if we want to be one with the Universal Church, we can also participate in praying the Liturgy of the Hours. There are also the devotions of Eucharistic Adoration, the Way of the Cross, the Rosary and all the other devotions that the Holy Spirit suggests for our souls.

Prayer at the beginning of a fast day

At the end of our daily prayers, we should offer a series of specific intentions for the days of fasting and prayer.

In the name of the Father and the Son and the Holy Spirit. Amen.

O God, come to our aid
O Lord make haste to help us

• Father, help me to understand that on this earth I am a pilgrim. So, in the moment when I have to pass through to the next life, I cannot take anything of what I now have with me. I guard meaningless objects with so much attention. Yet all I can take are those good deeds that I have done during my earthly life.

Grant that I grow in awareness that nothing of what I own is really mine, because everything I have was only given to me so that I could better serve You. Grant that this fast helps me to grow in humility and sanctity, and that it will purify me from my selfishness and pride. Grant that this thought liberates me from all my bad habits, calms all my fears, and increases virtue in my soul. May your grace purify me and fill me with peace and true joy. **Amen.**

• Father, I offer you this coming day of fasting. Through this self-abnegation, I want my heart to be purified. I want my communion with You and with my fellow men to be intensified. I put myself totally in Your hands and beg You to give me true peace. Today, I want to renounce material goods and satisfactions in order to gain a greater interior freedom, to make me more capable of listening to Your Word, living it today and making it my only food. Father, I would like that through this fast, my understanding and sympathy for the hungry, the thirsty and the suffering would grow. Open my heart to the needs of my neighbor. May I be ready to give of myself to my brothers and sisters with love and charity. **Amen.**

• Father, You who are holiness and mercy, You are the God of our forefathers, look down on us who are living this day, that from this meager table, works of charity may be born in favor of peace. We beg You to multiply the fruits of our penance. Convert them into blessings for those who live in need and uncertainty. With the action of Your Holy Spirit, make this seed sprout into reconstruction and re-conciliation for mankind. **Amen.**

• Lord Jesus, Creator of the world, I thank You for having ordered the whole of creation in such a marvelous way. Thank You for all the fruits that mother earth brings us. Father, I rejoice for the gift of all Your creatures and I thank You. Thank You for all those who have much and are always giving to others. Thank You also for those who are hungry, who today have nothing to eat, because I am sure that soon You are going to send them all the necessary help.

Father, today I have decided to fast in petition that I may never be thankless for Your creatures and Your gifts, but rather that through fasting I can rediscover them in their true value, and see them only in the light of Your love. **Amen.**

• Mary, your heart was free and totally tuned in to the will of the Father. Pour out on me, today, the grace of a joyful fast-day. May I be able to raise up a hymn of praise to the heavens from my heart, united with yours. May my decision to fast remain firm and constant.

I want to offer you, today, all the problems that this fast will bring about, and the hunger I will feel, for the salvation of all men. May your intercession and strength of protection distance be from all evil and satanic temptations. Mary, teach me how to fast and to pray so that every day I may become more like you and your Son, Jesus. **Amen.**

Eucharistic Adoration on fast days

Mary invites us to a life of bread and water. The most profound meaning of this life is a preparation for the encounter with Jesus in the Eucharist. The most important encounter takes place during communion in the context of the most holy sacrifice of the mass, but, apart from this, there is also an essential encounter with Jesus in adoration.

In the name of the Father and the Son and the Holy Spirit. Amen.

O God come to my aid.

O Lord make haste to help us.

Glory be to the Father

Jesus, I adore You in this day of fasting and prayer, present in this consecrated host. I wish to adore You. O Heavenly Bread. Please keep all of the things that hinder me from experiencing You in this host, far away. I want to have a real experience of the living God, the God who chose to remain with us in this simple way. I, too, want to choose to be with You in this moment. Remove all of my invasive thoughts and feelings. Correct and guide my desire for You and grant that right now I may be in complete peace in front of You.

(brief pause in silence)

I adore You Jesus, Living Bread and I thank you for the words: "I am the bread of life, whoever comes to me will have life. Whoever believes in me will never hunger. I am the living bread come down from heaven. I am the bread of life."

Jesus, living today only on bread I ask You to open my heart so that I can understand the love that You have for us becoming the bread of life. I want to have a profound hunger and longing for You, the bread of life. Awake in me a profound hunger for Your word and Your love.

(In silence now, speak to Jesus in your own words.)

I adore You Jesus, Living Bread, bread of heaven for my life and for the life of the world. I thank You for having loved me so much that You became the bread of my life. Mary, your mother, invites me to love within You.

Today, living only on bread, grant me the grace that my heart loves completely in You, and that from now on, You have the first place in my thoughts, my words and all my actions. I beg You, grant me the grace to accept the way of bread without fear so that I, like You can say: "This is my body given up for you" and am able to say in family, in community, and to all those who are in need, "Here I am on the table of life in front of you as the good bread, as love, hope, mercy, forgiveness: Bless and know the love, the forgiveness, the mercy and forgiveness and the goodness of God."

(In silence now, let me experience the love of Jesus.)

I adore You Jesus, Living Bread and I thank You for having accepted the way of the cross and for having accepted death. It is through your death that life begins again.

I now present to You my thoughts, plans, words and actions. I present to You my pride, my selfishness and my envy; my attachment to material things and all of my bad habits which hinder me from becoming the bread of life for others. I place before You all which renders my life bitter and painful. Thank you because You will give me the strength of Your spirit and I will be free to love like You.

(In silence now, I entrust to Jesus all those things that are not in keeping with the will of God and hinder me from becoming bread for others.)

I adore You Jesus and I thank You because in the desert, during Your fast, You didn't give in to Satan.

While You fasted, Satan said to You: 'if you really are the Son of God, order these rocks to become bread". Jesus, You answered; "it is written man does not live on bread alone, but on every word that comes from the mouth of God".

(In silence now, I entrust to Jesus, all my dependencies, all my worries and all the frustrations of mankind.)

I adore You Jesus, alive in this bread, and I thank You because in Your fasting and prayer in the desert, You showed complete obedience to the Father when You were put to the test. Satan, the tempter had brought You to the Holy City, and brought You to the top of the temple and said; "If You are really the Son of God, throw yourself down because it is written, 'I will order My angels to guard You lest You hit Your foot against a stone". Thank You for having replied "It is also written 'do not put the Lord Your God to the test."

I offer You this day to compensate for all those times in my life when I didn't trust the will of the Lord, when my pride and my selfishness, my disobedience and my fears, led me up the wrong road. I offer this day for all those times when I followed the inspiration of Satan and put God to the test. May the spirit of total obedience, of light and truth, enter my heart so that I may always recognize the temptations of satan, and to conquer them and crush them with the strength of Your Spirit.

According to the will of the Father, I want to commend to You, Jesus, all those who, lost in pride, selfishness and atheism, have contempt for You. I also commend to You all those who have sunk to the deepest levels of human evil and sin, living unworthily the dignity of the Sons of God. Grant them the grace not to put God to the test, but rather to serve Him with devotion.

(In silence, I speak with Jesus about my life,
I offer Him my heart and present to Him the people
with whom I am in contact.)

I adore You, Jesus, and I thank You for having loved the Father so much that You were obedient to Him. During Your temptation, Satan led you to a high mountain and He showed You the whole world and said; "I will give You all this if You prostrate Yourself before me and adore me. Thank You for Your answer and your attitude when You said: "Be gone from me Satan, for it is written, 'You will adore the Lord your God and you will serve Him'.".

I offer you my prayer and fasting this day so that my heart may be purified so that with the Father, in the Holy Spirit, You will take the first place in my heart. You are my God and my Lord. I renounce earthly things and in Your name I beseech you to distance Satan and sin from all my thoughts, feelings, decisions and behaviour. In Your name,

Jesus, I renounce satan and all his works and seductions and with all my heart I desire to love You, adore You and give You the first place in my life.

(In silence now I renounce in a concrete way, all that now occupies the first place in my thoughts words and actions, and which distances me from the Lord.)

Jesus, I now entrust my family to You *(I recall their names).* With the strength of prayer and fasting, grant them the grace to renounce Satan and all his works, to the point that they love You and want to consecrate themselves fully to You. I also want to entrust to You all those who occupy positions of responsibility within the Church and in the world, but have chosen Satan and have chosen to adore and serve him. I bring to You now all those who are posessed by him, all those who practice occultism and spiritism, masons and satanic sects.

Through the power that You received from the Father, Jesus, crush Satan and liberate mankind, the world and nature from his influences, so that all can be in the service of the Father, through the Holy Spirit. Grant that every knee will bow and every tongue proclaims: "Glory to You Jesus, Son of God, in the Holy Spirit".

(In silence now, pray concretely for all those who we know occupying important positions in the Church, for politicians and all those bearing positions of responsibility.)

Benediction prayer

Jesus, living in this host, I thank You for Your presence. Bless me and guide me along the journey of peace, grant me the grace to live in You, Bread of Life, and to become bread of goodness, love and mercy for others. Thank You for the love You have shown to the sick and the weak.

Heal my soul and my body, heal all the sick and the weak. Living this day in prayer and with bread alone, I pray for the spiritual healing of all men. Strengthen us in faith, hope and love. Please take up the first place in all hearts.

Bless families, communities, the Church and the world so that we may become a people who do not live on material bread, but on every word that comes from Your mouth. Deliver the world from Satan and his works so that we can live in peace. **Amen.**

The Stations of the Cross on fast days

In the name of the Father and the Son and the Holy Spirit. Amen.

O God come to my aid.
O Lord make haste to help us.

Jesus in the garden of Gethsemene

While the apostles sleep, you pray alone, abandoned. Forgive me Lord because often I am spiritually weak and asleep. You know how weak I am in the face of lifes' trials. Grant me the grace in this day of fasting and prayer to be able to follow behind you as you carried your cross like Mary, your faithful mother. Finally Lord, you know how much sorrow betrayal provokes, make us aware of how much pain we cause others by our infidelity. Never let our embraces and handshakes become the gestures of a Judas.

Have mercy on us O Lord
Have mercy on us

At the cross her station keeping
Stood the mournful Mother weeping
Close to Jesus to the last.

THE FIRST STATION
Jesus, Pilate condemns you to death

We adore you O Christ and we bless you.
Because by your Holy Cross,
You have redeemed the world.

Thank you Jesus, because even though You were unjustly judged, you received your condemnation with love. Your heart was free, because you always loved, prayed and fasted. I pray to You and I offer this fast for all the powerful of this world and all those carrying positions of responsibility in the Church, so that, armed with this fast and prayer, you can direct their decisions towards justice, love, truth and peace. I offer you this fast and time in prayer for all those who are suffering because of unjust decisions. Help them to accept their unjust condemnation in peace so that you can heal their heart and soul until peace surrounds their hearts and the hearts of all mankind.

A short pause for reflection

Our Father • Hail Mary • Glory be to the Father

Have mercy on us O Lord
Have mercy on us

At the cross her station keeping
Stood the mournful Mother weeping
Close to Jesus to the last.

THE SECOND STATION
Jesus takes up his cross

We adore you O Christ and we bless you.
Because by your Holy Cross,
You have redeemed the world.

Thank You Jesus because you took the cross upon your shoulders, You took the most frightening tortures and the most terifying of deaths upon yourself. In this day of fasting and prayer, grant me an interior light until in humility and freedom of heart I can become Your disciple and You my master. I want to offer this fast and time spent in prayer for all those who place heavy burdens on the shoulders of others and cannot see what they are doing and don't try to change it, but only see their own rights and pleasures and cannot see the incorrectness of their own behaviour. Grant that fasting and prayer can begin to purify hearts and bring peace and order in the way man relates to man. And finally Lord, give us courage when we have to face trials and help us to comprehend that our life finds its fulness only if we know how to take up our crosses with You and in the same way that You did. We ask this through the merits of Your Holy Coss with which You saved the whole world.

A short pause for reflection

Our Father • Hail Mary • Glory be to the Father
Have mercy on us O Lord.
Have mercy on us

Through her heart, His sorrow sharing
All His bitter anguish bearing.
Lo! The piercing sword had passed!

THE THIRD STATION
Jesus falls for the first time under the cross

We adore you O Christ and we bless you.
Because by your Holy Cross,
You have redeemed the world.

Thank You Jesus because you accepted the cross spontaneously and You offered this moment in love for all of us. In this day of fasting and prayer, grant me the grace to be able to recognise my falls and my behaviour during my falls.

I offer you those times when I fell and lost my faith, hope, peace, patience and mercy. Accept also the consequences of these falls in my heart which stopped me from getting up again and walking with You. I present to You also those whom I accused for these falls and my bitterness towards them together with all those who fell influenced by my weakness. Grant them the grace to get up again and to forgive me to the point that in peace and communion we can tolerate each others' mutual burdens, to pick ourselves up after our falls and to continue our journey towards You.

A short pause for reflection

Our Father • Hail Mary • Glory be to the Father

Have mercy on us O Lord
Have mercy on us

Oh, how sad, and sore distressed
Now was she that Mother Blessed
Of the sole-begotten One.

THE FOURTH STATION
Jesus meets His Mother

We adore you O Christ and we bless you.
Because by your Holy Cross,
You have redeemed the world.

Thank You Jesus for this meeting with Your Mother. Thank you Mary for this meeting with Your son. In this day of fasting and prayer, I have more time to think about my meetings in my family. I thank You for all those meetings which were beautiful and good, but I offer you also those times when my family offended me or when it was I who made others suffer. I want to offer now this fast and time spent in prayer for the healing of the wounds which were inflicted out of pride, selfishness, intolerance, lack of forgiveness, and a lack of love or lack of openness to others. Grant that fasting and prayer can render our hearts capable of love and forgiveness, mercy and comprehension. Grant us a listening heart and the virtue of obedience. I want to offer my fast and prayer also for those whose vision is clouded by an attachment to material things, for those who are attached to alcohol or drugs, those who are limited by their lack of faith or inability to obey. Grant that peace may enter their families.

A short pause for reflection

Our Father • Hail Mary • Glory be to the Father

Have mercy on us O Lord
Have mercy on us

Woe-begone, with heart's prostration
Mother meek, the bitter Passion
Saw she of her glorious Son.

THE FIFTH STATION
Jesus, Simon of Cirene helps You carry your cross

We adore you O Christ and we bless you.
Because by your Holy Cross,
You have redeemed the world.

Thank You Jesus because You came to help everybody and You accepted the help of Simon of Cirene! Thank you Simon for the good deed which you did for my Saviour!

Today Jesus I offer You my fast and prayer so that You may purify my heart from pride and selfishness, from hatred and all that hinders me from carrying the crosses of others or from helping my neighbor. Heal the wounds in the hearts of those who expected my help, when I didn't even notice their need because I was so wrapped up in myself, in chasing after material things, after pleasures and a false life, without any need to sacrifice myself. Let me pray and fast for all the wealthy so that they notice the needs of the poor around them and help them. Let me pray and fast too for all of us who enjoy good health, that they recognise the needs of the sick. And let me pray too for all those who have their youth, that they may notice the needs of the elderly. Be blessed in all those who have helped me till now and all those who I have been able to help.

A short pause for reflection

Our Father • Hail Mary • Glory be to the Father

Have mercy on us O Lord
Have mercy on us

Who could mark from tears refraining,
Christ's dear Mother uncomplaining
In so great a sorrow bowed?

THE SIXTH STATION
Jesus, Veronica offers You a towel and dries Your face.

We adore you O Christ and we bless you.
Because by your Holy Cross,
You have redeemed the world.

Thank You Jesus, because You left the image of your face on Veronicas' towel as a sign of gratitude. Jesus, I offer you my fasting and prayer so that You can purify me from all my bad habits and evil so that my face can reflect Your joy, peace, love and hope. I want my face to reflect Your face, my words to be an echo of Your words and the peace that surrounds me, reminiscent of Your divine peace. Grant that the signs of that desperation of a heart that is not free, diseappear from my face through fasting and prayer, and let my expression be one of inner freedom and love. On seeing this, may those around me, whose words come from turmoil and who blaspheme, fill their hearts with words that are sweet and loving, words of prayer and thanksgiving to You.

I offer You this prayer and fasting for the grace of a good confession. Through this sacrament we are purified and glow with a light that can only come from You. I pray also for my confessor. May he be the outheld hand of Your mercy. Amen.

A short pause for reflection

Our Father • Hail Mary • Glory be to the Father

Have mercy on us O Lord
Have mercy on us

Who, unmoved, behold her languish,
Underneath His cross of anguish,
'Mid the fierce, unpitying crowd?

THE SEVENTH STATION
Jesus falls for the second time under the cross

We adore you O Christ and we bless you.
Because by your Holy Cross,
You have redeemed the world.

Thank You Jesus for having gotten up after this second fall which was more painful than the first. I offer this day of fasting and prayer for all my weaknesses and falls so that I can have the strength to get up again and follow You.

I offer You in a special way this day of fasting and prayer for all those who today, because of suffering and difficulty decide not to let Gods 'gift of life' continue.

Give them the grace and the strength to love this unborn life and to choose in its' favor. To all those who have commit a crime against the unborn, grant them the grace of repentance, conversion and grace so that from now on they may serve life. So I want to offer this day of fasting and prayer for all mothers who are now carrying new life, for future fathers, for their families, for their doctors and for all those who help women with problem pregnancies. Give them the grace to respect and protect life.

A short pause for reflection

Our Father • Hail Mary • Glory be to the Father

Have mercy on us O Lord
Have mercy on us

For His people's sins rejected
Saw her Jesus unprotected,
Saw with thorns, with scourges rent.

THE EIGHTH STATION
Jesus consoles the women of Jerusalem

We adore you O Christ and we bless you.
Because by your Holy Cross,
You have redeemed the world.

Thank You Jesus, because You permit the women of Jerusalem to cry for what was to happen to you. You stopped and invited them to conversion so that they could be saved and they could help save their families and nation too.

I offer You this day now for the Pope, the bishops, priests, missionaries and catechists, so that they may become first listeners of the Word and then announce it to others.I offer this day in a special way for priests who consciously take up this call to announce the good news, to forgive sins, to heal the sick and to liberate from evil spirits.

Grant that your kingdom of freedom, peace, justice and life may come to all mankind. I pray also for the new missions in the Church so that young people can respond to the call.

A short pause for reflection

Our Father • Hail Mary • Glory be to the Father

Have mercy on us O Lord
Have mercy on us

Saw her Son from Judgment taken,
Her belov'd in death forsaken
Till His Spirit forth He sent.

THE NINTH STATION
Jesus falls for the third time under the cross

We adore you O Christ and we bless you.
Because by your Holy Cross,
You have redeemed the world.

Thank You Jesus because you got up again after this third fall under the cross. I offer this fast today for all those who have compromised their interior liberty in alcohol, drugs, gambling, immorality, prostitution and other vices.

Grant them the strength to overcome evil, to get up again and walk with You. Give them the grace not to be afraid of sacrifice, renouncement and to receive faith, hope, love and trust again. Grant that joy and peace can return in their hearts. Grant them the strength to forgive themselves and all those who accuse them for their falls. Sustain them in their witness to the strength that comes from You.

I offer this fast for all those who don't have the strength to get up again, and who do not admit to needing help. Illuminate their clouded minds, strengthen their weakened will, free them from evil influences, so that all mankind may live in peace. Amen.

A short pause for reflection

Our Father • Hail Mary • Glory be to the Father

Have mercy on us O Lord
Have mercy on us

Fount of love and Holy sorrow
Mother, may my spirit borrow
Somewhat of thy woe profound.

THE TENTH STATION
Jesus, they stripped you of your clothes

We adore you O Christ and we bless you.
Because by your Holy Cross,
You have redeemed the world.

Thank You Jesus, because with love and patience You even tolerated the outrage of nudity when they stripped You of Your clothes. You were exposed to the gaze of men who derided and beat You. I want to offer this day of prayer in thanksgiving for Your immeasurable love but also for those for whom I was humiliated, for all the sins of the body which I have commit and for all the sins of the world which humiliate mankind.

I offer you this day of fasting and prayer for all those who in their childhood suffered humiliations by those who were closest to them, for those who were refuted, who underwent sexual violence. I want to pray for all those who commit sins against the dignity of the unborn, for all political prisoners, for all those who were deprived of liberty because of their crimes. I pray too for those who abuse their position, their power and their money in order to take advantage of others and humiliate them.

A short pause for reflection

Our Father • Hail Mary • Glory be to the Father

Have mercy on us O Lord
Have mercy on us

Unto Christ, with, pure emotion
Raise my contrite heart's devotion
Love to read in every wound.

THE ELEVENTH STATION
Jesus, you are nailed to the cross

We adore you O Christ and we bless you.
Because by your Holy Cross,
You have redeemed the world.

Thank You Jesus, crucified Saviour. I offer you now this day of prayer and fasting for all evil-doers who take advantage of their own position, power and money and crucify others in different ways,with atrocious suffering. These people live hatred and bitterness and for this reason are ready to take revenge and repay evil with evil.

I want to pray and fast that they may be able to see their sinfulness and unjust behaviour. I want to pray for all those who cause division in families, in the church and the world, for those who cause wars and I want to pray too for those who carry out violence on children the sick and the poor the innocent and the weak. Grant them the grace to recognise their own violent behaviour, so that they convert to You, O God of Peace, love and forgiveness and become workers of peace.

A short pause for reflection

Our Father • Hail Mary • Glory be to the Father

Have mercy on us O Lord
Have mercy on us

Those five wounds on Jesus smitten.
Mother in my heart be written,
Deep as in thine own they be.

THE TWELFTH STATION
Jesus, You die on the Cross

We adore you O Christ and we bless you.
Because by your Holy Cross,
You have redeemed the world.

O my dead Saviour! I offer You this day of fasting and prayer so that love opens my eyes. May Your pain, and your words of forgiveness find an echo in my heart and change my whole life. Grant that everything that is tripping up my path to total union with Your will, dies within me.

I renounce sin and all evil and with the strength of fasting, prayer and sacrifice, free me so that I can offer with You my salvation and that of the whole world.

Grant interior strength to those who are now crucified because they have given in to evil, and are blinded by power and glory, because with their hatred and violence they are crucifying all those surrounding them. May evil die and goodness rise up, may all disturbances die down and peace rise up, may desperation cease and hope be born again.

A short pause for reflection

Our Father • Hail Mary • Glory be to the Father

Have mercy on us O Lord
Have mercy on us

Thou my saviour's Cross who bearest,
Thou thy Son's rebuke who sharest,
Let me share them both with thee!

THE THIRTEENTH STATION
Jesus, they take You down from the cross and place You in the arms of Mary

We adore you O Christ and we bless you.
Because by your Holy Cross,
You have redeemed the world.

Thank You Mary for your tears, you are crying for your Son in agony, tortured and pulled apart, but you are crying also for love which is not understood, not appreciated and refuted. You cry because mankind didn't pick up on this mystery. You cry because the biggest gift went unrecognised. You cry for the frightening stunted-ness which invades the human heart so much that it becomes blind and cruel.

I offer you O Mary this day of fasting and prayer so that you can use it to liberate me from whatever blocks me from consecrating myself totally to You and becoming fully yours. I offer you my past present and future so that you can heop me to remain faithful. I entrust all families to you, all parents, children, all widows, orphans, the youth, the Church and the world. I offer you this fast and prayer for all your intentions and for the victory of Your Immaculate Heart.

A short pause for reflection

Our Father • Hail Mary • Glory be to the Father

Have mercy on us O Lord
Have mercy on us

In the Passion of my Maker
Be my sinful soul partaker,
Weep till death, and keep with thee.

THE FOURTEENTH STATION
Jesus, they lay You in the Sepulchre

We adore you O Christ and we bless you.
Because by your Holy Cross,
You have redeemed the world.

Mary, often men think that they have had the last word about Christ, by cancelling His name. But exactly when everything seems to be over, the return begins and the resurrection takes place. The grain of wheat which falls to the ground dies, but in order to bear fruit. For whoever follows Christ, the exit point of every cross and every defeat is the splendour of the Resurrection. Together with You, I want to thank once again Your Son for coming into this corrupt world, for having lived among us sinners, and for all those things for which He was never thanked.

I offer this fast and prayer for whoever has strayed from the narrow path, to follow the ways of evil for whoever doesn't believe in the final victory over death and sees life as an end in itself, for all those who do not believe in eternal life and do not prepare seriously for their passing from this life to that which has no end.

A short pause for reflection

Our Father • Hail Mary • Glory be to the Father

Have mercy on us O Lord
Have mercy on us

Mine with thee be that sad station
There to watch the great salvation
Wrought upon th' atoning tree.

Concluding Prayer

Lord, You have gone through all the stages of our living and our suffering. Grant that we may always look at you as our only guide and model, so that together with You we may experience the joys, the trials and the defeats of life and arrive with You at the glory of the resurrection. Amen.

Prayer in front of the Cross

Let us bow in front of Your cross, because it is a symbol of Your love, and through the strength of Your most precious blood, wash us from all our sins and protect us from the works of satan. May rivers of peace and reconciliation run from this place into the parish community, into the Church and the whole world.

Bless and receive into heaven all those who honour the cross. Bless all those who have prayed and who will pray in front of it that they may realise what Mary Your Mother has told us; " pray in front of the Cross, from this great graces come". Blessed be Your name Jesus, because through Your Cross You have redeemed us for eternal life. I offer You this fast for my own salvation and for that of all mankind. Amen.

5 Our Fathers

in honour of the wounds of Christ

The Rosary on Fast days

In the name of the Father and the Son and the Holy Spirit. Amen.

O God come to my aid.
O Lord make haste to help us.
Glory Be to the Father
Invocation of the Holy Spirit

On the crucifix, pray:

I believe in God, the Father Almighty, Creator of Heaven and earth and in Jesus Christ his only son Our Lord, who was conceived by the Holy Spirit, born of the virgin Mary, suffered under Pontius Pilate, was crucified, died and was buried. On the third day, he arose from the dead, ascended into heaven and is seated at the right hand of God the Father almighty; from thence he shall come to judge the living and the dead. I believe in the Holy Spirit, the Holy Catholic Church, the Communion of Saints, the forgiveness of sins, the resurrection of the dead, and life eternal. Amen.

On the five beads between the crucifix and the beginning of the five decades:

1st bead: Our Father
2nd bead: Hail Mary for faith
3rd bead: Hail Mary for hope
4th bead: Hail Mary for love
5th bead: Glory Be

The Joyful Mysteries
(Mondays and Saturdays)

Introductory Prayer
Father, Creator of the world, I want to thank you now for inspiring me with a desire to pray. I want to spend this fast day together with You, with Your Son Jesus and Mary Our Mother, in peace and joy. I offer You my heart so that it can be filled with your light and your strength. Amen.

The First Joyful Mystery
The Annunciation

Thank You Mary, because your heart was free enough to put the will of the Father in the first place in your life, and for saying: "Father, let it be done unto me according to your will".

With you Mary, in this day of fasting, I want to pray to Our Lord to purify my heart which is a prisoner of the illusions of this world. Liberate me from all that is makin me blind and deaf to the will of the Father.

Our Father • 10 Hail Mary • Glory be

O my Jesus, forgive us our sins, save us from the fires of hell, lead all souls to heaven, especially those who have most need of your mercy.

The Second Joyful Mystery
The visitation

Thank you Mary for having gone to Elisabeth and glorifying the Lord together with her. Thank you for having gone there to help her. Through this fasting and prayer, can I open myself completely to you and to others so that in this way we make up a communion of joy. I offer up this day of fasting and prayer for all families, so that parents and children, in full interior freedom, become the joy of family communion that they are intended to be.

Our Father • 10 Hail Mary • Glory be

The Third Joyful Mystery
The Birth of Our Lord

Thank you Mary, because despite your poverty, you brought Jesus, the King of Peace, into the world. In this day of fasting, I want to pray together with you O Mary, so that the Lord frees me from whatever ties I have with the things of this world,May I accept in freedom and love, all the situations of life, and overcome all disturbances, and become a person of goodwill, ready to embrace peace and pass it on to others.

Our Father • 10 Hail Mary • Glory be

The Fourth Joyful Mystery
The Presentation in the Temple

Thank you Mary, that with Saint Joseph, with a free and loving heart, you presented Jesus for our salvation. In this fast day, I am praying with you my mother, so that all Christians, in prayer and fasting prepare and dispose themselves for the encounter with the Lord. Grant that they recognise his presence in the Eucharist and in His Word. May they be able to meet him with an open and free heart in all the sacraments.

Our Father • 10 Hail Mary • Glory be

The Fifth Joyful Mystery
Jesus among the doctors in the temple

Thank you Mary, because together with Joseph, you sought and found Jesus in the Temple.

In this day I present to you my fast on bread and water and my prayer, for all those who have clouded their interior liberty because of the false values which they picked up in the home. Some of them have even taken the wrong paths and walk the way that conducts far from Our Lord. Seek them out Mary and lead them back to the house of the Father.

Our Father • 10 Hail Mary • Glory be

Concluding prayer

I bless and I praise you O heavenly Father, with your Son Jesus Christ, our Lord, in the Holy Spirit, because today you have given me the grace to stay with them in this fast. May perfect joy and peace enter in my heart throught this fasting and prayer and in the hearts of those who pray and fast. Help us to love you more and more. Amen.

The Mysteries of Light
(Thursday)

Introductory prayer

Jesus, You are the light of the world and whoever lives in You has no fear of darkness or death. Today in this day of fasting and prayer I want to immerge myself in You and in a concrete way, I want to put into practice that seed that I received at Baptism, that call to be a living Eucharist. I want to be a light for my brothers, salt of the earth. I want the power of the kingdom of God to be expressed in my life.

The first Mystery of Light
The Baptism of Jesus in the Jordan

Thank You Jesus because on the banks of the river Jordan You began your path of penance in order to be like men in all things except sin. You submitted Yourself to the Father under the guidance of the Holy Spirit so that You have gone through all situations before us. You conquer sin, satan, death, and You open up to us the road to the resurrection. In this day of fasting Jesus, grant us a vivid sense of our own sinfulness and the grace to repent. Intercede for us to the point that we remember what You did to save us and we no longer wish to offend you.

Our Father • 10 Hail Mary • Glory be

The second Mystery of Light
Jesus presence at the wedding of Cana

Jesus, You began your life of preaching and teaching, enlightening your disciples with a miraculous sign transforming the water into wine. This sign came about at the intercession of Mary who was there present. In this day of fasting and prayer, reveal to us once more how important it is to "do everything" that you tell us, because You always did the will of the Father

Our Father • 10 Hail Mary • Glory be

The third Mystery of Light
The Announcement of the Kingdom and invitation to conversion

Jesus, you had a concrete objective that was very clear to you, to install the 'Kingdom of God', which is that unique relationsip of love, destroyed by men through sin. Only Your forgiveness O Father, can re-construct it and only a continuous conversion prevents us from destroying it anew. In this da of fasting and prayer, help us to understand and participate, through this bread and water in an active way in the plan of salvation and to bring all men to God.

Our Father • 10 Hail Mary • Glory be

The fourth Mystery of Light
The Transfiguration of Jesus on Tabor

Jesus, on Tabor You were accompanied by some of the disciples who later on would accompany You at Gethsemene. In this day of fasting, give me the grace to be one of the faithful disciples, and in the depths of my soul may I be capable of receiving the light which You are sending me today and for the rest of my life.

Our Father • 10 Hail Mary • Glory be

The fifth Mystery of Light
The Institution of the Eucharist

Jesus, so many times the disciples dined with You. On that evening though, there was something different, something special. You were awaiting that last meal together to show them how much you .loved them, that You loved them to the very end. You turned Yourself into bread and wine making Yourself the victim and altar of salvation. In this day of fasting and prayer, Mary I ask You the grace of getting to discover Jesus alive in the Holy Eucharist. Help us to love him adore him and honour him with the fearsome respect that we owe him. May the bread that I will eat today, keep the memory of your act of love alive in my heart. May I constantly remember how you broke bread and transformed it into your body and blood.

Our Father • 10 Hail Mary • Glory be

Concluding prayer

I thank You Jesus for this day passed in fasting and prayer; thank You especially for the gift of the Eucharist; forgive me all those masses when outside life was more important; when I was distracted, when You were ignored, when I remained cold, those masses that had no fervor of charity, those masses where I remained distant like an embrace which is insincere. Amen.

The Sorrowful Mysteries
(Tuesdays and Fridays)

Introductory Prayer

Thank You Jesus for having chosen suffering in order to save mankind. Today I offer You my hunger, so that you can replace it with another hunger; the hunger for superior values, according to the will of the Father. Mary, teach me to fast and pray in order to follow Jesus on the road of suffering. **Amen.**

The first Sorrowful Mystery
Jesus in Gethsemene

Thank You Jesus for Your suffering in the garden of Gethsemene. In this day of fasting and prayer, I ask You Jesus to give me the grace to struggle with all my bad habits that cause suffering and pain. I present all those who suffer dependencies on alcohol or drugs or other substances. These addictions provoke in themselves, their families, their spouses and children those difficult moments needed in Gethsemene. For all of them, I want to offer my prayer and this day of fasting and I want to thank You because You will grant them the interior freedom, the peace, the spiritual health, necessary to change. And after this will follow health of soul and body.

Our Father • 10 Hail Mary • Glory be

The second Sorrowful Mystery
The Scourging at the Pillar

Thank You Jesus for having allowed Yourself to be scourged. Let me offer this day of fasting and prayer for all those who carry in their hearts a wound from their childhood and through this wound keep fallin back into more bad situations and more dependencies. In this way they continuously scourge themselves and others. Free our families from all evil. May all these tortures end. Through fasting and prayer may they reach peace and joy and health in mind and body.

Our Father • 10 Hail Mary • Glory be

The third Sorrowful Mystery
The Crowning with thorns

Thank You Jesus for having tolerated everything in order to redeem us and to free us from evil.

I want to offer up my day of fasting and prayer in reparation for all the offenses and humiliations received in all black masses and occult rites. I offer it too for all those who enter satanic sects and participate in them, for all those who deal with spiritism, magic and witchcraft and who, for these reasons, end up under the influence of evil spirits.

Our Father • 10 Hail Mary • Glory be

The fourth Sorrowful Mystery
The way of Calvary

Thank You Jesus for having carried Your cross with patience. Although You fell under the weight of it You got back up again and continued that walk that You dicided to do for us. I want to offer this day of prayer and fasting for all the sick and the weak, for all those who have lost hope, and for all those who serve the sick and the suffering. I pray to You for all parents with sick children. Be light, strength and consolation for them.

Our Father • 10 Hail Mary • Glory be

The fifth Sorrowful Mystery
Death on the Cross

Thank You Jesus because You accepted crucifixion and death on a cross. I offer up this fasting and prayer for an easy passage from this life to the next. I want to pray for all souls who have to die today. Let fasting and prayer bring to death of all that is not of God within me. May all links with sin be broken, and all relationships with myself, others, with material goods and with You which are incorrect come to an end.

Our Father • 10 Hail Mary • Glory be

Concluding Prayer

Thank You Jesus for Your passion, thank You for Your suffering and death. Through fasting and prayer, may I be able to carry all the crosses of my life with love, and let some of them be a prison to praise.

The Glorious Mysteries
(Wednesdays and Sundays)

Introductory Prayer

Jesus, my heart sings Your praises because you have defeated death and You are risen. I bow down before You. Alleluia! Today, in fasting and prayer, by the power of the Holy Spirit, free my heart from entering into the glory of the resurrection with You.

Mary, may my heart be like yours: Early on the day of the Resurrection, you were resplendent with joy because of the victory of good over evil.

The first Glorious Mystery
The Resurrection

Jesus, You arose gloriously from the sepulchre. I offer up this fasting and prayer for myself and for all those who freeze up in the sepulchre of sin, bad habits, hatred, dependencies, in envy, selfishness, in pride, atheism or in violence. I pray too for all those who have been wounded by the sins of others and fall into the darkness of the sepulchre. May all hearts experience this victorious glory and continually render You praise and thanks.

Our Father • 10 Hail Mary • Glory be

The second Glorious Mystery
The Ascension

Father, I offer You this day of fasting and prayer for all those who are so attatched to themselves, to other men and to material things, that they gave in to power and have no more place for You in their hearts. Their outlook is restricted to the earth. May the wealthy people of this world raise their gaze, and in the liberty of their own hearts, recognize in the poor, brothers and sisters and reach out to them with joy. May You occupy the first place in their hearts, and may they remain faithful to You for always.

Our Father • 10 Hail Mary • Glory be

The third Glorious Mystery
Pentecost

We praise You Jesus, because faithful to Your promise, You sent Your Holy Spirit. I offer You this day of fasting so that You can fill those without peace with Your Spirit of tranquility. Fill those who have lost their trust with the Spirit of prayer and fill atheists with the Spirit of faith. Grant to the weak Your Spirit of Fortitude, to the afflicted, Your Spirit of consolation and joy and to prisoners of sin, Your Spirit of interior liberty. Grant to those who hate, Your Spirit of love. Grant to those who have lost hope, Your Spirit of hope and to the violent Your Spirit of Peace.

Our Father • 10 Hail Mary • Glory be

The fourth Glorious Mystery
The Assumption of Mary into Heaven

I praise You O Father, because You assumed Mary into heaven body and soul. In a special way I want to offer You my fasting and prayer for the youth of today, so that in you Mary, they find a Mother and a teacher so that they can overcome all the difficulties of life and the trials of this world. Through fasting and prayer, may they recognise evil and its seductions and suceed in turning away from all the degeneracy of this world.

Our Father • 10 Hail Mary • Glory be

The fifth glorious Mystery
Mary is crowned as Queen of Angels and Saints

Father I praise You because You crowned Mary as Queen of heaven and earth and You sent Her to us as Queen of Peace. Thank You Mary, because

You do not become tired of us and you continue to pray and intercede for us.

I offer this day of fasting and prayer which You sought, for the intention that peace comes to every heart, to every family, in the Church and the world, and that all discord may be resolved. Grant that all non-believers experience the love of the Father, that families begin to pray and that evil and all ills will be defeated.

Our Father • 10 Hail Mary • Glory be

Concluding Prayer

Father, fill all your children with a spirit of fasting and prayer, so that they can recognise and carry out Your Divine Will. May we love You above all things, and love our neighbours as ourselves. May we protect and love nature as a special expression of Your love for us. Grant Your peace to all hearts through the intercession of Mary, in the name of Your Son Jesus Christ, King of Peace. Amen.

Salve Regina

Hail Holy Queen, Mother of mercy. Hail our life our sweetness and our hope. To thee do we cry poor banished children of Eve. To thee do we send up our sighs, mourning and weeping in this valley of tears.

Turn then most gracious advocate thine eyes of mercy towards us, and after this our exile, show unto us the blessed fruit of thy womb Jesus. O Clement, O loving, O sweet virgin Mary.

The Litany of the Blessed Virgin Mary

Lord, have mercy on us

> Lord, have mercy on us

Christ have mercy on us

> Christ have mercy on us

Lord, have mercy on us

> Lord, have mercy on us

Christ, hear us

> Christ, hear us

Christ, graciously hear us

> Christ, graciously hear us

God, the Son, Redeemer of the world

> Have mercy on us

God, the Holy Spirit,   "

Holy Trinity, One God,   "

Holy Mary,   pray for us

Holy Mother of God   "

Holy Virgin of Virgins	**pray for us**
Mother of Christ	"
Mother of the Church	"
Mother of divine grace	"
Mother most pure	"
Mother most chaste	"
Mother inviolate	"
Mother undefiled	"
Mother most amiable	"
Mother most admirable	"
Mother of good counsel	"
Mother of our Creator	"
Mother of our Saviour	"
Mother of Mercy	"
Virgin most prudent	"
Virgin most venerable	"
Virgin most renowned	"
Virgin most powerful	"
Virgin most merciful	"
Mirror of justice	"
Seat of wisdom	"
Cause of our joy	"
Spiritual vessel	"
Singular vessel of devotion	"
Mystical rose	"
Tower of David	"
Tower of Ivory	"
House of gold	"

Ark of the covenant

pray for us

Gate of Heaven

Morning star

Health of the sick

Refuge of sinners

Comforter of the afflicted

Help of Christians

Queen of Angels

Queen of patriarchs

Queen of prophets

Queen of Apostles,

Queen of martyrs,

Queen of confessors

Queen of virgins

Queen conceived without original sin

Queen of the most holy Rosary

Queen of the family

Queen of peace

**Lamb of God, you take away
the sins of the world.**
Spare us, oh Lord.

**Lamb of God, you take away
the sins of the world.**
Graciously hear us oh Lord.

**Lamb of God, you take away
the sins of the world.**
Have mercy on us.

Pray for us, oh Holy Mother of God.
That we may be made worthy of the promises of
Christ.

Let us pray
O God, whose only begotten Son by His Life, death
and resurrection has purchased for us the rewards
of eternal life, grant, we beseech You, that
meditating upon these mysteries of the most holy
Rosary of the Blessed Virgin Mary, we may imitate
what they contain and obtain what they promise.
Through the same Christ our Lord. **Amen.**

TOTUS TUUS

"What I tell you in darkness, speak in the daylight; what I whispered in your ear, proclaim from the rooftops". (Mt 10:27). The theme here echoes the words of Jesus and could not be otherwise because we preach of Christ alone (...) Today proclaiming faith from the rooftops means proclaiming the Word of Jesus within the dynamic world of social communications and by means of it".
Pope John Paul II.

In these times, when our faith in the unique Church of Christ is put to the test, it is essential that we include submission, obedience and communion with the Pope as part of our Christian experience, enlivened by the bond of Trinitarian love and encouraged and guided by Mary. The Pope has renewed his invitation to us to proclaim the word of God "from the rooftops", that is, using the means of communication and the technology that the modern world offers us and Shalom Publishers feel called personally to embody this invitation through the publication and distribution of religious publications. In accordance with the appeal voiced by Cardinal Ratzinger to defend the greatest gift that we have: faith, while maintaining the utmost respect for other cultures and religions, we too welcome the invitation to be courageous in defending the great gift that we have been given: Christian life and faith. A faith that is certainly open to dialogue, but that may only be built upon by beginning from a strong conviction, founded on a single cornerstone: Jesus Christ.

The pages that follow are a mere "taste" of the general catalogue for 2004, that contains Shalom's entire production of books, holy pictures, images and various objects, along with books and merchandise produced by other catholic publishers. You may order it and have it delivered to your home by contacting us by phone, fax or e-mail or by visiting our Internet site (see page 4).

Our books contain orthodox texts (that is, texts written in absolute obedience to the laws of the Catholic Church) published by SHALOM, a catholic and Marian publishing company that aims to promote prayer among the largest number of readers possible and to re-establish Eucharistic faith as the centre of human life. In order to make this goal attainable, although it is a commercial enterprise, SHALOM publishers has renounced all profit and does not pay any type of royalties (either ownership royalties or moral royalties) for texts, translations, photos, drawings or illustrations of any kind. This initiative is developed with the aim of contributing to the triumph of the Immaculate Heart of Mary in the certainty that in doing so we are serving the Kingdom of God and participating in the faith and obedience of Mary, Servant and Mother of the Lord, entrusting ourselves entirely to her protection and that of St. Joseph and St. Michael the Archangel. Printed in April 2006 by Sograte, Città di Castello.

"PRAY,PRAY,PRAY"

Format: cm. 12 x 19
Pages: 1280
Price: € 9,00
Code book 8148

code 8148

Series: THE MOTHER OF GOD

This book proposes prayers, rosaries, acts of consecration and novenas, all gathered together in a very rich collection which is subdivided according to the following subjects: Monsignor Nicola Rotunno, former Apostolic Nuncio and Bishop, in one of his letters, described the book with the following words: "Honest people, who find themselves in an arid desert devoid of human values, lost, and without strength, not knowing which road to take, but yet certain of their belief in Jesus, Son of Mary the Virgin Mother, Son of God, they will know how to find in this book: "Pray, pray, pray", the voice of God which will encourage them and show them the right path to take. This book, in the light of the Second Ecumenical Vatican Council, promotes devotion towards the Blessed Virgin, it holds in high esteem the practice and exercises of devotion towards her, recommended down through the centuries by the Magistery of the Church, and it does not contain fanatical exaggeration neither does it contain narrow minded thinking. True devotion does not consist of sterile and passing sentimentalism, nor of vain belief, but arises rather from true faith which encourages us to imitate Mary's virtue"…

ISBN 978-88-86616-16-4

Collaborators
Sr. Maria Gabriella Turrin of the Annunciation cmop

• Everyday prayers
• To the Mother of God
• To the Most Holy Trinity
• To Saint Joseph
• To the Father
• To the angels
• To the Son
• To the Holy Family
• To the Holy Spirit
• To the Saints

"PRAY THE HOLY ROSARY EVERY DAY, PRAY TOGETHER"

Format: cm. 12 x 19
Pages: 256
Price: € 5,00
Code book 8118

code 8118

Series: THE MOTHER OF GOD

ISBN 978-88-86616-14-0

Collaborators
Father Slavko Barbaric ofm

Continue to love the Holy Rosary

I would like to make many
recommendations to you,
but I will mention just one essential one:
continue to love the Holy Rosary
and spread its practice in all places
wherever you come together.

It is a prayer
that will educate you according to the school
of the living Gospel,
it will educate your soul to be holy,
it will make you persevering in good,
it will prepare you for life
and above all,
it will bring you close to Mary
the Blessed Virgin
who will protect you and
defend you from the snares of evil.

Pray to Our Lady for me,
and I will entrust all of us
to her maternal protection.

John Paul II

TRUE DEVOTION TO MARY

Format: cm. 11 x 17
Pages: 320
Price: € 5,00
Code book 8143

code
8143

A book by *Saint Louis-Marie G. de Montfort*
Comments by *Father Battista Cortinovis, s.m.m.*

I often remember a little book with a blue cover, dirty of soda... . When I used to work by the Solvay, I always brought that book with me, together with a piece of bread. For the afternoon and night-shifts.

ISBN
978-88-86616-03-4

Series:
THE MOTHER OF GOD

THE SECRET OF MARY

Format: cm. 10 x 14
Pages: 128
Price: € 3,00
Code book 8263

code
8263

"The book that the reader has in their hands when reading "The Secret of Mary" is quite small but is dense with contents that have a very particular aim. "The Secret of Mary" aims at discovering the special role of the Mother of the Lord in the mystery of salvation and the manner in which this must be recognised by means of an authentic relationship with him.

ISBN
978-88-8404-020-6

Series:
THE MOTHER OF GOD

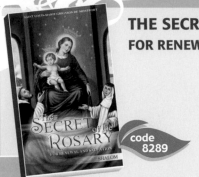

THE SECRET OF THE ROSARY
FOR RENEWAL AND SALVATION

code 8289

Format: cm. 11 x 17
Pages: 256
Price: € 5,00
Code book 8289

ISBN
978-88-8404-054-1

"I look at all of you, brothers and sisters of all conditions, you Christian families, you the old and the sick, you young people, faithfully take the rosary into your hands, rediscover it in the light of Scripture, in harmony with the Liturgy and in the context of daily life. Do not fail to heed my appeal!"

John Paul II

Series:
THE MOTHER OF GOD

FIFTEEN PRAYERS OF SAINT BRIDGET

code 8241

Format: cm. 10 x 14
Pages: 64
Price: € 1,80
Code book 8241

ISBN
978-88-8404-033-7

"Saint Bridget was a woman of great courage since she had an uninhibited faith, a love she offered with all her heart. She loved the Church of the times just as it was. She worked for it, she suffered, she committed herself for its unity and to uphold the Vicar of Christ".

John Paul II

Series:
THE SAINTS

FULL CIRCLE

FULL CIRCLE

Pamela Oldfield

This first world edition published in Great Britain 2007 by
SEVERN HOUSE PUBLISHERS LTD of
9–15 High Street, Sutton, Surrey SM1 1DF.
This first world edition published in the USA 2007 by
SEVERN HOUSE PUBLISHERS INC of
595 Madison Avenue, New York, N.Y. 10022.

British Library Cataloguing in Publication Data

Oldfield, Pamela
    Full circle
    1.   Elopement - Fiction
    2.   Love stories
    I.   Title
    823.9'14 [F]

    ISBN-13: 978-0-7278-6404-8 (cased)
    ISBN-13: 978-0-7278-9193-8 (paper)

Typeset by Palimpsest Book Production Ltd.,
Grangemouth, Stirlingshire, Scotland.
Printed and bound in Great Britain by
MPG Books Ltd., Bodmin, Cornwall.

One

Madeline was checking her husband's breakfast tray, which the housekeeper was offering her for inspection.

'A boiled egg, toast, butter and an apple – but not marmalade, Sarah,' she said. 'Mr Swain had that yesterday. You know how fussy he is about variety in his meals.'

From across the large kitchen, Sarah Gravely sighed. 'I do, ma'am. I'm sorry. Shall it be lemon curd or the honey?'

'Honey, I think. There is very little lemon curd left. I shall have to make some more.'

Sarah smiled. 'It's young Louise who eats most of it. It's a wonder she's not turning yellow!'

Louise Legrand could do no wrong in Sarah's eyes, but Madeline knew that, at eighteen, her daughter was already changing from a lively, imaginative child into an impulsive and passionate young woman. Madeline recognized the signs with some anxiety for she had been exactly the same at her daughter's age.

She picked up the tray and carefully negotiated the broad staircase. At the top she met Louise. She had already washed and dressed, her dark hair neatly brushed and held by a red satin ribbon. The likeness between them was obvious. Both were dark-eyed with pale complexions and neat features. Only age separated them. Where Louise's attitude was bright and eager, her mother's was calmer with a hint of caution. Louise was only just losing her gawky, coltish looks, but Madeline's body had rounded a little over the years.

Louise glanced at her stepfather's tray. 'Not honey again!'

'Again?' Madeline looked startled. 'Oh! Don't say I've . . .'

Louise grinned. 'It's a joke, Mama!'

1

Madeline let out a sigh of relief. 'You wretch! For a minute there you had me worried.'

Laughing, Louise hurried down the stairs and Madeline pushed against the bedroom door to open it. She entered a large room made gloomy by dark oak panelling, large furniture and three sombre paintings. Heavy drapes that hung at the window kept out much of the July sunshine. It seemed that Oscar only appreciated sunshine if he was walking in it. He liked the house cool and she had long since become reconciled to the idea.

Oscar Swain, her second husband, was sixty-nine and in failing health. A serious heart attack ten years earlier had left him weak and fearful. He feared a second attack, which the doctor had warned might prove fatal. Madeline smiled at him as she approached the bed. Oscar still slept in the double bed they had once shared, but after his attack he had decided that Madeline was too restless in bed and kept him from his much needed sleep. She had moved without regret into the third bedroom.

These days the difference in their ages was painfully obvious. He was almost bald with only a few thin wisps of grey hair, his face and body were thin and the hands that clutched the bed covers were claw-like. Madeline, however, regarded him with affection. She had regarded him more as a father figure than a husband since their wedding night when he had explained that the marriage bed held no interest for him. He had married, he told her, simply for affection and companionship. Madeline had received the information with mixed feelings as she had never found him physically attractive although she had great respect for the kindness he had shown her and her daughter and mother. She also felt a deep sympathy for the man who, she knew, found it difficult to show his feelings. Oscar Swain, for the most part, kept his emotions under lock and key.

Oscar looked up at once from the bible he was reading, closed it carefully and laid it on the bedside table. He didn't smile, but regarded the tray through narrowed eyes.

'No lemon curd?'

'There is only a scraping left in the jar, Oscar. I'll make some more.'

2

'Do that, please, dear.'

With difficulty, he struggled into a better sitting position and smoothed the covers, and Madeline set the tray on his lap. Years of being bedridden had taught him how to manage his meals without any spills or minor disasters. He now poured milk and tea into his cup, added sugar and stirred it seven times.

Madeline stared out of the window across the bay, through cream lace hung between heavy brocade curtains. She was willing herself not to lose patience over the familiar ritual. You'll be old yourself one day, she reminded herself. She turned to sit beside him on the bedside chair while he tapped three times on his boiled egg to open it and slowly cut his toast into quarters.

She bided her time as he began to eat. He liked her to 'share' his breakfast and this morning she was particularly willing because she had a favour to ask.

He said, 'The toast was burned. It's been scraped. I can always tell. Please tell Sarah to be more careful.'

'I will, Oscar.' She stared down at her hands folded demurely in her lap, trying to plan her approach. After a moment or two she pulled a letter from her pocket and opened it.

Oscar eyed it sharply. 'Is that from who I think?'

'Yes, dear. It's from Gertrude. She asks if . . .'

'Not another visit, surely. She was here in the New Year!'

'But she always comes over at least once in the summer.'

Gertrude Legrand was Madeline's mother-in-law from her first marriage. A sprightly woman about the same age as Oscar, but who kept the exact date of her birth a secret.

Oscar finished his egg and toast and reached for the apple. Using a small sharp knife he peeled it, carefully keeping the coil of peel unbroken. 'That woman wears me out.'

Madeline hid a smile. The truth was that the cheerful Parisian was so full of life that she made Oscar look feeble in comparison. She also made Madeline feel extremely unadventurous with her frequent trips, to and fro, across the English Channel, while wild horses would be needed to drag her daughter-in-law anywhere near a seaport. Since her first husband's death, and even before, Madeline had never

3

desired to travel. She had never set foot on alien soil and never wanted to. Not that she wasn't interested in other countries, she just couldn't face the prospect of crossing so much cold grey water in what she regarded as flimsy unsafe boats.

'Gertrude is coming to England to visit some friends in Sussex and wonders . . .'

'Which part of Sussex?'

'East Sussex. She will be visiting in Hastings and would like to come to St Mark's Bay and call on us first – to see Louise. I suspect she would like to be invited to stay at least overnight.'

Oscar laughed but not unkindly. 'When has she ever stayed overnight? You know she will stay for days if not weeks.'

Madeline did not deny it. 'Let me read you her letter,' she suggested.

> Dear Madeline,
>   I think it is time my granddaughter began to take
> private art lessons and I would like to pay for these.

He glanced up sharply. 'Would like to meddle, more like!'

'Oh, Oscar! That is so unfair. She has been very generous to Louise over the years.'

'Hmm! I call it meddling. She unsettles the girl whenever she visits. Always talking about the past and the girl's father. Roland this and Roland that!'

Madeline bit back a sharp reply. Gertrude could never win as far as Oscar was concerned. She was a wealthy widow who liked to spoil her only grandchild, but if she spent too much Oscar complained she was flaunting her money. If she didn't, he decided she was mean with it. The truth was that he was jealous of her wealth.

Madeline continued to read the letter.

> The artist I have in mind, Mr Daniel Grant, is highly
> thought of as an artist in his own right, but also gives
> classes, as well as taking students separately, if they
> wish, for intensive coaching. He lives not far from you

      on the outskirts of St Mark's Bay and I will also pay
      for Louise to travel there and back . . .

'It goes on with dates and other matters,' she explained. 'What do you think, Oscar? Shall we accept her offer? I think Louise would benefit from the instruction. She does show promise.'

'No doubt you have already told Louise of this offer. That makes it difficult for me to refuse.'

Madeline had, in fact, discussed the offer with Louise the previous day when the letter arrived, but Oscar needn't know that. Louise had been enthusiastic. She certainly did have some artistic talent inherited from her father's side of the family. Her latest report from school spoke of 'a promising talent' in flower drawing. A framed study of sweet peas in a glass jar hung on her bedroom wall. So all that was necessary now was to persuade Oscar to agree to the lessons.

'I think art lessons might prove a calming influence,' Madeline suggested. 'Louise is becoming rather self-willed and it would help if we could fill her days with suitable activities. I'd like your advice on the matter.'

'I think I agree,' he said with obvious reluctance. 'We don't want to curb her spirit, but she does have a long way to go yet before we can consider her ladylike!'

They both laughed.

Although Louise was not Oscar's child, he had taken the place of her father in 1886 when he married Madeline. She had then been a widow for two years, struggling to raise a daughter and to care for her own ailing mother. Oscar had offered them all a home in his rambling, five bedroom house in St Mark's Bay, not too far from Folkestone on the southeast coast of Kent. Her mother had died within the year, but to Madeline's surprise the taciturn bachelor had grown fond of the child. Nowadays, his hesitation with regard to Gertrude's visits was not so much a personal animosity, but the fact that she would insist on extolling the virtues of her dead son. Madeline understood that this made him jealous of the young husband, but she also felt it important that Louise should know as much as possible about her real father whom she knew only from photographs.

5

She said, 'I did tell Louise and she is certainly interested. However, I've told her she must talk it over with you.'

He brightened as he sipped his tea. 'Send her up after she has had her breakfast. It depends on whether she will keep going or lose interest the way she did with the singing lessons.'

'Poor Louise.' Madeline smiled at the memory. 'She wanted to please you, Oscar, but we all know that she has no singing voice. Unfortunately Miss Downey told her so. It was tactless of her, but I daresay she thought she was being cruel to be kind.'

He tidied his plate and sat back. 'I suppose I can tolerate Gertrude for a day or two.'

'Thank you, Oscar.' Madeline picked up the tray. 'She'll be very pleased. I think she has a lot of respect for you, Oscar. She was *very* pleased when we married.'

The latter remark was true, but the former, about respect, was a deliberate lie that Madeline hoped would flatter her husband into feeling more kindly towards her ex-mother-in-law. As she carried the tray downstairs, Madeline was feeling rather pleased with the way she had dealt with the matter.

Louise tackled her as soon as she re-entered the kitchen. 'What sort of man is he, this art master?' She regarded her mother artlessly.

'You mean is Mr Grant young and attractive or old and boring?'

Louise laughed. She carried her crockery to the sink where Sarah was waiting to wash up the breakfast things and clear away before she started preparing lunch. The housekeeper had been with Oscar before he married and ran the house smoothly and comfortably with very little supervision. She had seen Louise grow up and had a special place in her heart for the girl. She had always wanted a daughter, but had been blessed with two sons instead. Both had enlisted in the army and were frequently abroad and writing infrequent letters home.

Louise asked, 'Any news from your boys, Sarah?'

Sarah rolled her eyes in mock despair. 'Not a line, but that's sons for you, my dear. I should have had daughters.'

'Mama wanted a boy,' Louise told her. 'She told me so.

If Papa hadn't died she might have had another child and then I might have had a brother.'

Madeline glanced at her. 'But you might have had a sister. Or two or three sisters. Girls seem to run in the family.'

'But Grandmama had Roland.'

'True.'

Louise grinned. 'I shall try very hard to give you a grandson, Mama. All my suitors will be required to show proof that boys run in the family!'

Sarah said, '*Suitors!*' She rolled her eyes. 'Don't talk of suitors just yet, Louise! You are far too young to be looking for romance.'

Madeline felt the familiar tug of anxiety. 'Sarah's right. You've only just finished your schooling. I appreciate the offer of a grandson, Louise, but not just yet. Your father and I are . . .'

'Stepfather!'

'Your stepfather and I don't want you to marry too young. I made that mistake and . . .'

'But now you have me! So it was obviously not a mistake.'

Sarah and Madeline exchanged amused glances.

Sarah shrugged. 'You know what they say: "You pays your money and you takes your chances." I waited until I was twenty-four and they all said I was on the shelf.' She sighed. 'I married for love, but I still chose a wrong 'un. Poor Bert. He was a weak man. Easily led astray.'

Nobody referred to the fact that Bert was in prison for burglary.

Sarah said nothing about the fact that Gertrude was coming to visit. She had a sceptical view of the French and resented the recipes which Gertrude brought with her as 'froggy rubbish'. Rather than put up with friction in the kitchen, Madeline often gave Sarah a day off so that Gertrude could work in the kitchen in peace.

Louise said, 'Perhaps I shall become a well-known artist and show my work in a London gallery with a champagne launch party and . . . and rich and famous people will come from far and wide to see my pictures. And buy them, of course!'

Sarah smiled. 'I don't doubt it for a minute, but you won't

7

have time for painting if you marry young and have a brood of children. You've still got some years of childhood ahead of you. Enjoy yourself.' She stacked the plates and attacked the cutlery.

Louise ignored this little homily. 'If I do become famous, Sarah, I'll give you one of my paintings as a gift.'

'I shall hold you to that, my dear.'

Madeline regarded them gratefully. She had no complaints about her life and knew she was far better off than many people. The exterior paintwork on the house was fading and inside there was much in the way of maintenance that needed to be done. But they had a roof over their heads, good food to eat and a warm fire in winter. Madeline was content.

She had no idea at that moment that their lives were about to change and that the catalyst for this unwelcome change would be the art master.

Later that day, just after Madeline had returned from a session at the dressmaker's, she became aware that someone was in the kitchen. Sarah always went home after the midday meal so she assumed it was her daughter.

'Is that you, Louise?' She unpinned her hat and laid it on the hat stand. The expected answer failed to materialize, but she heard the pantry door open and close. 'Louise?'

Her daughter appeared at the kitchen door. She looked flushed and anxious. 'You're back early, Mama!' she said, her voice holding a hint of reproach.

'Mrs Barrett had another client immediately after me so there was no time for a chat.'

'I've . . . I've been out for a walk.' Louise pulled the kitchen door to behind her, but not before Madeline had heard a scuffling sound that made her raise her eyebrows. Her daughter looked decidedly worried and Madeline's heart sank. 'I hope that's not another stray cat I can hear!'

Her large brown eyes regarded Madeline warily. 'A cat? No! Why should it be? You wouldn't let me keep the last one!'

'Because it was diseased and Mr Granger said the kindest things was to . . .'

'To kill it!'

'To put it down humanely. Do be sensible, Louise.'

The scuffling from the kitchen had now become a distinct whine.

Louise said, 'It's a dog! And it's not diseased and I want to keep it!'

'A *dog*!' Madeline's voice rose. 'Louise, how could you? We've been through this before!' Exasperated, she stepped forward and reluctantly Louise opened the door of the kitchen so that her mother could enter.

'Where is it?'

'In the larder. It's only a small dog and . . .'

'The larder?' Madeline groaned. 'Get it out of there at once. Really, Louise. How could you be so foolish?'

Arms folded, she watched her daughter open the larder door. A small black dog peered out. It took a few tentative steps into the kitchen and sat down. At once Louise bent to scoop the animal into her arms.

'Oh, the precious thing!' She buried her face in the dusty fur. She turned to face her mother, defiance written large on her young face. 'She won't eat much, Mama, and she'll be a watch dog.'

'She's a he, Louise.' Madeline hid a smile. 'And you must take him back where you found him.'

The dog trembled in Louise's arms. It had a small pointed face and sharp stand-up ears. He looked thin and obviously uncared for.

Louise said, 'Can't we just give her – I mean him – something to eat. He's so thin.'

'And dirty! The answer's no, Louise. I know you mean well but you are too tender-hearted. You haven't done it any favours by bringing it here. You must take it back where you found it. The owner is probably looking for it.' She didn't believe this for a moment, but she knew from previous battles that her daughter could be very stubborn. Madeline also knew she would have to take prompt action.

'I can't,' Louise told her. 'He was being teased by some boys. They were throwing stones at him.'

The dog whined, caught Madeline's eye and barked hopefully.

Louise put the dog down and it stood there, whimpering,

tail down, ears back. Madeline was aware that Louise was watching her closely.

'We can't keep it,' she repeated firmly. 'I suggest you take it to the park and release it there. I'll give you some scraps. You put the dog down, give him the scraps and sneak away while he's eating them.' She thought that a reasonable compromise.

Louise hesitated. 'Can't I just brush him first? I think his coat would look much better without all the dust.'

'No, Louise. It would be most unfair to make the poor creature feel at home. There's a nice bone left from Sunday's joint. He can have that as well. He'll be happy in the park. Probably chase a few squirrels or birds.'

Louise crouched beside the dog and patted it. The dog licked her hand and she looked up quickly. 'Suppose he doesn't want the bone. Suppose he just follows me home.' She stood up and her expression changed. 'If you won't let me keep him, I shall ask Papa!'

'He'll be sleeping.'

'Then I'll wake him up!' Her eyes flashed and before Madeline could summon any further objections, she snatched up the dog and ran down the passage.

Madeline understood her daughter's desire for a pet, but they had a very small backyard. Added to this, neither she nor Oscar were particularly keen on animals. They had once agreed that ten year old Louise could have a rabbit, but she had quickly lost interest and it had fallen to Madeline to look after it. A kitten that had followed a year later had been run over. Louise's ensuing grief had settled the matter for Oscar. There would be no more pets, he decreed.

'No more pets!' Madeline muttered as she filled the kettle and set it on the stove. She knew what Oscar's response would be and dreaded the scene that was even now threatening. From the bedroom above she could hear her husband's measured tones and Louise's angry screeches. Obviously disturbed by the clamour, the little dog joined the argument, barking excitedly.

Madeline heard her husband say, 'Get him off the bed!' and sighed. What Louise really needed was someone to love. Not a pet but a young man. Her best friend, Agatha, who was a few years older, already had an admirer – a shy young man who worked in the bookshop in the High Street. He was very fair with deep blue eyes and, although Louise scoffed that he was rather silly, she was nevertheless deeply envious. The girls' friendship was under strain because although Agatha often invited Louise to join them, she told Madeline that she felt like an interloper and so frequently refused.

'If I were courting we could be a foursome,' she had confessed. 'As it is, I feel more like a chaperone. I know she feels sorry for me and I can't bear being an object of pity.'

For Madeline's part, she was rather glad that she could still think of her daughter as a child. Louise was still very immature, prey to irrational mood swings and the odd childish tantrum, but she was also full of romantic notions and was increasingly inclined to defy the accepted wisdom of her parent's generation. Madeline understood that in young people, there was always a deep need to grow up, and she sympathized. Oscar always sided with the girl. She has to spread her wings, dear, he had told Madeline on more than one occasion. Perhaps he was right. Madeline told herself she must be patient. She knew that when a young man entered the arena Louise would be lost to her and she was aware of how lonely she would be without her daughter.

Upstairs, the bedroom door slammed and Louise thundered down the stairs. She burst into the kitchen, tears streaming down her cheeks. The dog, tucked under her arm, was struggling to get free and finally fell to the floor.

'I hate you both!' Louise shouted. 'You don't care a fig for my happiness, either of you!' She rushed into the larder, found the promised bone and picked up the dog who was now cowering under the table. 'When Grandmama comes I shall ask if I can live with her in Paris!'

In a flurry of furious skirts, she was off down the passage and out of the front door, banging it behind her so hard that the flap of the letter box rattled. Madeline hurried into the front room and crossed to the window to watch her daughter's progress. Somehow, as she watched her daughter's flight, a deep sense of unease settled within her followed by another sensation which she defined as a feeling of impending loss.

11

Soon she would lose her daughter, she thought, with a flash of panic. One way or another Louise would find her wings and take off into her future.

'Please God, not just yet!' she whispered.

She made a pot of tea and took it upstairs on a tray with two cups and saucers.

Oscar smiled at her when she entered the room. 'Don't fret, dear,' he advised kindly. 'She has always been tempestuous. No one can ever say our lives are dull!' He took a cup of tea and stirred it absent-mindedly.

Madeline sat down beside him. 'She says she wants to live with Gertrude.' Her voice shook a little.

'Live with Gertrude?' He laughed and patted her hand. 'You mustn't upset yourself, my dear. We both know how headstrong she is. She's young and speaks without thinking of the hurt she's inflicting. Gertrude would never agree to take her in. Her little flat is much too small and she values her freedom too much. After a week with Louise, Gertrude would be begging us to bring her home.'

Madeline managed a smile, grateful for his reassuring words. To change the subject she said, 'It was quite a sweet little dog.'

'Probably full of fleas!' He sipped his tea. 'How did the do-gooders' meeting go?'

'Oscar!' she protested, laughing in spite of herself. 'You have to stop calling us that! Someone has to care about the unfortunates of this world.' She forced her mind back to the moments before the storm. She was a member of the Ladies Charity Group who raised funds to help the local poor of whom there were too many. St Mark's Bay had its share of poor and it was never difficult to find people in need.

'We are going to have another jumble sale,' she told him, 'and with the money we make we shall arrange a delivery of milk to twenty of the poorest families. A pint for each every day until the funds run out. If we give the money to them as cash in hand, the husbands will most likely spend it on baccy or beer. We had quite a discussion about who should go on the list. Some of our members are reluctant to help two of the women because their husbands have been in prison, but I don't feel we should punish the wives and children for the sins of the fathers.'

'Does Sarah's next-door neighbour qualify for help, do you think? Louise was telling me that he has just lost his job and they have three young children.'

Madeline raised her eyebrows, pleased that he had reminded her. Samuel Watts had been a cooper at a nearby brewery but was now crippled with arthritic hands and could no longer work. 'I'll put his name forward,' she promised, 'and see what I can do.'

The warm sweet tea soothed her and she felt marginally better. Her life was very fulfilling, she reminded herself, and she had plenty for which to be thankful. If a rebellious daughter was the worst of her worries she should be grateful. Smiling at her husband over the rim of her teacup, she felt her confidence returning.

Suddenly, entirely unbidden, a memory came to her of the young Louise on the beach at Brighton. Her daughter standing with a bucket in one hand and a spade in the other, glaring at Madeline, her face red with anger.

'But I want to! I *want* to!' she had cried.

Nearly five at the time and still emotional from the death of her father, Louise wanted to go barefoot on the sand, but Madeline had seen plenty of broken shells and feared her daughter's tender feet would be cut by the sharp edges. From the corner of her eye she caught sight of a middle-aged man who was eyeing Louise with obvious disapproval. Madeline saw him every day about the same time and found him a rather strange figure. Surrounded by holidaymakers in various stages of undress, he always looked incongruous. It was as though he had stepped straight out of his office wearing a neat business-like suit, highly polished black shoes, walking stick and bowler hat. Out for his daily constitutional, she had decided.

Madeline had returned his uncompromising glance with one of her own, then returned her attention to her daughter.

'Make me a nice big sandcastle,' she suggested in an attempt to distract her. 'I'll help you.'

'Don't want to!' Louise tossed the bucket in one direction and the spade in the other.

The businessman caught Madeline's eye and said, 'Dear me!'

13

Madeline ignored him. She was mortified by the comment, but pretended she hadn't heard it. No doubt a bachelor, she thought bitterly. A selfish, self-satisfied bachelor! What does he know about the traumas of life? How much does he care for the problems of others? Probably rich. She immediately wrote him off as a miserable old devil because he made her feel like an unsatisfactory mother.

Louise sat down and began to tug at her new kid boots. Her small fingers failed to undo the knots Madeline had tied earlier and she let out a scream of frustration. Madeline's patience was almost at an end. She knew what was coming and swallowed hard. She was aware of other glances directed towards her troublesome daughter. Some were amused, others supportive of Madeline's firm handling of the situation.

One man called out, 'You tell her, missus!' and some of the onlookers laughed.

'I want my Daddy!' Louise shouted. 'I don't want him to be dead!'

There were tears in Louise's eyes and her own tears threatened. She understood her daughter's sense of loss for she, too, was still grieving. She felt like shouting, 'So do I! He was the love of my life!' But she didn't. No one understood how lonely life could be for a widowed mother. No one cared. Why should they? They had problems of their own. Louise's lips trembled and Madeline held out her arms.

'Come here, dearest girl,' she begged.

Instead, before Madeline could guess her intention, Louise turned and ran down the beach and into the water. As Madeline scrambled to her feet she saw Louise tear off her new straw hat and throw it as far as her small arm could manage. Seeing her mother approaching at a run, she panicked and turned to wade further into the water, but at that moment a wave knocked her over and she went under with a thin scream of terror.

To Madeline's astonishment the 'selfish, self-satisfied bachelor' had at once waded in and snatched the little girl from the next wave, then carried her back to shore in his arms. His trousers were sodden to the knees and the sleeves of the jacket were also wet. His feet squelched in the waterlogged shoes.

14

Full of apologies for Louise's behaviour, Madeline had stammered her thanks.

He listened politely, then handed her a small white business card. 'Let me know if your daughter needs rescuing again. I'll be happy to oblige.'

Ignoring the little ripple of applause, he turned and squelched away, minus his walking stick which, in the meantime, had floated out to sea. Somehow he still maintained a sense of dignity.

The man was Oscar Swain. After Madeline had taken Louise home, she had written to the gentleman, thanking him properly for his timely assistance and asking if she could help him in any way. She had not expected a reply. To her surprise he wrote back a few weeks later. Did she by any chance know of a reliable woman, possibly herself, who would act as his live-in housekeeper? He lived in a large house, his mother had recently died and he was alone. With some misgivings, Madeline suggested herself, but pointed out that she had a dependent mother and a troubled daughter. That would no doubt deter him, she thought.

His reply – a few words on headed notepaper – said simply, 'It sounds quite perfect!'

By eight thirty that evening Louise had not returned home and Madeline was in turn angry and worried. Was Louise punishing her or had something happened to her? She talked to Oscar who suggested she walk to the park and see if Louise was there.

'Where else could she be?' he asked.

Madeline set off. It was already dusk by the time she reached the park, but she soon spotted her daughter. Louise was huddled on one of the park benches, the dog in her arms.

Madeline's reaction was one of reluctant admiration laced with annoyance. How dare her daughter put her through so much worry? How long had the silly child intended to stay there? Later it would be dark and Louise would be vulnerable to all the tramps that inhabited the park after dark.

Madeline moved nearer and saw an old man approach the seat on which Louise sat. Madeline could not hear what he said, but she heard Louise's crisp rejoinder.

15

'Go away! I have nothing for you!'

The man moved closer. Louise stood up. 'I have a whistle and I shall call the police if you come a step closer!'

The man hesitated but at that moment Madeline came to an abrupt decision. She would give the dog a chance. If the experiment worked, he would have a home. If not, she would personally see that he was removed. She would advertise for a good home for him. She knew she was weakening, but the sight of her daughter in this predicament tore at her heart-strings.

She pushed past the old man. 'Bring him home, Louise,' she said. 'We'll see how he gets on.'

There was no way she would allow her eighteen-year-old daughter to run into another sea.

In spite of her reservations, Madeline admitted that the dog had a certain charm. Once he had been brushed, fed and placed on a warm cushion in a corner of the kitchen, he looked passable. Oscar had given in gracefully and Louise was in seventh heaven.

'He's your responsibility,' Madeline warned. 'Don't expect me to walk him twice a day or bath him or remember his food. That's your business. He's your dog.'

Louise agreed. She seemed happier than she had been for a long time and Madeline marvelled at the change in her daughter. Louise named the dog Midnight, but immediately shortened it to Middy. The animal flourished as well he might. Madeline wondered if the animal appreciated how lucky he was. For the moment peace reigned in the household. A fragile peace, Madeline was to discover.

Two

A week passed – a week which Madeline found thankfully trouble free. Her daughter, full of smiles, was wrapped up in her little dog. He had been bathed and fussed over and the vet had clipped his nails which he told Louise had been sadly neglected. Louise had bought him a collar and lead, and was taking him on regular training sessions in the park. She had also borrowed two books on dog care from a private lending library and studied them religiously, frequently quoting extracts to whoever was available to listen. When Agatha invited her to join her and Albert for a walk in the park, Louise had agreed willingly, eager to show off her new pet and impress them with his amazing progress under her management.

The art lessons, which Gertrude had already organized, were temporarily forgotten but Gertrude's visit was not. Louise had changed her mind about wanting to share her grandmother's flat in Paris, but she was desperate to hear her opinion of Middy.

'He looks so much better already, doesn't he, Mama?' she asked – at least three times a day. Fortunately Madeline was able to agree whole-heartedly. The dog, she thought, was really rather handsome in his own small way – his legs, body, tail and head all in proportion – and he seemed to have only one bad habit. That was stealing food. Anything edible that was left below four feet would abruptly disappear, and a rule was quickly established that all food must be returned promptly to the larder and the door firmly closed. Stealing, all three agreed, was the natural behaviour of a stray animal who had been forced to scavenge to survive.

Madeline said, 'He'll grow out of it as soon as he realizes he will always be fed. Don't fret Louise. We'll forgive him a few mistakes.' She was reluctantly becoming fond of the dog who was slowly learning to trust them and no longer shrank back in fear when anyone approached him too suddenly or raised an innocent hand in his vicinity. Louise spent countless wasted hours trying to imagine a dramatic history for him.

'Someone ill-treated him,' she had insisted, 'so he ran away and became a stray. That shows an independent spirit.'

Another day, another theory.

'Maybe he was the runt of the litter and they just abandoned him. He's had to fend for himself all his life!'

Sarah had suggested a kinder scenario. Perhaps he had been loved but his owner had moved house and somehow the dog had been lost. Oscar's feeling was that he may have been stolen by dog thieves and had somehow managed to escape a terrible fate.

'Dog thieves?' Louise's eyes had widened in horror. 'What sort of fate?'

'Animals are stolen every day for their fur . . .' he'd begun, but Louise had fled from the bedroom at the very idea.

Madeline, enjoying the calm that Middy had brought, prepared the spare room for Gertrude's arrival. She aired the bed, dusted the furniture, washed the curtains and applied lavender polish wherever it was possible. As a last touch she bought a leafy plant in a pot and set it in the window.

Eventually, the day of Gertrude's arrival was upon them. Louise and Madeline hired a cab to take them to Folkestone to meet the packet from Boulogne. The wind had ensured a rough crossing and many of the passengers staggered from the gang plank with white faces, their grim faces reflecting their longing to be on firm ground again. An excellent sailor, Gertrude was among the exceptions. She hurried towards Louise and Madeline, holding on to her hat with one hand and carrying a small carpet bag in the other. She was beaming with delight and was soon hugging and kissing them, and saying all the right things when Louise told her about Middy. They drove home in high spirits and within minutes Gertrude was heading upstairs to greet Oscar.

'My dear Oscar!' she cried, her arms outstretched in welcome. 'How well you look!'

18

She leaned forward and he kissed the withered cheek that existed somewhere beneath the lavish layer of expensive face powder.

'I've been dying to see you all again,' she told him. 'It's been so long!'

'Not that long, surely!' he offered, extracting himself from her perfumed embrace. 'It was the New Year, I believe.'

Gertrude stood back and surveyed him. 'Was it as long as that? *Mon Dieu!'*

She had acquired the habit of tossing the occasional French words into her conversation and Oscar complained to his wife that he found this pretentious, but secretly he rather enjoyed it. It seemed to give Gertrude a cosmopolitan aura which he found rather exciting.

'I'm so grateful, Oscar,' she went on, 'that you are going to allow Louise to take art lessons. It has always been my wish that she should follow in my son's footsteps – but only if she has real talent. I propose that we invite Daniel Grant to visit here so we may judge him. I've heard good things, but one should never take a recommendation at face value. Don't you agree?'

'Invite him here? Why not? If my wife is happy with the idea.'

'And you feel Louise's heart is in the plan? We mustn't overlook her wishes. I do feel, Oscar,' she leaned forward confidingly, 'that she should have something positive to focus upon. She's at a very awkward age and we don't want her to spend her time drooling over a young man. So many young women do, you know. She has plenty of time to marry. Now she should be enjoying her life. Exploring. *N'est ce pas?'*

Oscar nodded. As usual she gave him very little time to consider her proposals before demanding an answer. 'I dare say,' he said, cautiously. 'At the moment, of course, she has her little Middy. He is the focus of her attention.'

'I'm very glad to hear it. You were very wise, Oscar, to encourage it.' She gave his hand an approving pat. 'Now I must leave you in peace. Madeline and I have a lot to discuss and I mustn't tire you. *Au revoir, mon ami!'*

She left the room, leaving a hint of the familiar face powder lingering in the air. Oscar grinned to himself and relaxed.

She had a kind heart, he mused. She meant well. He did hope, for her sake, that Louise showed real promise and that the art lessons would be a success.

Madeline and Gertrude sat in the small back garden an hour later. Lunch was over and Louise had taken the dog for a walk. The two women discussed the art master's visit with growing enthusiasm. At first Madeline had thought a visit unnecessary, but she was coming round to the idea.

Gertrude tapped the table with an imperative finger. 'If we don't take to him, the lessons are off!' she told Madeline. 'We have to be sure he will be an influence for good before she starts the lessons. One never knows. He is a stranger to us at the moment.'

'I know what you're saying, Gertrude, and as usual you are right. Suppose we invite him to lunch one day. How would that be?'

'Lunch? Mmm?' Gertrude looked dubious. 'Or maybe afternoon tea? If we don't approve for any reason, we don't want him eating us out of house and home.'

Madeline laughed. 'All that really matters is that he is fully qualified to teach, that Louise likes him and that he is a reliable person. We don't want to send Louise for private lessons to a man who isn't . . . respectable.' She shrugged helplessly.

'If he is another Jack the Ripper, you mean!' Gertrude raised amused eyebrows. 'Or has a lunatic wife locked in the cellar!'

'Something along those lines!' she replied and they both laughed. 'I also hope he is not young and single and good looking. I don't want Louise to fall in love with him. Or anyone else.'

Gertrude shook her head. 'It will happen sometime, Madeline. She is eighteen.'

'But Roland and I . . .' She knew she must avoid hurting Gertrude's feelings. Roland was her only child. 'We were so unfit for married life. Neither of us had any experience of the world. For both of us it was the first romance . . . but then you did approve, Gertrude. I always wondered why. I thought you would say we were much too young.'

20

Gertrude hesitated then steepled her elegant fingers. 'It was because I had guessed your secret. The child you were expecting. I saw the signs. I recognized the change in you and the change, the *strains*, between you.'

Madeline stared at her, shocked by the revelation. 'You *knew*!' she gasped. 'Yet you didn't say a word.'

'It was your secret, Madeline. Yours and Roland's. I hoped you'd share it with me but you didn't so I held my counsel. I knew you must have the child. No illegal backyard abortionists for my son and his girl. It was a dreadful dilemma for you and I wanted to help. So I asked no questions. As soon as Roland asked your parents if you could marry and they said "yes", I gave you my blessing. I thought you would need it!'

Madeline sat back in her chair. 'You are an amazing woman, Gertrude.'

Gertrude didn't deny it. 'Did you confide in *your* parents?' she asked.

'I told my mother and she told Papa. We were all in a panic. All we could think of was to get married as soon as possible. Roland wanted to save you the hurt of knowing we'd been so . . . so rash.'

'It happens all the time, dear!'

'I know that now, but then . . . Roland blamed himself for persuading me. I should have known better but I couldn't refuse him.' She smiled at the memory. 'Your son was very appealing. He also believed that nothing would happen the first time we . . . did it.'

Gertrude threw up her hands in an exaggerated way as her laughter rang out. 'How very unoriginal of him! Men have been using that ploy since the beginning of time, Madeline, but thousands of charming people have been born as a result so let's not condemn them. What's the phrase I'm looking for? Ah yes! "It was ever thus!"'

Madeline said. 'You are just as persuasive as your son, Gertrude. As you say, we have Louise and although we married in haste, we didn't regret it. Is it too late to thank you for giving your blessing?'

Gertrude waved an airy hand. 'You and Roland gave me Louise, dear. She is all the thanks I need. If you hadn't had

21

Louise, then when Roland died, I would have had nothing and nobody. In a way, it was a kind fate . . . But I wouldn't want it for Louise. You were quiet and willing to take advice. Louise is – ' she rolled her eyes – 'so unpredictable. The Lord only knows what she might do!' She paused. 'But I can put your fears at ease, Madeline, about the artist. Grant is a middle-aged man. Daniel Grant. He has lived alone for the past eight years, ever since his wife deserted him for another man. A much richer man, by all accounts. You know how people gossip.'

'The way we are gossiping now?' Madeline asked lightly.

'We're not gossiping, dear. We're *discussing*. It's not at all the same.' Gertrude regarded her indignantly. 'Daniel Grant is very successful artistically and he studied years ago in Italy for some considerable time. That's when his wife ran off. He came back to England and settled in Folkestone. Recently he opened his own gallery there where he shows his own work and that of others. I understand he is currently preparing for an exhibition.'

'He sounds a decent enough man.' Madeline considered the facts for a moment or two longer, then gave a satisfied nod. 'We'll ask him to tea then, shall we?' Before Gertrude could agree, she changed her mind. 'No, on second thoughts I think lunch would be better. It will give us longer to get to know him. Later this week. Sunday lunch.'

'Perfect. Then we shall have a chance to attend his gallery before and see his work for ourselves. Of course, he's not in the same field as Roland. He liked to paint in oils – almost exclusively portraits. Grant prefers watercolours and mostly paints landscapes. They're much easier to sell. There's always a market for land- and seascapes. If I like his work I shall hope to buy something for my hallway. I've thought for some time it looks rather bare.'

The decision was made and Louise was informed. As Madeline had expected she had lost interest in starting art lessons, but agreed willingly to meet her new tutor. Madeline wrote a brief letter of invitation for the 17th of July and it went into the post the following morning.

A few days later Madeline and Gertrude decided to go to the gallery to see for themselves just how good an artist

22

Daniel Grant was. Gertrude had realized that it was no good liking the man when they met him for lunch on Sunday, if they didn't like his work and thought he would be an unsuitable teacher. 'That,' Gertrude had insisted, 'would be very embarrassing. We'd have to cancel the lessons.'

'Are you coming with us, Louise?' Madeline asked as they lingered over breakfast. 'We'll only be there about an hour, if that.' Louise shook her head.

'But surely you want to see what kind of work Mr Grant does.'

'I can't. I'm invited to lunch with Agatha and her family. It's her mother's birthday and they are having a goose. Her uncle's a farmer and he always gives them poultry as presents.'

'We could use an uncle like that!' Madeline laughed. 'Have you warned them you will have to leave promptly after lunch as you have your first lesson with Mr Grant.'

'They know, Mama. Do stop fussing.'

'What about Middy. He's never been left alone in the house.'

'He's been invited too.' Louise's face glowed. 'They all adore him. Agatha wants a puppy too. All she has is an elderly cat.'

'See Middy behaves himself,' Gertrude warned. 'They won't appreciate him quite so much if he does a puddle on their carpet!'

Louise looked genuinely horrified. 'Of course I'll keep an eye on him, but he wouldn't do such a thing. I've been house training him.'

'You've only had him about ten days, Louise. You can't expect miracles.'

By ten o'clock Madeline and Gertrude were pushing open the door of Daniel Grant's gallery in the High Street. From outside, it was somewhat unprepossessing with an old-fashioned façade painted in dark green. It was squashed between a shop selling carpets and a florist. Inside, however, it was well lit and surprisingly spacious. There was a table inside the door where a young woman sat, handing out lists of the pictures on sale.

23

She greeted them and asked, 'Have you visited us before?' She was very dainty with exquisite features and beautiful green eyes. The sort of woman who immediately made every other woman feel dowdy and uninteresting. Madeline was no exception and immediately regretted her choice of jacket.

Gertrude spoke up at once. 'No, we haven't been here before, but you've been recommended to us. I've just come over from Paris to see for myself.' Her voice carried and several people turned to look at her.

The girl pushed a leather-bound book towards them. 'Then perhaps you would sign our visitors' book?' She offered a pen and indicated the elegant brass inkwell.

While they were signing the book, the girl continued in what was obviously a well-rehearsed speech. 'Mr Grant's own work is on the far wall – mostly watercolours, with a few charcoal or pencil sketches. We are also exhibiting work by Miss Diana Fletcher – one of Mr Grant's pupils. It's her first exhibition so she is very excited and we are delighted to be offering her work. Hers are the miniatures over there . . .' She pointed with a pencil towards an alcove on the right. 'We are also proud to be displaying hand thrown pottery by a local man, Isaac Gray, and to your left we have a selection of works by Damien Lester. Mostly oils. Mostly still life.' She smiled. 'I do hope you find something to your taste.'

The two women murmured something suitable and moved on. Gertrude made a beeline for Daniel Grant's watercolours, but Madeline lingered by the pottery. She was wondering whether Daniel Grant was in the gallery. She wanted to observe him before they met on Sunday for lunch. Glancing round she saw two young women earnestly discussing one of the miniatures. The youngest one, possibly Diana Fletcher, was explaining that because of their size, miniatures really looked better grouped in threes or fours and her companion, presumably a potential buyer, was saying she could only afford two but might be able to add others later on. Madeline tried to imagine Louise in the gallery in a few years time, talking in the same way when her own work was being exhibited for the first time.

Glancing across the room, Madeline saw a man and a

woman standing together in front of one of Daniel Grant's watercolours – a seascape which looked remarkably like a view of Hastings' seafront.

'If there's anything about it that you don't like, you mustn't buy it,' he warned his companion. 'Over time it will come to irritate you and that will spoil your pleasure in the picture. What about this, Mrs Lesley? Low tide at Dungeness. Does this appeal? Does it "speak to you"?'

'Are they supposed to? Speak to me, I mean.'

'Hopefully. A picture should somehow resonate.'

Mentally, Madeline raised her eyebrows. It all sounded a little pretentious, she thought. Why did people have to pretend to be so knowledgeable when probably, like herself, they knew very little about art? She studied the man. He was of stocky build with graying dark hair and was comfortably dressed in tweed trousers that had seen better days and a velvet jacket. By contrast, his female companion was elegantly dressed with an elaborate hat, and lorgnettes which she waved about when she was not peering through them.

A slightly bedraggled elderly woman was examining the pottery, picking up each piece and examining it, in spite of the notice requesting that the objects should not be handled. Madeline moved to stand near her. The pottery was rough grey with surprising patches of random blue glaze which Madeline found extremely attractive. The prices quoted in the list, however, were more than she had expected and she gave up the idea of owning even a small piece.

Gertrude appeared at her side and whispered, 'Do take a look at his work. It's very good.'

'I will. You should look at this pottery. It's different, and expensive, but Isaac Gray is very talented.'

The miniatures didn't interest Madeline, so she made her way to the far end of the room where the comfortably dressed man was still talking to his companion.

'What can I say, Mrs Lesley?' he asked, his tone a trifle weary. 'Why don't you buy the one you like and if, in six weeks' time, you no longer like it, I'll buy it back from you?'

Madeline's eyes narrowed. So was this the owner of the gallery? Was this Daniel Grant who would be her daughter's teacher?

Mrs Lesley looked at him sharply. 'At the same price?'

'Yes.' He laid a hand on his heart – a gently mocking gesture – and added, 'You have my word on it.'

'Hmm?' She peered at the picture through her lorgnettes while he turned away from her, slipped a half-hunter watch from his waistcoat pocket and snatched a quick glance at it. Before he turned back his glance rested briefly on Madeline and she was flattered to see a spark of interest in his grey eyes. It was the first time she had seen his face and it was not a handsome face in the traditional sense. A square face framed by untidy hair. He had a plain face but one full of character. Pleasant, cheerful, friendly, perhaps, but not handsome. In the brief moment their eyes had met, she'd sensed gentleness and, maybe, a certain resignation. It was what her mother would have called a 'lived in' face. There was experience there, she thought, and not all of it happy.

He was moving away now towards the desk and Madeline watched him go. The woman was fumbling in her handbag for her cheque book, while the receptionist hurried to one of the pictures and stuck a red dot in a corner of the frame, presumably to indicate that it was sold.

Daniel Grant was smiling at his customer. 'As soon as we close this exhibition, your picture will be delivered at a time to suit you.'

'And when will that be?'

'At the end of next week. We shall then be closed for a week while we set up the next exhibition.' Glancing up again, he met Madeline's gaze, smiled and turned back to his customer. 'I'm sure you'll be happy with the picture you've chosen.'

'I'll see what my friends think. If not I'll hold you to your promise, Mr Grant.'

'I shan't fail you, Mrs Lesley.'

Madeline studied his paintings. They were painted in very delicate colours, and outlined here and there in a fine black line. She recognized the local scenes, but there were others – Devon rivers, Thames bridges, snowy landscapes in the Lake District.

Gertrude sidled up to her. 'That's him at the counter. He's

not at all how I imagined. You'd never think he was an artist, would you? Ah! He's free now. I'll have a word with him.'

Mrs Lesley had left the gallery and Daniel Grant was moving towards them. Before he could speak Gertrude introduced herself and his face lit up.

'The lady from Paris! The grandmother of my new pupil.'

They shook hands and Gertrude said, 'And this is Louise's mother, Madeline Swain.'

Madeline shook hands with him and they exchanged smiles. Gertrude told him how much she admired his work and his gallery and how talented Louise was.

She added, 'She inherits her talent from my son who sadly was killed years ago in an accident.'

'I'm so sorry. That must have been dreadful.' He was looking at Madeline as he spoke and she was once more aware of the kindness in his eyes. How could she ever have thought him less than attractive? she thought guiltily. It was the first time since Roland's death that she had even noticed a man's face. Oscar had been a knight in shining armour, but he had never moved her in that way.

Surprised by her reaction to a comparative stranger, Madeline stammered, 'I know my daughter is looking forward to her lessons. She did well in art classes at school.' Even to her own ears it sounded trite.

He nodded and glanced round the room. 'I'm sure if she has talent we can help reveal it. Is she here?'

Gertrude said quickly, 'Unfortunately she had a prior invitation, but I'm sure she will call in before the exhibition closes. Diana Fletcher's miniatures are charming. Has she been studying with you long?'

'Ever since she was fifteen and she's now in her early twenties. It's never too early to start. Is your daughter passionate about art?'

Madeline thought guiltily about Louise's obsession with the dog, but said, 'I think she needs to be convinced that she does have a flair for the subject. She's eighteen, but a very young eighteen.'

The pretty receptionist appeared at his elbow and said, 'Damien Lester's here about his talk in the town hall next week. He seems worried.'

'Last minute nerves, I expect.' Grant lowered his voice and said, 'Poor chap. I'll talk to him.' He turned back to Madeline and Gertrude. 'I'm sorry. I'm needed elsewhere, but I'm looking forward to meeting your daughter today – and to Sunday.' He looked directly at Madeline before returning to the reception desk.

Gertrude gave Madeline a satisfied look. 'Well, I think Louise will be safe in his hands,' she said. 'Shall we go now? I think tea and a jam scone at Peggotty's is in order before we make our way home.'

Later that afternoon Madeline and Gertrude watched the clock, eager to hear Louise's account of the lesson. Also awaiting her return, Middy refused to budge from the hall where he lay on the carpet with his front paws aimed at the front door. From time to time he whined anxiously, occasionally casting reproachful glances at Madeline or Gertrude as though blaming them for his beloved mistress's disappearance.

At five minutes to five, when Louise was due to return, Madeline made a pot of tea and carried a cup and some biscuits up to her husband who was also eager to know if the art lesson had been a success.

'Thank you, dear,' he said with a glance at the bedside clock. 'Is our girl a little later than expected?'

'A few minutes, perhaps, but it was the first lesson and I daresay they chatted a little afterwards. Also the hackney cab might have been later than arranged. I'll send her up when she gets in and she can tell you all about it.'

He stirred his tea and nibbled a biscuit while Madeline, sensing there was more to come, hovered in the doorway.

'I suppose she does have some talent?' he said. 'I'd hate to set her up for disappointment.'

Madeline had been thinking the same thing, but didn't want to add to his worries. 'We did have a good report from the school,' she said.

'But was it good enough?' He frowned. 'Gertrude has rather steam-rollered her into these lessons. Just because Louise's father was an artist, it doesn't mean Louise has to follow in his footsteps. Does she want to be an artist?'

'I doubt she will ever be an artist in the sense of making

a living, but then she won't need to, will she? She will presumably marry and bring up a family, but she might as well enjoy painting as a pleasant pastime . . . and the time will come when her children leave home and she has time on her hands.' Madeline gave him a reassuring smile. 'Let's not worry about her, Oscar. Learning is never wasted and she might surprise us. Maybe this time next year or the year after, we may see some of her pictures on the wall of Daniel Grant's gallery!'

At that moment the front door opened and shut and Middy began to bark ecstatically. Madeline and Oscar exchanged smiles of relief.

'Mama! I'm back!'

Moments later they were all in Oscar's bedroom, including Middy who was being clutched as usual in Louise's arms. Louise, her face flushed with excitement, was giving them a detailed account of her session.

'I showed him some of the work I'd done at school and I think he was impressed. He kept nodding and . . . and I told him about my real father being an artist and he said, "How wonderful" and then . . . Keep still, Middy! Oh, what a fidgety dog you are! Oh! Go down then!' She tipped him unceremoniously on to the carpet and went on. 'He asked me what my strengths were and I didn't know the answer, but he meant whether I prefered still life or figure drawing or . . . Of course, I'm not sure what figure drawing is, but I couldn't say so and it might have meant nude people and I wasn't sure so I said flower drawing. I do like drawing flowers.' She looked at her father. 'Do you remember the daisies I painted for your birthday when I was about seven?'

'Indeed I do! They were very good. I still have them somewhere.'

'I know they were blue, and daisies aren't, but white daisies on white paper wouldn't show up.' She paused, breathless, and took a gulp of air.

Gertrude seized the opportunity. 'So did you draw anything today?'

Louise nodded. 'He didn't have any flowers handy, so he set up a little still life for me to sketch in pencil. A small brown jug, an orange and . . .' She screwed up her eyes. 'Oh,

29

yes! Two books, one on top of the other. I did quite a good sketch, but the jug went a bit wrong so I said I wouldn't bring it home and he has put it in a folder with my name on it and the date.' She stared at them all, waiting for a response.

Gertrude clapped her hands so hard that her gold bracelets jangled. 'Well done! I can see you've enjoyed yourself.'

Oscar said, 'What sort of man is this Daniel Grant? Respectful, I hope.'

'Respectful of me, you mean? Oh, yes. He called me Miss Legrand and when he asked me something, he didn't interrupt my answer . . . except once when he said, "You are very like your mother", but I said, "And my father. I have his temperament and some of his faults. Papa was very impatient and so am I." I told him my father was killed in an accident and I can hardly remember him.'

Oscar said quickly, 'Did you say your mother had remarried?'

She hesitated. 'I may have done, Papa. Probably. I can't remember everything I said, word for word.'

Madeline said, 'Well, it obviously went very well. Has he set you any work to do for next week?'

She nodded. 'Another still life. I can choose it myself, but it must contain something made of glass.' She jumped up and gave Oscar a quick kiss. 'I must give Middy her walk in the park.' She was halfway out of the door when she turned, a slight colour in her cheeks. 'By the way, Agatha's Albert has a friend called Stanley Bridger who would like to meet me. She has suggested . . .'

Oscar's expression changed. 'A young man? What does he do, this Stanley Bridger?' he asked, with studied carelessness.

'He's a clerk with the railway. He's twenty and has two younger brothers. Agatha has suggested we all meet by the bandstand in the park on Sunday morning at eleven. I thought it was possible so I said . . .'

Oscar frowned. 'Will Agatha's parents be with you?'

'Yes, Papa.'

Madeline was shaking her head. 'We have invited Mr Grant to lunch. Have you forgotten? I know you when you are with Agatha, you'll never come home in time. No idea of time!'

30

Louise's face fell. 'But I've said I will and I expect Albert has told Stanley I'll be there. I can't disappoint him. It will ruin everything. Can't we put Mr Grant off?'

Gertrude tutted. 'Don't be silly, dear. That would be very rude. Your mother is right. You must . . .'

Oscar held up his hand. 'Why not arrange the meeting for after lunch, Louise? Say half past two? Then instead of having to rush home, leaving poor Stanley on his own, you will have the whole afternoon together. I'm sure Agatha could change the time if you explain the problem.'

After a moment's deliberation, Louise nodded. 'Thank you, Papa! I'll do that. I'll go round to see her now.'

In her haste to be gone she almost tripped over Middy who scrambled out of the way with a reproachful look, then chased after her. They listened in silence as the girl and dog clattered down the stairs together and breathed again as the front door closed behind her.

Gertrude said, 'Well! Sunday should be *très intéressant*! A young man called Stanley is now on the horizon.'

'Very interesting indeed,' Oscar agreed. He raised his eyebrows. 'I wager this heralds our daughter's first romance.'

'I didn't know you liked to gamble, dear!' Madeline teased.

He laughed. 'It's one of my few vices.'

Gertrude said, 'Spoken like a true man!'

Lying in bed that night, Madeline tried to concentrate on Sunday lunch. Tomorrow she would do the shopping. They could have a nice piece of pork. She would score it and rub it in a little salt to make sure the crackling crackled. She must ask Gertrude about his religious persuasion. If pork, then she would do apples, roasted potatoes, carrots and maybe cauliflower.

She thought about Daniel Grant and the way he had looked at her in the gallery. Had she imagined that flash of interest? Or had she exaggerated it to be more than it really was – simply a polite interest in a new face at the gallery? Presumably he was always interested by possible new clients. She felt a pang of guilt for thinking Daniel Grant plain. He had a homely, good-natured face, not unattractive at all . . .

Madeline! she silently scolded herself. What on earth was

31

she doing, thinking of him at all? She was a respectable married woman.

With an effort, she wrenched her mind back to her Sunday lunch menu. He might prefer lamb, she mused. A leg of lamb was always nice and it was one of Gertrude's favourites. A leg of lamb. Perfect. She would spike it with rosemary and serve it with some of her homemade redcurrant jelly. For a change she could serve boiled potatoes, peas and chopped cabbage, the way Oscar liked it. A fruit jelly would be a light dessert or she could make a trifle.

She narrowed her eyes. Why had Daniel Grant said that Louise resembled her? Had he really taken that much notice of his pupil's mother during their brief time at the gallery? A question now arose in her mind – was there a woman in his life? Gertrude had said his wife left him years ago, but had he remarried? She should have asked Louise . . . And Oscar had quickly picked up on Daniel's comment. 'Did you say that your mother had remarried?' Did that suggest that he might be a little bit jealous? The thought at once shocked and thrilled her. It was years since she had even considered such a thing. Oscar, she was sure, was very confident of his place in her affections, but no other man had ever shown the slightest interest in her since their marriage. Nor had Madeline ever given her husband cause to feel jealous. Bringing up Louise and being a good wife had been enough for her.

And I'm still a good wife, she thought, reassuring herself. I'm only thinking about him. Curiosity. Nothing more.

Once again she forced her thoughts towards the meal, which was somehow becoming desperately important. Beef, perhaps. Yes, beef on the bone and fluffy Yorkshire pudding and . . . But Oscar disliked Yorkshire pudding. Would Daniel like it?

'Oh, *no!*' she muttered and her hand went to her mouth in alarm. She must never think of him as Daniel. He must always be Mr Grant. It would be deeply embarrassing if his Christian name slipped out. What was she thinking?

With a groan of frustration, she turned over and buried her face in the pillow. Stop being ridiculous, Madeline. Of course he isn't interested in you . . . But if he *did* see her as attractive it was rather flattering. She might as well relish the idea for a few more days because when Sunday arrived he would discover that she was happily married and that would be that. A few harmless dreams. That was all it was.

Gertrude was always boasting about the men in her life – the Antons, the Claudes and the Philippes who seemed to be constantly beating a path to her door. And Gertrude must be nearing seventy if she was a day! Her admirers were always young, always amusing, adoring and artistically gifted. One of them had been a pianist, she recalled and another was a writer. Listening to Gertrude often made Madeline feel dull and unappreciated.

So if I want to simply think about another man, I will. And I'll cook him lamb, peas and carrots and we'll have a nice fruit salad.

Three

All her well-made plans were reluctantly abandoned when she came down to breakfast the next morning after taking up her husband's breakfast tray. Gertrude glanced up from the breakfast table where she and Louise were eating stewed apples.

'I've come to a decision, Madeline,' Gertrude announced with a smile. 'It's Sunday tomorrow and you are going to have day off to relax and enjoy yourself. Louise and I are going to prepare lunch for Mr Grant. A *pot au feu*! Everyone enjoys that. I've made a shopping list and we shall . . .'

'Oh, but I've already decided on a roast,' Madeline protested. 'A leg of lamb and then a fruit salad.' Her heart was already sinking with disappointment. 'You love lamb, Gertrude.'

Louise shook her head. 'I'm going to help Grandmama and learn how to make it. *Pot au feu* is a classic French dish recognized all over the civilized world and Grandmother thinks I should learn how to make it.'

Gertrude smiled. 'We can have lamb next Sunday. I shall still be here, dear.'

But Daniel – *Mr Grant* – won't, thought Madeline. She realized suddenly just how much she had been looking forward to cooking for him. So perhaps this was fate's way of preventing her from making a fool of herself.

Louise said, 'Oh, do please agree, Mama. I'd like to help Grandmama. You are always saying I should take more interest in household affairs.'

'I am?' She looked from one face to the other and saw that her daughter had inherited some of her grandmother's ways. A certain steely determination to get her own way while smiling graciously! 'But what shall I be doing meanwhile?' she asked.

'You'll be taking Middy for his walk in the park,' Louise said. 'The exercise and fresh air will do you good.' She pushed aside her dish and reached for a slice of toast.

Madeline longed to fight this, but she saw that if she protested too much she would simply draw attention to herself and she had no way to explain her reluctance to have a morning off from the chore of preparing Sunday lunch. Maybe a walk in the park would be pleasant. 'Is Middy good when he's out?'

Louise nodded. 'Very good. You can let him off the lead. He won't run away. And if you take a few biscuits in your pocket, you give him one when he comes back to you. That's his reward.'

Middy pricked up his ears as though he understood this. He certainly looked very angelic, sitting in his basket, watching the breakfast without soliciting snippets from the table. Really, thought Madeline, he was a good little dog and perhaps it would be fun to take him out.

'It might rain,' she objected belatedly.

'It won't, dear.' Gertrude wagged a finger. 'It's July and the weather is very settled. Just give in gracefully, Madeline, and look forward to tomorrow.' She glanced at Louise. 'Your poor mother is unused to having leisure time.' She turned back to Madeline. 'Maybe Sarah should work a few hours more, one day a week. You should get out more.'

'I don't care to leave Oscar alone,' Madeline told her. 'He feels nervous when there is nobody in the house. Since that terrible heart attack . . .'

'Nonsense, Madeline. That was years ago! He must understand that you are not his nurse. You are entitled to a little time to yourself.'

Madeline gave up. She buttered a slice of toast and spread some of the new lemon curd.

So be it. She would not be cooking for Mr Grant. But, she reflected rebelliously, there might be other Sundays when Gertrude had gone back to Paris. With half an ear she listened to Louise and Gertrude discussing the main course. A large chicken cooked with a selection of root vegetables in plenty of red wine. It was going to be rather rich, she thought, but

35

it was no longer her problem. Tomorrow she would take the dog and go to the park as instructed – and there she would brood on her ruined plans.

Sunday found Daniel Grant standing outside a florist's shop, deep in thought. He wanted to take a small expression of thanks to his hostess, but he wasn't sure what to buy. He stood outside the window and surveyed the flowers on offer. If only he knew whether or not Madeline Swain was a widow or had possibly remarried. He should have asked Louise. If the former, then maybe a small bouquet of flowers would be suitable. If she was not unattached, a bouquet might seem too personal. A small potted plant, perhaps? He considered the African violets but thought them rather sombre in colour. There was a small basket with a ribbon bow which contained a plant with striped leaves. Did she even like flowers? Perhaps she would prefer a box of expensive chocolates.

He had set out much too early, he realized. A woman passed by and he studied her reflection in the mirror, comparing her to Madeline Swain. Taller but not as good-looking, he decided. Another woman stopped beside him and studied the window display. Shorter than Madeline, and plumper, and with no dress sense at all. Women! He sighed. He had long ago decided, since the end of his marriage, that he had very little understanding of women and their ways, but suddenly he wanted to know more.

Sensing his interest, the woman turned to him abruptly. 'What can you take to a man who is dying?' she asked. 'My hubby doesn't like sweets and he's not allowed fruit. Upsets his insides.' She frowned. 'You on your way to the hospital too?'

'No. Thankfully.' He suddenly felt the need to talk to someone. Anyone. He wanted advice. 'I'm on the way to a Sunday lunch. I don't know what to take. Spoilt for choice here. It's been a long time since I bought flowers.'

'Family, is it? Carnations are a safe choice and they do last well.'

'No. Not family.'

'Friends, then?'

Could he call them friends? 'Not exactly. That is, they're new friends.'

'A woman?'

'Er . . . Yes.'

'Take a few roses . . . or a single orchid. Is it romantic?'

'Romantic? No-o. I don't think . . .' He wished he could say 'yes' but it would be untrue. 'No, it isn't. It's three women, actually. All the same family.' He was beginning to regret the conversation.

'Make it carnations. A dozen.' She returned to her own problem with a shrug. 'What's the use. He'll be dead before the flowers die. They've given him twenty-four hours.'

Daniel was momentarily lost for words. 'I'm sorry,' he muttered.

'Don't be. I've never liked him.'

She walked into the shop and, taking his chance and feeling utterly foolish, Daniel hurried away.

When Madeline popped her head in at the kitchen door, the room seemed chaotic. Pans, chopping boards, cutting utensils and basins seemed to be everywhere, but Louise and Gertrude were chatting happily as they worked, so she said her goodbyes and left with Middy. She had the distinct feeling that neither of them would miss her.

The little dog trotted along beside her and Madeline was determined to enjoy her enforced exile as best she could. The streets were full of people in their Sunday best. A recruitment sergeant, using a loud hailer, urged young men to think about enlisting in the Queen's army. A small group of young men stood around, hands in their pockets, listening to him and muttering to each other. Madeline had always wanted a boy, but now she was grateful that she had a daughter and not a son. How dreadful it would have been to watch him march cheerfully off to war and then learn of his death in a foreign land.

'Fighting for Queen and country!' the officer shouted. 'What better way to serve the land that gave you birth? How better to protect your nearest and dearest? A chance to travel . . . A chance to share the camaraderie of enlisted men in the best army in the world.'

Dying for Queen and country. Madeline was aware of a flash of relief that she would never lose Louise. She uttered up a silent prayer for the young men who even now were being urged up on to the platform by the officer's persuasive talk. Hastily she hurried past and in through the gates of the park. She released the dog and said, 'There you go! Have a scamper, Middy, but don't go too far.'

In her pocket she had three lemon biscuits in a scrap of paper. Following her daughter's instructions she gave Middy about three seconds before she called him back. He came willingly and she gave him a piece of biscuit.

'What a good dog!'

Reassured, she strolled on, admiring the flower beds and the fountain. She paused to watch the children on the swings and roundabouts, then she sat down on a seat to watch the world go by. Unused to being on her own with time to kill, she felt rather out of place, but her parasol gave her a feeling of privacy as she tried to relax and enjoy herself.

A few moments passed before she remembered the dog and she stood up at once and called him. She looked in all directions, but there was no sign of him. Her mind was at once filled with dire possibilities. He had wandered out of the park and been run over! He had been stolen for his smooth black fur!

'Middy! Middy!' she shouted. She felt for the biscuits in her pocket but there was no need for them since there was no sign of Louise's precious pet. If anything had happened to him, Madeline knew that Louise would never forgive her. She would never remember that she and Gertrude had practically forced Madeline to take the dog for a walk in the park. But it was no excuse, she told herself. She, Madeline, had accepted responsibility for the dog and in less than half an hour she had lost him.

Madeline hurried towards an elderly man who was sitting on the next park bench. 'Have you seen a small back dog? He's run off and I . . .'

'I'm afraid not, madam.' He touched his hat courteously but turned away to signify that the conversation was at an end.

A young couple approached from the other direction

and Madeline asked them the same question. Both shook their heads. Madeline gave them a description and told them the dog's name. 'He's wearing a collar,' she added. They promised to be on the lookout for him and left her, arm-in-arm.

As Madeline hurried to and fro, she grew more worried. This was going to ruin the day, she thought desperately. She imagined herself turning up when everyone else had started lunch. She would break the bad news and Louise would scream and rush upstairs in tears. Gertrude would be furious that the lunch was no longer being appreciated and Daniel – Mr Grant – would be embarrassed by the scene.

'Middy!' she muttered. 'Where are you, you little wretch?'

At that moment a flurry of furious barking broke out somewhere beyond the swings. Madeline feared that a larger dog had attacked Middy and she would have to return home with *very* bad news. The worst possible news. Poor little Middy was injured or dead! Gathering her skirts, she set off at a run in the direction of all the noise. Others were also moving curiously towards the source of the commotion. All hope faded as she drew nearer. Middy was embroiled with a large black poodle. The two dogs were whirling furiously, snapping and snarling as though intent on killing each other, but Middy, free of his leash, had the advantage. The poodle was still on a lead, which was held by a rather elegant woman who was screaming for help. Several young boys were cheering the dogs on and seemed to be betting on which one would win.

Someone called, 'Fetch a bobby. He'll sort 'em out!'

'That's my dog!' Madeline cried breathlessly as she ran the last few yards. Her hat was askew, her parasol had been abandoned somewhere along the way and she was almost in tears. Please, she prayed, don't let him be hurt.

She was about ten yards from the fray when a man stepped forward, seemingly from nowhere, and grabbed Middy. He held the little dog high in the air while the elegant lady dragged her poodle back and bent to comfort him.

One of the children, jerking a thumb in the poodle's direction, said, 'He started it!' Madeline turned to Middy's rescuer and found herself staring into the amused face of Daniel Grant.

He lowered the dog to the ground, Madeline handed over the lead and together they gave the animal a quick examination. Daniel Grant stood up and handed back Middy's lead. 'No broken bones,' he said. 'No blood. I think it was all for show.'

Too out of breath to speak, Madeline simply nodded and looked for the nearest seat. Daniel Grant took hold of her arm and guided her towards it. Middy trotted along beside her, as though butter wouldn't melt in his mouth. Madeline's heart was thumping painfully and her eyes were full of relieved tears. Daniel Grant settled Middy and gave Madeline a large clean handkerchief. Then he walked over to the poodle's owner and asked if it was injured.

The woman shook her head. 'It sounded much worse than it was,' she acknowledged, 'and I have to admit my naughty Dancer started it. Your dog was only defending himself. I'm so very sorry.'

'It seems there's no harm done.'

'This is the third time it's happened. I shall try to find somewhere else to walk him.'

Madeline watched the encounter and thanked God for Daniel's timely interference. He returned with a comforting smile and sat down beside her. 'Nothing to worry about, Mrs Legrand.'

Madeline hesitated. 'I'm Mrs Swain now,' she said and saw his eyes darken as he understood the comment.

For a moment they stared at one another.

At last he said, 'I should have guessed. You are much too attractive to have remained single all these years.'

Nonplussed, Madeline stared at him speechlessly. Then she said softly, 'I'm sorry.'

To cover her confusion she drew a biscuit from her pocket and gave it to Middy who swallowed it in one eager gulp. Madeline made a fuss of him, struggling to regain a little of her normal composure.

He said, 'I wanted to bring you some flowers, but I didn't know . . . your daughter didn't make it clear. In the end I decided it was better not to.'

Madeline imagined him turning up at the front door with a bouquet of flowers and was filled with regret. 'Probably better you didn't,' she said. 'Oscar might have been . . . a little wary.'

'I could have given them to your mother-in-law, I suppose – or to Louise.'

They both laughed.

'Why are you lurking here in the park?' she asked. 'Not that I'm objecting. You were here when I needed you. In fact I haven't thanked you yet. You might have been badly bitten.'

He said, 'I wanted to buy the flowers and didn't want to be late so I came out much too early. I had no idea it was your daughter's dog when I saw the scuffle, although Louise had given me a very accurate account of his charms. Are we going to tell her? About the fight?'

Madeline began to tidy her hair, wishing that she had taken more trouble with her appearance, but walking the dog had not inspired her and she had worn a comfortable skirt and light jacket. She said, 'I think I'm going to have to explain why I look a little the worse for wear. Let's say they had a bit of a tussle but make light of it. The point is that Louise ought to be wary if she meets that poodle again. I'd like to warn her.'

It was agreed, their secret, and they strolled back in search of the abandoned parasol, but found it had vanished.

After the slightest hesitation, Daniel offered to buy her a replacement. 'Instead of the flowers,' he insisted.

For a moment Madeline almost threw caution to the wind and accepted his offer but prudence won out. 'It's a very kind thought,' she told him, 'but I . . . I do have another. Hopefully it will make someone else happy.'

As they walked, she explained her own presence in the park. 'So I hope you like the lunch.'

'I don't know. I've never had it, but I love roast lamb!'

'I . . . We shall invite you again after Gertrude has returned to Paris.'

An hour later they went home to lunch and told the tale. Middy was welcomed as the walking wounded and made much of by his owner. Madeline took Daniel upstairs to meet Oscar who then heard the story from Madeline and was suitably grateful for the art teacher's intervention. The superb lunch was enjoyed (although Madeline, feeling rather mean, was secretly glad that the potatoes were a little underdone) and the two cooks were duly complimented.

That evening, long after Daniel Grant had left them, Gertrude asked Madeline whether she had enjoyed her time in the park. 'Excepting the scuffle with the dogs, of course.'

'Yes I did.' Madeline met her eyes calmly. 'You were right, Gertrude. I did need some time on my own.'

'Not that you *were* on your own!'

'True. Fate decided otherwise, but Mr Grant was good company. I had an enjoyable morning and a wonderful lunch.'

Louise said, 'The potatoes were a bit hard.'

'Hard?' Madeline feigned surprise. 'If they were I didn't notice!'

Gertrude gave her a keen look. 'Well, I do think you have a little more colour in your cheeks than usual! Your little adventure has done you good.' She turned to her granddaughter. 'And from your account, you were rather taken with young Stanley Bridger.'

Louise laughed. 'I think he was rather taken with me, too. And he loved Middy.'

'So-o!' Gertrude glanced at Madeline. 'It sounds as though romance is in the air at last!'

'It sounds that way,' said Madeline innocently and wondered just how much Gertrude had guessed about her feelings for Daniel Grant.

Madeline tossed and turned in bed that night, thinking about her daughter's young man. An admirer at last. It was what Louise had longed for and Madeline was pleased for her, but she was beginning to realize that this might well be the beginning of the end as far as her little girl was concerned. From now on Louise would see herself as a young woman and she and Oscar must try to do the same. Which was an advantage in one way because now they could reasonably expect sensible behaviour from their headstrong girl. If she wanted to be treated as grown up, then she must act accordingly. Less tantrums and more co-operation, thought Madeline hopefully.

But how would young Stanley find Louise's behaviour? Was he mature enough at twenty to deal with a sometimes wild-spirited female who liked to get her own way? Madeline smiled into the darkness. The poor young man had no idea what he was letting himself in for. She understood because Roland had had to deal with her all those years ago. But he had been very resilient and took Madeline's excesses in his stride. He had been relaxed about her sudden changes of mood and her impatience with the rest of the world. Would Stanley be as flexible? Would the young railway clerk pass the test of time or would there be a succession of admirers before Louise finally met her future husband?

Gertrude had expressed her determination to meet Stanley Bridger before she returned to France, but Louise was equally convinced that it was too early.

'You'll terrify him!' she had insisted. 'We hardly know each other, and you'll ask him all sorts of questions he might not want to answer. You will, Grandmama! I know you both. He'll think he's being interrogated. Wait until I know him better.'

There was something in what she'd said, thought Madeline, but Gertrude could be very determined and Madeline had foreseen fireworks. She had talked to Oscar about it and as usual he had come up with a sensible solution.

'Ask him to call here to collect her next time they go anywhere together,' he suggested. 'Then say that I'm an invalid but would like to meet him. I shall size him up pretty quickly, man to man, without any questions. Then we can tell Gertrude that I approve and that's enough for the moment. Louise can write to her and tell more as time goes on.'

'You think that will satisfy Gertrude?'

Oscar raised his eyebrows. 'Gertrude is not mistress in this house, Madeline. I am the master and you are the mistress and she is a guest. A family member, maybe, but one who is also a guest. If necessary I will deal with her.' His eyes gleamed suddenly. 'That might be fun!'

43

Now, in the darkness, Madeline could still recall the expression on Oscar's face. Amazing, she thought. He was strong without being a bully and she really should appreciate him more than she did. She had often wondered what he was like as a much younger man.

She turned restlessly in the bed. It was a warm airless night, even with the windows wide open – the sort of night when normally she struggled to get to sleep. Not so tonight. Tonight she had Daniel's visit to think about and no longer cared whether or not she stayed awake.

We walked in the park together, she thought happily. Just the two of us. Not arm in arm, naturally, or hand in hand, but together. An unexpected gift from fate. And she had Gertrude and her *pot au feu* to thank for the stolen moments. If Gertrude and Louise hadn't chivvied her out of the house – and if Daniel hadn't arrived early – they might never have had that precious time together. Not that it meant anything, she warned herself. Certainly not. Nor was it at all romantic. They had both tried hard to make sure it wasn't. Hadn't they? He had hinted that he'd hoped she was still a widow . . . and that he *had* been interested when he first caught sight of her in the gallery. Or had she been reading too much into the words? She had confessed to him that she'd been looking forward to Sunday and his visit – but it had gone no further than that. Madeline was absolutely determined to do nothing to which Oscar could object, and Daniel was obviously determined that he would do nothing that might embarrass her or create problems in her life. That unwritten pact was enough to reassure Madeline – if it really was an unwritten pact.

You are too old for this nonsense, she decided. She tried to imagine him asleep in his bed . . . but suppose he wasn't sleeping. Suppose he, too, was lying awake, thinking about her. No. That was quite ridiculous!

Nothing would come of today's encounters. Daniel would remain Louise's teacher and possibly, in time, become a family friend. And that would be enough.

But they had shared confidences. She recalled those quite clearly so they were not figments of her imagination. She had told him about Roland and his death and how she met Oscar

44

on the beach. Daniel told her the way his first marriage had faltered. It seemed that his young wife, Elaine, was desperate for a family but after five years had still not conceived. The specialist had informed her that she had various problems that would almost certainly prevent her from ever having a child of her own and had suggested they might adopt.

'I was willing,' he'd told Madeline, 'but Elaine couldn't bring herself to make the decision. Then she met Gerald, a widower with three young children . . .'

She had left Daniel three months later after a tearful farewell. She and her new family had gone abroad shortly afterwards and now lived in New York. Since then Daniel had had several half-hearted relationships but nothing that led to marriage.

Madeline was sad for him. It seemed he was destined to remain alone.

Gertrude went off to her friends in Horsted Keynes a week later, still complaining that she had not been able to inspect Louise's admirer. From there, she would return to France. At first the house was quiet without her, but the following day it was Oscar's birthday. It arrived with the usual lack of attention – he detested fuss and hated being reminded how old he was. Madeline bought him an intricate jigsaw puzzle and spent time each day helping him put it together. She did this by way of a penance – for the crimes she had never committed with Daniel but had thought about. She had also been alerted by Gertrude to the fact that her husband was noticeably frailer than when she last visited.

'His voice is weaker, Madeline, and his memory is not as good. Haven't you noticed how many times he searches for a word?'

Madeline had now decided to help Oscar surreptitiously. If she told him her worries he would be mortified. The fact that he was much older than her had always troubled him and now that he was bedridden, the thought plagued him incessantly. She had no wish to make matters worse. A jigsaw would help his concentration, she thought. She also asked if he was interested in studying another language. French, perhaps. He had shied at the idea. 'Not French, dear! For heaven's sake! I would be faced with long sessions of Gertrude putting me through my paces.'

There, for the time being, the matter of another language rested.

On the 27th of July, Daniel arrived at the gallery a few moments before nine o'clock. He let himself in and locked the door behind him. He had asked Miss Maddock not to arrive until nine thirty because he liked to spend time alone in the gallery when it was empty. He stood in the middle of the empty room and breathed deeply. Five days until the next exhibition opened. He loved these moments when the walls had been cleared of art and the new exhibition was about to be planned – when success or failure was in his hands. Setting up an exhibition was an exacting and highly professional undertaking and as usual he would have help. Slowly he turned, eyeing each wall in turn, imagining the various works he was going to include and trying to see where each picture would be shown to best advantage.

'Simmon . . . Now where can we put you?' he murmured. Peter Simmon's oil paintings were dark and mysterious. If he put them in a shaded corner he worried they would be difficult to appreciate. Perhaps they should go on the wall to his left near to the window. He gave a cautious nod but then frowned. There was a problem. Simmon had fewer paintings to exhibit so it didn't make sense to give him the largest wall. Dodie Fisher's portraits were larger and would look cramped anywhere but on the left wall . . . unless he put up a separate stand, dividing the room into two but providing more space. Or he might have some extra candles to give more light. Maybe a circular tray of stout candles mounted on a pedestal of some kind. That was something worth considering.

'Tricky!' he muttered. There was also the jewellery to consider. Derek Wiseman made exquisite pieces of silver – brooches, tie pins, pendants and rings. They would be best displayed in a small glass-fronted display cabinet. Perhaps they would look good right inside the entrance by Miss Maddock's desk, where she could draw attention to it. He also wanted to find a corner for six flower paintings by

46

Dorcas Reed, one of his very able pupils. He pushed his hands into his pockets and perched on the edge of the desk, then, leaning over, he fished a sheet of paper and a pen from the top drawer and began to sketch the planned layout. It looked fine, but had he forgotten anything?

A tap on the door alerted him to Miss Maddock's arrival. Early, he thought, but never mind. At least she was conscientious, which was more than he could say for the previous receptionist. Miss Maddock came in, smiling cheerfully as usual. She was not nearly as precious as she appeared to clients and now waved a sheaf of papers.

'Good morning, Mr Grant. I've been thinking of the new launch and I've had a few ideas. You did tell me to think about it.'

'Good morning, Miss Maddock. Yes I did.' He moved from her desk and peered into her green eyes. He had always thought her a very pretty young woman. No wonder Dodie Fisher had painted her portrait. It would be in the exhibition with a red sticker on it because Miss Maddock's father had already bought it. The sale ticket would hopefully inspire others to purchase something.

She took off her jacket and slipped it on to a hanger which went inside a cupboard in the adjacent room. No extraneous clutter was allowed to mar the ambience of the gallery. 'I thought we could have a change from cheap champagne and serve a good rosé wine,' she said. 'My uncle has something rather special from the Côte d'Azur which he thinks you should . . . Mr Grant?'

Thinking of pretty women had reminded him of Madeline Swain. He jerked his attention back to the present and saw that Miss Maddock was regarding him reproachfully. 'I'm so sorry. I'm a little distracted this morning. A private matter. You were telling me about the rosé wine.'

'Very suitable, he says, for an occasion such as a launch, and he would let you have it at a special price.' She perched on the table on the spot recently vacated by her employer. 'Also I've found some rather nice invitation cards and I've started to make a list of important people. I think we might ask Mr Thwaite from the *Folkestone Gazette*. He's a bit lascivious, but . . .'

'Lascivious? Is he really?' Daniel was startled.

She laughed. 'Oh, nothing serious. Nothing I can't deal with. He likes to pinch my arm when he thinks no one's looking! But he did write a good report last time for the *Gazette*.'

'You don't think he'll pinch the arms of our guests, do you? I have a friend I want to invite. Two actually, and I wouldn't like to think . . .'

'Oh, no!' She laughed. 'They'll be quite safe. Give me their names while you think of it and I'll add them to the list.'

'A Mrs Swain and a Miss Legrand, her daughter who's a new pupil of mine. She'll be excited to be at the launch.' And I shall be excited to see her mother again, he thought. On the back of Madeline's invitation he would write, 'Sorry, no dogs admitted!' He knew she would appreciate his joke and wished he could have a new exhibition every week so that he could see her more often.

The following day, Sarah was polishing in the dining room. The sun shone in on the mahogany table and chairs. It fell across the heavy matching sideboard and glinted on the newly polished brass coal scuttle in the fireplace. There was a distinct smell of lavender from a bowl of potpourri on the windowsill, and an aspidistra took pride of place on the occasional table which was covered with a tasselled velour cloth. This room, unlike Oscar's bedroom, was light and welcoming with a well polished floor of light oak. The wallpaper was striped in ivory and cream and a bowl of pink roses graced the dining table. Sarah glanced up eagerly when Louise entered, her face glowing with excitement. Although Louise and Madeline frequently ate in the kitchen, the dining room was always used at weekends and whenever visitors came to stay.

'Did Mama tell you?' Louise demanded and rushed on without waiting for an answer. 'I went to meet Stanley's parents yesterday afternoon. Nothing too serious. Just a cup of tea and a slice of cherry cake. He's got two younger brothers – twins – and his mother is rather on the plump side but a very cheerful sort of person. I was very nice to her, of course, and I think she liked me. She wasn't too keen on Middy, though, because he was in a funny mood and kept barking.'

She paused for breath and Sarah said, 'My aunt was bitten by a dog once . . .'

'Middy didn't bite her,' Louise rushed on. 'His father's a bit stern. Rather stiff and starchy, not at all like Papa, but Stanley says he was brought up by a dreadful old battleaxe of a grandmother and that accounts for it. Poor man.'

'Poor man indeed. So you are getting fond of this Stanley, are you?' Sarah applied polish to the first of the six dining chairs.

Louise threw herself on to the nearest chair. 'I think I am. He tried to kiss me, but I wouldn't let him. The first time, that is. The second time I weakened.' She laughed.

'Then you'll no doubt be inviting him here to tea. Tit for tat, eh?'

'I might suggest it, but he might take it as a sign that I'm serious about him.'

'But you say you are.' Tucking a stray lock of hair under her white cap, Sarah started on the next chair. 'Does he strike you as a man you could spend your life with?'

Louise frowned. 'I don't know about that. He's only twenty so hopefully he will grow up a bit over the next few years. He is still a bit boyish. Doesn't take life too seriously. Still larks around with his brothers. I'm wondering if I prefer older men. Not that I know any, but some women do, don't they? Mama seems very happy with Papa and he's much older than her.'

'But her first husband – your father – was very young when they married. Most women marry men of their own age or thereabouts. I daresay there are advantages to both. Your Stanley will probably be much more grown up in a year or two – or you might find a young man with a steady head on his shoulders. Then you'd have the best of both worlds. My sister married a much older man and he lived to be ninety-one and she died before him. You can never plan these things.'

Louise stood up and looked at herself in the mirror for a moment or two. 'Is my nose too big, do you think?'

'Too big? Certainly not. It's just right. What's got into you, Louise?'

'There's a receptionist at the art gallery. Very pretty. Petite, too, with the most amazing green eyes.'

'Pretty women are good for business.' Sarah paused in her polishing long enough to pluck a dead leaf from the aspidistra and tuck it into her apron pocket.

Louise lost interest in her reflection and turned. 'I realized last night that if Roland had lived, he'd be about the same age as Mr Grant, who is also an artist. So my father might have been famous, too, with his own gallery and some pupils to teach. If so, I could have been his receptionist and if he'd . . .'

'A lot of "ifs", dear.'

Louise seemed not to hear her. 'I wonder if she is Mr Grant's lady friend?'

'None of our business, Louise!' Sarah ignored the tightening of Louise's mouth and continued. 'So are your pictures going to be on display there? In Folkestone, I mean?'

Louise stared at her. 'She wouldn't be right for him because, from what Mama said, she's efficient. Probably too efficient. She sounds almost domineering. Some women are like that. Mr Grant needs someone gentler. Someone more natural.'

'She could be married.'

'They refer to her as Miss Maddock.'

'Then she may be engaged to someone. If she's so pretty . . .'

'I hope so for his sake.'

Sarah shrugged. 'I'm sure Mr Grant knows what he's doing, Louise. Is he pleased with your work?'

'I don't know yet. As for being hung in the gallery, who knows? Mr Grant has made it clear that nothing goes into the gallery that is less than first class. I think it was a warning.' Absent-mindedly she ran a finger along the mantelpiece and stared at the dust she had collected.

Sarah said sharply, 'I haven't done that yet!'

'Sorry. I didn't mean anything by it.'

Sarah held out her polishing cloth and Louise wiped the offending dust on it.

Louise said slowly, 'I've got a lot on my mind, Sarah.'

'Haven't we all!' Sarah smiled. 'Try not to worry. You'll do well at your art, dear, if you put your mind to it.'

'Another if!' cried Louise and with a heartfelt sigh hurried out of the room in search of Middy.

Four

M onday, the first of August was the opening day of the exhibition and Madeline handed over the elegant invitation card. It was edged in gold with fine antique lettering inviting her and Louise to the opening of the new exhibition in the Daniel Grant Gallery. The gallery looked splendid, with several tasteful flower arrangements and a display of candles. On the desk there was a tray of pale pink wine and a young woman was circulating with a tray of canapés.

Miss Maddock welcomed Madeline and Louise in turn. 'Mrs Swain and—'

'I'm Louise Legrand, one of Mr Grant's pupils.' Louise's look was a trifle frosty, thought Madeline, but her own smile was warm enough for two. She had been looking forward to the event much more than she dared admit and it had seemed an eternity before the time came to catch the train.

'Ah, yes! Miss Legrand. Mr Grant has spoken about you. Is this your first visit?' She took two catalogues from the pile and handed one to each of them.

Louise said airily, 'I have looked in from time to time.'

It was news to Madeline, but she said nothing. She was looking for Daniel and almost immediately saw him, surrounded by an eager crowd.

Miss Maddock said, 'Do please help yourselves to a glass of rosé wine. It's from the Côte d'Azur region of France and comes highly recommended.'

'A nice change from champagne,' Madeline agreed.

She and Louise each took a glass, sipped it and pronounced it perfect for a summer's morning.

Louise turned to her mother. 'I can see Mr Grant's busy. I shall have a good look round first.'

For a moment Madeline felt abandoned as her daughter moved away, but within minutes Louise was back. 'Would you believe!' she hissed. 'That Miss Maddock, the receptionist, has had her portrait painted and someone has already bought it! What vanity! Really! Mind you Mr Grant has flattered her! She's not *that* pretty!'

'Did you get a chance to speak to Mr Grant?'

'A few words. He said how alike we are, you and me.' She tossed her head impatiently. 'I said I didn't agree. We are not at all alike.'

Before Madeline could digest this barbed comment, Louise had drifted away again. Almost at once, Madeline caught Daniel's gaze and, with a few quick words, he broke away from his group and moved towards her. Madeline was shocked at the delight that flooded through her as drew near.

'My dear Mrs Swain! This is such a pleasure. I was hoping you'd be able to spare the time.' He was looking at her intensely, struggling to sound detached, she thought, aware of the same problem. In fact she had an overwhelming desire to hug him, but that was utterly ridiculous and she knew it. Her throat was so dry she had to sip the wine before she felt able to reply.

'I wouldn't have missed it for anything. The invitation has been on the mantelpiece ever since it arrived.' Did she sound giddy with excitement? She prayed not. 'And I didn't bring the dog!' She laughed. 'But you spoke to Louise, I gather.'

He laughed. 'She rather bit my head off.'

To Madeline's relief, a tray of bite-sized vol-au-vents appeared at her elbow and she accepted one. 'Mmm. It's delicious.'

'Chopped chicken in cream,' he told her and she nodded, her mouth full, her throat tight. She coughed as a few flaky crumbs went down the wrong way. The canapé had been unwise, she decided.

'We have some very good work here today,' he said, coming to her aid. 'I should like to show you . . .'

A large man with a whiskery face touched his elbow and Daniel turned, hiding his reluctance.

'Won't keep you long, old boy,' the large man promised, 'but my good lady wife has taken a fancy to a little picture by this Simmon chappie! Don't care for it myself, too dark for my liking, but I have to humour her. You know what these women are like!' He burst into loud laughter and winked at Madeline. 'Present company excepted, naturally.' This provoked another burst of laughter.

Daniel said, 'Best if you speak with Mr Simmon himself. He's the gentleman with the spectacles, in the black smoking jacket.'

'Ah! That's him, is it? I'll have a word in his ear.'

He wandered off. Madeline was trying to hide her amusement. Daniel whispered, 'That's one of the cons of owning a gallery. You meet all sorts.'

'But if he's going to buy a picture . . .?'

'There you have it. But how have you been?' He lowered his voice. 'Dare I say I've missed you?'

'I don't think you should!' she said, but she was so glad that he had. To hide her confusion, she sipped her wine and looked for Louise who was talking to an earnest looking man and looking very happy. Madeline relaxed. Her daughter had been in a strange mood, but now she seemed to have recovered.

Daniel said gently, 'I don't suppose you missed me at all.'

'Not at all!' she told him with a smile. 'Married women aren't allowed to dwell on the charms of other men.'

He clutched his chest. 'Straight to the heart, Mrs Swain, but I take your point and you are right, of course. Forgive me.'

A middle-aged woman now hovered at Daniel's elbow and he turned his attention to her. She wanted a piece of jewellery for her daughter's twenty-first birthday and wondered if Daniel would be kind enough to give her advice on what to choose.

'If Mrs Swain will excuse me,' he murmured and Madeline watched him as he crossed to the display stand behind Miss Maddock's desk.

Louise appeared suddenly beside her. 'What were you two whispering about?' she demanded. Excitement had brought a spot of bright colour to her cheeks and her eyes flashed. Madeline could not quite read her daughter's expression and immediately regretted her little tête-à-tête. She had promised herself that she would do nothing untoward that would draw attention to her and Daniel, but within minutes she seemed to have annoyed Louise. Inwardly she cursed her foolishness.

'We were laughing at some of the people here,' she confided, lowering her voice. 'You have to admit that art lovers come in all shapes and sizes. Glance to your left and you'll see what I mean.' Disarmed, Louise turned obediently. A large woman was haranguing a young man, in a loud horsey tone. Despite the fact that it was summer, she wore a heavy tweed suit and dabbed frequently at her face with a handkerchief.

'Miss Dodie Fisher is my niece,' she bellowed. 'I coached her when she was a child. Spotted the talent, you see. I have an eye for a good line and can recognize a sound composition when I see it!'

Louise turned back, grinning, and Madeline was relieved to see that she had accepted the small lie.

'I saw you were talking with the rather nice-looking man – the one with ginger hair.'

Louise's face lit up. 'That was Henry Godden. He's engaged to Miss Maddock. They're getting married next year. I could see he adores her and no wonder. She is very sweet. Someone called Dodie Fisher painted her portrait, but her father bought it.' She rolled her eyes. 'That's cheating in a way, don't you think?'

'Then I mustn't buy one of yours, must I, when they eventually appear on the wall?'

'Oh, that's different, Mama!' Louise said airily. She tugged gently at Madeline's arm. 'I've found a small painting that Grandmama might like. It's by one of Mr Grant's pupils and it's quite good. I wondered if we could afford it as a thank you to Grandmama for my art lessons. It's number seventeen in the catalogue. Do go and have a look at it. I'm going to look at the jewellery.'

Another tray of canapés was being offered. This time it was crab meat on squares of toast. Madeline shook her head but Louise took two.

Number seventeen in the catalogue – the one Louise liked – was one of a series of six, all animals. The subject was a young foal, finding his feet with difficulty. His feet were in straw, the background was the interior of a small barn. Madeline knew at once that it would appeal to Gertrude and saw that the price was reasonable. She collected Louise and together they found Miss Maddock and bought the painting. As the small red dot was stuck to the frame, Madeline was aware of a growing pride in her daughter. Considering all the other distractions of Louise's young life, it was thoughtful of her to think about a thank you gift for Gertrude.

It was satisfying, too, to know that the decisions she and Oscar had taken throughout Louise's life had proved to be the right ones. Gertrude, understandably, had been inclined to interfere when she could. At one time she had wanted Louise to spend a year with her in Paris so that she could attend a dancing academy, but Madeline and Oscar had had doubts about allowing their daughter to be away from them for so long. They also disliked the idea that Louise would have no room of her own but would sleep on the rather elegant chaise longue that Gertrude had described so lovingly over the years. They had also fought off Gertrude's suggestion that Louise should go to a girl's boarding school, despite her insistence that she felt Louise would gain confidence and independence away from home.

Oscar and Madeline had scotched the plan. 'Gertrude doesn't know Louise as well as we do.' Oscar had laughed. 'She is already a sight too independent. The Lord only knows what she would get up to, given the chance!'

Tactfully they had resisted all efforts to lose daily contact with their daughter and now it seemed they had been right to do so. Once or twice Madeline had wondered secretly whether it had been fair to deny Louise the opportunities Gertrude had offered, but lately she had felt reassured. Oscar had suggested that, in a year or two, marrying a man like Stanley, steady and with a good career ahead of him, would calm Louise down and help her mature. Madeline, with a woman's deeper understanding, doubted that Louise was anywhere near ready for matrimony. From her own experience she thought a young marriage could present all sorts of problems for both the husband and wife.

'Stanley is simply the *first* admirer,' she had argued. 'Hopefully she will meet and consider other partners before she makes up her mind to settle down.'

Madeline already thought she detected a certain lack of enthusiasm on Louise's part for Stanley Bridger. We shall see, she thought. She watched her daughter across the room, talking to Dorcas Reed, and felt content. Stanley was probably too young for a girl like Louise, but she would find the right man in time. There was certainly no hurry.

Madeline had always dreaded the day when Gertrude's age would finally win, beating her indomitable spirit. The following morning the postman brought a letter which rekindled all her fears. Moments later she was sitting beside Oscar's bed, rereading the familiar spidery handwriting.

> Dear Madeline,
> I regret to say I have to entrust this letter to André who has been an absolute rock ever since my fall, yesterday – I somehow lost my footing within an hour of arriving home. I did hope that I would recover quickly from the accident (I fell down the stairs) and you know how I hate lying in bed. I become bored very quickly although dear André has been reading to me. Bless the boy! The point is that the doctor thinks I have a sprained ankle and two cracked ribs so he forbids me to get up until they are healed . . .

Oscar said, 'I hope this isn't leading where I think it is!'
'So do I.'

> André is an angel and has cooked for me and taken care of me since the fall, but he is due to go to Italy in a fortnight's time and I shall be alone. If my various bones have failed to heal I shall need someone else and wonder if you will make yourself available . . .

Madeline felt a frisson of terror. She had always feared the prospect of a sea crossing and had remained firmly on English soil.

Oscar said promptly, 'I won't allow it, dear. I know how much you hate the idea of a sea crossing. Gertrude knows it full well and has no right to ask.'

Deeply grateful for his understanding, Madeline nevertheless felt obliged to protest.

'But who will care for her, Oscar, if I don't go?'

'He's not going to Italy for another week or so. She might be healed by then. Anyway, she can afford a private nurse. Surely she doesn't need to drag you across to Paris, knowing how frightened you are of the water. And what about me? Don't you have a duty to me?'

Madeline felt a spark of hope. Of course, she had a very good excuse. She had a bedridden husband. What was Gertrude thinking of, expecting her to make such a dangerous journey?

> . . . I'm sure Sarah would be willing to put in a few
> more hours each day to care for Oscar.

'What damnable cheek!' Oscar exclaimed. 'Sorry, dear, but I really am astonished at the woman's nerve. This is Gertrude at her very worst.'

> . . . It wouldn't be for long and Louise will be there
> to keep us informed if there is an emergency of any
> kind . . .

'Hah! So if I have another heart attack, Louise telephones to you and you take so long getting back that I die waiting for you to return. Really! Gertrude has gone too far this time.'

Reluctantly Madeline had to agree, but she was still hoping that somehow the moment for a decision would be averted.

Madeline read the last few lines which were general enquiries. Slowly she folded the letter and pushed it back in the envelope. 'She will hopefully recover quite quickly, Oscar,' she suggested optimistically. 'What surprises me is how she came to fall down the stairs. True, they are narrow by all accounts, but she has lived there for more than twenty-five years.'

Oscar raised his eyebrows. 'Maybe a little too much champagne from one of her adoring young men!'

'Oscar! Really. What a thing to say!' She grinned. 'But I daresay it's possible . . . So how shall I answer this letter?'

He pursed his lips thoughtfully. 'Delaying tactics, Madeline. Express regret, explain that you cannot make an immediate decision because just at present I am feeling particularly frail and in very poor health and cannot be abandoned to the care of the daily woman and Louise. Add that the doctor is expected.'

'Which reminds me, Oscar. That isn't a white lie because he is calling Monday morning after his surgery.'

Oscar shrugged. 'It suits me, dear. I feel as fit as ever.' He put a finger to his lips. 'But don't tell Gertrude that!'

That night, while the rest of the household slept, Madeline awoke suddenly and sat up in a panic. Something had woken her but what? Her pulse rate quickened and her mouth was dry. Yet there were no unfamiliar sounds. So what had woken her? She slid from the bed and went to the window. There was no sign of anybody in the street outside and after a moment or two Madeline told herself she must have been aroused by a nightmare which had left her frightened of something intangible. She was halfway across the room towards her bed when she heard a sound that immediately sent her heart racing even more erratically.

'Someone's knocking at the front door!' she gasped with a glance at her alarm clock. It was a quarter past four! Snatching her dressing gown from the back of the door she crept out on to the landing. There was no sign that either Oscar or Louise had been disturbed so she started down the stairs. Perhaps it was a neighbour – some kind of emergency, perhaps. Or a stranger passing by who was taken ill suddenly . . . Or the police! The latter frightened her most. A visit from the police usually meant bad news. Had something happened to Gertrude?

'Please, God, no!' she whispered.

She felt deep remorse as she remembered how she and Oscar had plotted to ignore her plea for help.

Cautiously Madeline opened the door a little to find a complete stranger standing on the doorstep.

He said, 'Where's Sarah?'

'There's no Sarah living her. You've made a mistake . . . unless you mean our housekeeper.'

''Ousekeeper, is she?' He smiled. 'Good for her! Who are you?' Madeline pulled her dressing gown tighter around her. What could she do? No point in alerting Oscar who could not come to her aid, and she certainly wouldn't want to involve Louise.

He leaned forward and she could smell ale on his breath. 'I'm her 'usband and I've got a right to talk to 'er, ma'am, so I'd be obliged if you'd give 'er a shout and tell her Bert's 'ere!'

In the gloom of the nearest street lamp Madeline could now see that he was shabbily dressed and carried a small bag slung over his shoulder. It was Bert! Of course! Bert Gravely – the husband who was supposed to be in prison for burglary.

He grinned.. 'Worked it out, 'ave you? But I don't mean you any 'arm, ma'am. I just want to see my missus.'

'Have you escaped?' she stammered. 'That is, is she expecting you?'

'No, ma'am! I'm let out because I've done me time, fair and square.' He stepped forward, intent on passing her, but Madeline sidestepped to block his entry. He was obviously rather drunk.

'Sarah isn't here, Mr Gravely,' she told him as firmly as she could manage. 'Sarah doesn't live with us, you see. I'm sorry. She comes in daily from eight until twelve.'

He scratched his head.

From the top of the stairs, she heard Louise's sleepy voice.

'What's the matter, Mama?'

'Nothing, dear. Go back to sleep.'

Bert stared past Madeline. 'Is that you, Sarah?'

Madeline said, 'I've told you, Mr Gravely, Sarah doesn't live here. That was my daughter. I'm afraid we can't help you.'

He frowned. 'Then where does she live 'cos she's not where she used to be. I've bin there and there's new tenants. So she's gone somewhere. You must know where she lives.'

'I'm afraid I don't.' Unlikely as it sounded it was actually the truth. Sarah had never discussed her family except to talk about her two soldier sons. Bert had rarely been mentioned, her home address never. Now Madeline saw why. If she didn't know where Sarah lived, she couldn't be forced to tell Bert. Obviously poor Sarah wanted to have nothing more to do with him.

Louise suddenly appeared beside Madeline and peered curiously at their visitor. 'My mother has told you that Sarah doesn't live here, Mr Gravely, and we don't know where she does live. That's the truth.'

He raised his voice suddenly. 'Sarah! Are you there?'

Oscar shouted down the stairs. 'What's happening, Madeline? Who's that at the door?'

Madeline gripped her daughter's arm and said, 'Go up to your father, Louise. Calm him down. This won't do his heart any good. Tell him I'm dealing with it!'

'But I don't want to leave you alone, Mama. He might . . .'

'Please do as I say!' She pushed her daughter in the direction of the stairs and turned back to Sarah's husband. 'There is really no point in you staying here, Mr Gravely,' she said firmly. 'Sarah does not live in. If you want her address I suggest you write to her sons.'

'My sons?' For a moment he swayed to and fro, his face contorted by the effort to concentrate on what was being said. 'My sons? But they're in the army.'

'Then go to your local recruiting office and ask there. They'll have all the information you need. If not they can tell you how to find it. Now do please go away. You have woken the whole house up!'

He hesitated and Madeline held her breath. She was longing to close the door on him, and she was also unable to help him. What she hoped was that he would leave quietly.

Abruptly an upstairs window opened in the house next door and a man put his head out. This was Adam Carter, an assistant bank manager. Although large in stature, Madeline had always found him to be polite and well spoken.

'What's going on down there?' he barked, his tone unusually abrupt. 'It's the middle of the night. Decent people want some sleep.'

Madeline called up to him. 'I'm sorry but I can't persuade this man to go away.'

Bert glared at her but the other man's intervention had unsettled him. 'I want my wife!' he muttered.

The window was slammed down and a brief silence followed. Bert looked confused and Madeline crossed her fingers that he would leave. No such luck. He was still there when the neighbour opened his front door and stepped out on to the pavement. He wore an overcoat over his pyjamas and carried a walking stick. He towered over Bert who promptly took a step back and regarded him fearfully.

'You!' Mr Carter roared. 'Hop it!' To make his meaning clear he grabbed the man by his collar and began to urge him along the pavement. Then he released him and gave him a final push. 'And don't come back bothering this good lady.'

Together they watched the man shuffle away and Madeline tried hard not to feel sorry for him.

Mr Carter said, 'That's seen him off, I hope.'

'You were splendid, Mr Carter. Thank you so much.'

He raised an invisible hat. 'My pleasure, Mrs Swain. I don't think you'll see him again.'

Dorothy Carter now appeared at the window, a shawl round her shoulders, her head full of curling rags. 'Has he gone, Adam?'

Madeline looked up. 'Yes, he has, thanks to your husband. He soon scared him off.'

'You should see how he treats his staff at the bank,' Mrs Carter said and they all laughed. 'Come on back to bed, Adam. You know how easily you get chilled.'

After breakfast a few hours later, when Louise had taken Middy to the park, Madeline sat Sarah down with a cup of tea and broke the news about her husband's visit the previous night and the intervention of the next-door neighbour.

'He's out of prison, Sarah. He's done his full sentence, and wanted to come home – to you. When you weren't there he came to us. Whatever is going on, Sarah? You can tell me.' Seeing the woman's reluctance, she continued. 'You *must* tell me because if it happens again and he refuses to leave, we might have to call the police.'

Sarah swallowed. For a moment she didn't answer. 'I don't care what happens to him.'

'Oh, Sarah! You don't mean that!' Madeline was genuinely shocked. 'He's still your husband. He's paid his dues. Doesn't he deserve a second chance?'

To her surprise, Sarah shook her head. 'You don't know what he did. You don't know how he shamed me. If you did you wouldn't want me to take him back.' Her eyes began to water and she pulled a handkerchief from her apron pocket and wiped her eyes with a fierce dabbing motion as if they were somehow responsible.

Madeline said nothing and eventually the housekeeper continued. 'I moved after he was sent down – to get away from the neighbours' gossip! There were decent people in that street, respectable families . . . and we lowered the tone. They stared if they saw me in the street, but mostly they just avoided me and I knew what they were thinking.' Her voice dropped to a whisper. 'I couldn't bear it. Every time I went outside to hang up a bit of washing, I knew they were peeping from behind their curtains. Fortunately the boys were away in the army. Thank heavens they were spared.'

'I'm sorry, Sarah. I didn't realize. So . . . So you moved house.'

'I had to – for more than one reason. I couldn't afford to stay there. It was a nice little flat, but I found something cheaper in a different area. I moved again a few years later. And that's why I never told you where I lived, because I did not want him to find me.' She sniffed. 'You may think me harsh being his wife for better or worse but I couldn't bear it. All those lies!'

Sarah began to cry in earnest and Madeline watched helplessly. She didn't want to add to the poor woman's misery, but she felt she should know exactly what Bert had done. Was he really violent? If so, she would definitely feel obliged to call the police if he came to the house again.

She pushed the cup of tea closer and said gently, 'Drink some tea, Sarah, and then tell me what happened.'

Sarah obeyed. She was making valiant efforts to halt the flow of tears. Perhaps, thought Madeline, it was good for her to get rid of the pent-up emotion.

Sarah recovered at last. 'I'm sorry you were upset last night,' she said and drew a deep breath. 'He used to work for the brewery and he brought home good money. Sometimes he worked a night shift, or so he said, and brought home a bit extra, but he always said he'd earned it. It turned out he was burgling. Not in a gang or anything but now and then, on his own. Can you imagine? Lordy, that upset me – when I found out, I mean. Learning that he was a burglar.'

Madeline said nothing, but she could imagine what a shock it must have been.

Sarah drew a long breath and went on. 'Then one night he was burgling, thinking the big house was empty, but the owner and his son were asleep upstairs and came down the stairs with a gun. It wasn't a real gun, but Bert thought it was and grabbed the poker from the grate and had a go at him.'

Madeline tried not to react to the words, but this was what she had feared.

'Bert hit the man's arm that was holding the gun and then the man's grown-up son appeared and between them they caught him and tied him to a chair. He was arrested, natu-rally.' She shrugged. 'He was such a nice man . . . or so I thought. Before I knew the truth I thought the world of him. Kind, funny, never looked at another woman. He wasn't that sort . . . It was such a . . . a disappointment.'

At least he hadn't murdered anyone, thought Madeline, but he could have done. If he'd hit the man's head instead of his arm, he might have killed him.

'I know you're going to say it was a long time ago but that doesn't mean Bert didn't hurt him. They said in court that he was drunk and lost his temper.'

There was a long silence. Sarah was exhausted and started to sob quietly and Madeline wondered what to say.

The silence lengthened until a bell rang, breaking it. It was Oscar, Madeline guessed, waiting for a fresh carafe of water so that he could take his pills.

She jumped to her feet. 'I'll take it up,' she said. 'I'll have a word with Oscar. He'll have to know.'

'Will he want to keep me on after this?'

Madeline stared at the anxious, tear-stained face, and put

a hand on Sarah's shoulders. 'Of course he will. You've done nothing wrong so there's no question of you leaving us. But there is a bit of a problem and Oscar is very wise.'

Oscar swallowed his pills and restored the pillbox to the bedside table. He had listened to Madeline's hurried explanation of Sarah's dilemma. He tutted at regular intervals and then paused while he thought about the options.

'Ask her if she would come up and talk to me,' he requested. 'I think she's panicking a little. It may not be as bad as she thinks.'

'Not as bad? But he's a thief! A burglar! And he drinks and loses his temper. I know she's his wife but can we expect her to . . .?'

Oscar held up a hand. 'Please, Madeline, trust me. I'm seeing the man's point of view here. He was either a bad 'un, as they say, or greedy or weak willed, but that was then. He must have had a lot of good points or Sarah would never have married him. It might be that he deserves a second chance. We don't know. Let me talk to her.'

Reluctantly, Madeline passed on the message and with equal reluctance Sarah made her way up the stairs. When she was sitting comfortably beside him, Oscar smiled kindly at her.

'You've had a very difficult time, Sarah,' he began, 'but this could be the end of it. Your husband has also had a miserable time for many years, but has now paid his debt to society.'

'I don't trust him!' she said, staring at her hands which were clasped together in her lap.

'But you did love him once?'

'Oh, yes!' She looked up eagerly. 'He was a charming man . . . once. So I thought.'

'Did he love you?'

'Of course he did! We were head-over-heels with it.'

'If you had done something terrible, would he have forgiven you, Sarah? Did he love you that much?'

Shocked into silence she stared at him, her mouth trembling. 'I don't know. I never did anything terrible. I never did anything to shame him. Nothing.'

'But if you had, Sarah. Do you think he loved you enough to give you a second chance?'

She shrugged. 'Not if I'd lied and cheated for years, pretending I'd earned all that extra money. When I thought about him breaking into people's houses . . . climbing in through windows and everything . . .'

Oscar sighed. 'And you believed his story about the extra money?'

She hesitated. 'I suppose I did wonder – but I was glad of it. We had the two boys and it was a respectable flat with a respectable rent!' She twisted the damp handkerchief. 'If you must know, Mr Swain, I thought he gambled. I thought he gambled at the pub with his mates and got lucky. I didn't ask.'

He nodded. 'So you turned a blind eye even though you didn't think he was perfect.'

'I suppose so.'

'Can't you give him one more chance – to see if there is still good in him?'

Again she paused, thinking it through. 'But what if he *hasn't* changed? If being in prison has made him even worse? I've thought about it, night after night, worrying what to do. Suppose he's made some bad friends and they come to the house. How will I get away from him then? It's fine for you and Mrs Swain but put yourself in my shoes.' Abruptly she stood up. 'I know you mean well and I hope he never shows up here again, but I don't think I could ever live with him and that's an end of it.'

When the door had closed behind her, Oscar sighed. 'So you didn't persuade her, Oscar,' he muttered to himself. 'Well, we'll just have to hope there'll be no more trouble.'

But he turned back to his bible with a strong sense of unease and a suspicion that they hadn't heard the last of Bert Gravely.

The doctor was a little later than expected, having been delayed by one of his female patients who had gone un-expectedly into an early labour.

'It was a fine healthy baby,' he told Madeline, as he took off his hat and handed it to Louise who always greeted him

66

like an old friend, which indeed he was, because he had known her since she was born. 'A lovely bouncing boy!'

'Oh, Mama! Don't listen.' Louise turned back to the doctor. 'Everyone seems to have boys except poor Mama.' To Madeline she said, 'But never mind. When I marry, you will have a son-in-law and that will be more or less the same. I might even give you one or two grandsons if I'm feeling *really* generous.'

Madeline laughed. 'Just don't rush me into it, Louise. I can wait a few more years.'

She watched the doctor make his way upstairs and hid her anxiety. The alarm caused by Bert had taken its toll on her husband. For a man who needed calm the episode had been a great strain. Knowing that his family was being threatened but being helpless to intervene had upset Oscar. He was also unhappy that his attempt to persuade Sarah to give Bert another chance had failed. He could see that until the matter was properly resolved, their home would be the focus of Bert's efforts towards a reconciliation and his family might well be at risk.

After about twenty minutes Madeline heard the doctor come downstairs and hurried to lead him into the privacy of the sitting room.

After they sat down he said, 'I am rather disturbed, Mrs Swain. Your husband's pulse rate has risen since the last time I was here. Do you know of any reason for that?'

She explained about Bert's visit and he sighed. 'Excitement. The very thing he needed to avoid!'

'Didn't he tell you about the incident?'

'I didn't give him a chance, I'm afraid. Too busy with my questions. Did you know he had a lot of chest pains yesterday?'

Her eyes widened. 'No! He said nothing to me. But he didn't eat as well as he usually does . . . and I thought he may have had a restless night, although he denied it this morning.'

'Mmm. He's obviously trying to spare you the anxiety and is—'

There was a noise from outside and they both turned.

Madeline said, 'That's the front door! Oh, I do hope it's not him again. Mr Gravely, I mean.'

Her hopes were not realized. The front door opened and they heard Louise say firmly, 'I'm sorry, Mr Gravely, but you can't come in. Sarah isn't here.'

Madeline jumped to her feet. 'It *is* him! Oh, dear!'

She hurried down the stairs but too late. Bert had pushed past Louise and was heading along the passage in the direction of the kitchen.

'Sarah, love!' he called. 'I know you're 'ere. I 'ave to talk to you. Sarah, love, I'm a changed man, I swear it.'

He had reached the kitchen door and Madeline prayed that Sarah would have the sense to hide herself somehow. It seemed she hadn't done so for Bert pushed the kitchen door open and barged in. 'Sarah! Sarah!'

Madeline caught her daughter by the arm. 'Please, Louise. Go upstairs and be with your father and the doctor. I'll deal with this.'

Without waiting for the protests she knew would be forthcoming, she hurried into the kitchen. To her surprise Sarah was nowhere to be seen. Hiding in the larder, perhaps?

'I just want to talk to 'er,' Bert pleaded. He had taken off his cap and now twisted it in his hands. 'If she says no to me, then I can take it, but she should listen to me. It's only fair.'

As she looked at him, Madeline thought he was typical of some of the men the Ladies' Charity Group was trying to help with the funds they raised. But Bert's sons were grown and fighting overseas and his wife no longer wanted him. How many more such splintered families inhabited the back streets of St Mark's Bay, she wondered. She was seized by an immense sadness.

'I'm sorry, Mr Gravely, but as you can see, Sarah isn't here. She went early today.' Today she smelled nothing on his breath – so at least he was sober. 'Now if you don't go I shall have to ask the doctor to send for a policeman.'

'Doctor?' He glanced round in confusion. 'What doctor?'

'The doctor is upstairs with my husband who is one of his patients. I only have to call him . . .' She allowed the threat to hang in the air.

Bert gave a last look round the kitchen. 'I know she's 'ere. I know you're lying and I reckon she put you up to this. But

68

I'll find 'er – tell 'er that from me! She's my wife and I deserve a chance to say my piece.' He turned and walked out of the kitchen. As he left, he slammed the front door behind him so loudly that the china rattled on the kitchen dresser.

Louise had not retired upstairs as instructed and now appeared from her hiding place behind the dining room door. She looked at Madeline. 'So, where is Sarah?'

'I've no idea.' They both returned to the kitchen to find it empty. They stepped through into the garden in time to see the housekeeper emerging from the garden shed. She was brushing dust from her clothes and paused to rub her shoes with a handkerchief.

Full of apologies, she left them in no doubt that she was still determined to keep her distance from her husband.

Tender-hearted Louise spoke up for him. 'Couldn't you just hear what he has to say? Poor man. I'm sure he is very sorry, Sarah.'

'Sarah sank on to a chair, covered her face with her apron and began to cry.

Louise regarded her unhappily. 'I'll make a pot of tea.'

Madeline nodded and went upstairs.

The doctor said, 'What a difficult man. I heard every word, but I didn't know whether or not to interfere, Mrs Swain, and I thought your husband needed me most.' He regarded Madeline gravely. Behind him, Oscar was breathing heavily, a horrid, rasping sound which sent a frisson of fear down Madeline's spine. There was perspiration on Oscar's forehead and his eyes appeared unfocussed.

'Oh, Oscar!' she cried and rushed to him. Leaning over him, she took his hands in hers. 'There is no need for alarm, Oscar. Truly there isn't. Bert went away without too much fuss. Sarah was hiding in the shed so he didn't see her.' She turned to the doctor. 'What's happened to him?'

Oscar whispered, 'I'm fine, dear. You mustn't worry about me.'

'But I do worry, Oscar. You look terrible. That wretched man turning up again has upset you.'

The doctor drew her to one side. 'Send your housekeeper round to the surgery in about half an hour and I'll give her a draught for your husband to take. It will make him drowsy and lessen the anxiety – but do try and solve the problem of your housekeeper's husband. One way or the other. I don't want Mr Swain to go through this level of anxiety again. It is very weakening for his nervous system and bad for his heart.'

Louise came up carrying a mug of hot, sweet tea and sat beside her father while he sipped it gratefully.

The doctor followed Madeline down the stairs and they stood at the front door, talking in low voices.

'I don't want to alarm you, Mrs Swain, but do you think the housekeeper's husband has his full wits about him? I do wonder if his years in prison have unhinged him a little. It wouldn't be the first time the rigours of prison life have broken down a man's mental defences. If you at any time suspect that his mind *is* deranged you must let me know at once. We might be able to help him before he gets any worse.' He picked up his hat. 'Talk to his wife. Find out if there is any history of mental fatigue or failure in his family. We may need to commit him. Now I must be on my way. I won't forget the draught . . . and call me whenever you need me. Your husband is not at all well and needs peace and quiet. He really should be protected if possible from the unpleasant side of life.'

Five

L ater that same evening, Madeline sat down to write the first draft of the long delayed answer to Gertrude's letter. When she had done the best she could with it, she took it up to read to Oscar who had had a good sleep and was feeling better. He was propped up against the pillows, reading the bible which, he claimed, always soothed him. He slipped in his book mark and closed it carefully.

Madeline settled herself on the bedside chair. 'I've tried to make it sound, Oscar, as though I didn't truly believe that she needed me. I do feel guilty about it, but I couldn't leave you now even if I wanted to go to her.'

'And if you had gone rushing over there, how would we have dealt with Bert, my dear? It would probably have been Louise who had to deal with him and she's little more than a child.'

'True.' Madeline felt marginally better and was grateful for her husband's reassurance. She began to read the letter aloud.

> Dear Gertrude,
>   I hope this letter finds you recovered from your fall. We were so sorry to hear that you were indisposed but thankful it wasn't worse. Knowing how many good friends and devoted young men you have around you, we assume you were well cared for . . .

Oscar smiled. 'Very cleverly put, Madeline. Very diplomatic. You have a way with words, my dear.'

'I'm glad you approve.'

> Meanwhile we have had several difficulties here
> which needed my attention. Sarah's husband left prison
> and came in search of her. It seems she has moved
> house several times in the hope of avoiding him, but
> presumably he was told by her original neighbours that
> she worked here. Bert Gravely was most unpleasant,
> almost violent, and we shall have to seek help from the
> police if he appears again. As you can imagine, the
> excitement had a serious effect on poor Oscar whose
> nerves were affected and whose general health has dete-
> riorated.

He glanced up in some alarm. 'You make me sound very decrepit, Madeline. Am I really in such poor shape? What has the doctor said to you that I don't know about?'

'Only that the worry is undermining your health and I must take care to keep you calm. Not easy in this house at present!' She laughed ruefully. 'Then I ended the letter as cheerfully as I could.'

> Louise is enjoying her art and she shows promise.
> She is always eager to go to her lessons and Mr Grant
> seems very kind and encouraging.
> The Ladies' Group are running the usual summer
> fair on the 20th and I am busy crocheting collars while
> Louise makes the inevitable lavender bags to sell. Pray
> for fine weather for us, Gertrude. Do write again and
> assure us you are on the mend.
> We all send our love,
> Madeline

Oscar nodded his approval. 'Very well done, dear. I have no alterations to suggest.'

'Then I shall write a fair copy.'

As the clock struck noon the following day, Louise and Agatha settled themselves on the park seat and Middy was released from his lead with instructions from Louise that he shouldn't venture too far or fight with any other dogs. For a while he apparently took this to heart and sat close to Louise's feet, but after a while he wandered off.

'He'll be good,' said Louise with unwarranted confidence.

Agatha moved a little closer to her friend. 'So . . .' she prompted. 'Tell me how you and Stanley are getting on. He seems awfully keen on you, Louise. Albert says he talks about you all the time. You must tell me all about it because I told you about me and Albert.'

Louise sighed. 'He is very keen on me. I know that. He keeps hinting about the things we can do in the future.'

'Things you can do? Like what exactly?' Agatha's eyes widened.

'Travel and suchlike.'

'Travel?' She groaned theatrically. 'I thought you meant . . . I thought *he* meant . . . in a *romantic* way. You know.' She rolled her eyes.

Louise looked at her in surprise. 'What? You don't mean . . . in bed?'

'That sort of thing but, of course, I don't mean that exactly. At least . . . You haven't, have you?'

'Certainly not! I didn't mean that so don't look quite so hopeful. I meant he asks how many children I'd like to have and where I'd like us to live, but he has never asked me to marry him. Not outright, like a proposal. I think he's hoping I'll understand what he means and give *him* a clue as to how strongly I feel for him.'

'And how do you feel, Louise? Will you marry him? You must surely love him a little bit. He is rather sweet, isn't he? And Albert says he would make a most devoted husband.'

'What on earth does Albert know about it?' Louise glanced round briefly, but there was no sign of Middy. She sighed. 'I don't think I could marry him. I do like him, Aggie, and if I wanted to marry a young man I might be tempted, but I think I prefer older men.'

Agatha sat back, astonished. '*Old* men?'

'Not *old*. Silly! Older. There's a big difference.'

'How much older?'

'About fifteen years older. An older man has lived, Agatha. He has experience of the world. He's . . . he's got more personality and understands things.'

The ensuing silence was broken by Louise rushing off after Middy who had reappeared suddenly and was racing towards a family who were seated on the grass some distance away. A mother, father and twin baby boys who were at the crawling stage.

'Middy! Middy! Come back here at once!' She caught up with him, grabbed him by the collar, led him back to the seat and gave him a smack. 'Now sit there and behave yourself,' she told him. 'Bad boy! Very bad boy!'

His ears went down and he threw his mistress a pleading look.

Agatha said, 'Oh, the poor thing. He didn't do anything naughty.'

'He was going to,' Louise told her loftily. 'Last time he saw that family he stole a knitted rabbit and chewed one of the ears off. I apologized and offered to buy something else for the baby, but they were quite unpleasant. They said his grandmother had knitted the rabbit for him. You see how they glare at me?'

'But how did poor Middy know it was wrong? He chases real rabbits and nobody grumbles at him.'

'He doesn't chew their ears off!' Louise was mortified. 'They said I should control him properly. They hate me.'

To prove her point, the family now collected up their belongings, picked up the babies and pointedly moved further away. 'You see what I mean. Dogs can be very embarrassing.'

'Rather like children.' Agatha grinned. 'When I was still very young we went to tea with my rather grand maiden aunt and I crawled underneath the table. When I wanted to try and stand up I pulled the edge of the table cloth and half the crockery and an iced cake fell off!'

Louise chuckled. 'Did she tell your mother to learn to control you?'

'I don't know and I don't want to know! The moral of the story is, avoid rather grand maiden aunts.'

Middy's disgrace was forgotten and the girls reverted to their former, and favourite, topic.

Agatha said, 'But, Louise, if you had a gentleman friend who was thirty five or more we couldn't go out as a foursome. Albert would hate it. He wouldn't know what to say to a middle-aged man. He likes it, now, just the four of us. Why do you have to be so difficult?'

Louise shrugged. 'I can't help falling in love with an older man. I can't fall in love just to please you and . . .'

Agatha twisted further on the seat to stare at Louise. 'You don't mean . . . You're not saying . . . You've actually fallen in love with someone else?'

Louise abruptly abandoned her intended secrecy because the need to talk about it was overpowering. 'I'll only tell you if you swear on your mother's grave never to tell a soul.'

'My mother's not dead.'

'Well, do it anyway.'

Middy whined and Louise gave him a biscuit. 'It's Mr Grant who teaches me art.'

'Mr Grant? Oh, don't be so silly, Louise. You said the other day he was *fatherly*!'

'I did not!'

'You did, Louise. You said he reminded you of your father – if you'd ever known him, that is.'

'Of course I knew him,' Louise snapped. 'Maybe not for long, but I did know him. Even if I don't remember him, I did know him.'

Agatha held up a hand. 'I get the point, Louise. Don't go on about it. So one minute he's fatherly and now you're in love with him? It doesn't sound quite right.'

'Well, it *is* right. And he likes me too.'

'Albert *loves* me. It's different.'

'He likes me a great deal.' Louise stared at her shoes, refusing to meet Agatha's gaze, disliking her friend more each minute for not relishing the news.

Middy spotted a squirrel and, twisting free, dashed off after it, barking furiously.

As if recognizing the danger she was in, Agatha said quickly, 'So does he love *you*?'

Louise hesitated. 'Of course he does, but he . . . I don't think he realizes it yet. He keeps saying how like Mama I am and asking me things about our family and Roland and Papa. He's desperately interested in me.'

Louise frowned. She was torn between the truth and the desire to impress Agatha. 'I can tell what's in his mind. It's the difference in our ages. He thinks it's a problem but it isn't. Not for me. And he's been married before and it ended unhappily.' She smiled. 'Poor lamb! He's afraid he'll be hurt again if he falls in love with me.'

'And when will you tell him? When will you put him out of his misery?'

Louise shrugged. 'I don't know yet. Mama and Papa will probably disapprove and say I'm too young for him. I don't want to say anything yet so I'm keeping it to myself – the fact that I love him . . . except for telling you. And you mustn't breathe a word to Albert or Stanley. You promised.'

'But aren't you going to tell Stanley that you don't love him? Is it fair not to?'

These were exactly the questions Louise had dreaded and she scowled. 'I don't want to hurt Stanley unnecessarily,' she explained. 'There's plenty of time. He shouldn't have fallen so completely for me, Aggie. It's exactly the sort of thing younger men do. Older men are wiser. They take their time and wait to be sure of their feelings. I think Daniel Grant is waiting for a sign from me.'

'Suppose he isn't. Suppose you've misread the situation.'

'I haven't.' She tossed her head. 'I shall make him admit his feelings. If he doesn't quite understand . . .' She straightened her back. 'I can make him love me, Agatha. I know I can. He must be very lonely. He must want to have a woman in his life. It's only natural.' Seeing that Agatha was still not reconciled to the idea she went on. 'Stanley and I can still be friends so the four of us can go out together as a foursome. We can still all be friends. Unless Stanley should propose and then, of course, I'll tell him my real feelings are elsewhere. I'll tell him.'

Agatha was silent, fiddling with the button on one of her lace gloves, and Louise decided she had offended her friend by her careless dismissal of young men and must make amends. 'You're lucky with Albert,' she said. 'He's young but he's also very wise for his age. Very sensible . . . No, not sensible . . . reliable. That's the word. He's *dependable*. Albert is mature for his age.'

Mollified, Agatha managed a smile. 'I know I am lucky. I do prefer younger men. They are better looking and healthier

76

and much more fun . . . So will you tell me when Mr Grant proposes?'

'Most certainly. And you tell me if Albert makes any of those *romantic* remarks!' She raised her eyebrows and Agatha blushed. Poor silly creature, Louise thought. Heading for marriage with a young, immature man like Albert. She, Louise, would remain friendly with Stanley while it suited her, but when the time came to break the news to him, she would be kindness itself and would convince him that she was not the right woman for him and, if she became his wife, would only make him miserable. For a while she was silent, imagining this romantic episode. Yes, she would be very kind to him and would ensure that they remained dear friends for the rest of their lives.

Saturday, the 20th of August – the day of the summer fair – arrived at last and, as predicted, the weather was fine with the obligatory sunshine and a gentle breeze. The fair was held as always in the large garden which belonged to Sir Leonard Brockwith and his wife Ernestine, who was the Ladies Charity Group patron and major benefactress. Her husband had once been a diplomat in India and had retired with a very generous pension which, added to Ernestine's inherited money, amounted to a very enviable sum.

As two o'clock drew near, Ernestine fluttered anxiously between the various stalls and gave an encouraging word to any who needed it. There was a cake stall, a bottled goods stall, a plant stall, a second-hand toy stall and a bric-a-brac stall. 'Nothing as humble as jumble' was Ernestine's catchphrase. Madeline was running the tombola, Louise was selling raffle tickets and Agatha was 'waiting tables' in the refreshment marquee, resplendent in a white cap and apron.

Since everything had been donated, the proceeds of the summer fair were always very gratifying and this year would be no exception.

'Mrs Swain!' cried Ernestine. 'Is everything satisfactory here? Have they given you enough change?' She beamed at Madeline who was sticking the last of the numbers on to the prizes. 'Always a popular game, tombola. I think secretly everyone enjoys a gamble. Very naughty but we all love a little flutter.' She checked the arranged prizes to see that her own lavish basket of fruit was in a suitably central position. Madeline had given it pride of place which obviously pleased her.

'Harmless fun,' Madeline agreed.

'I was admiring the crocheted collars on the handicrafts stall. Apparently they are yours. Very nice, Mrs Swain. Very neat work.'

'Thank you, Lady Brockwith. I hear our customers are already queuing at the gate.'

'Oh, they are. And the weather has been kind. Now I must have a word with Miss Livingstone about the children's fancy dress competition. Do excuse me.'

She hurried away as the clock struck two. Time to open the gates. Madeline braced herself. She enjoyed the fair, but was always exhausted at the end of the day.

Children came at a rush, hands outstretched, feeling lucky.

'Here's threepence, miss. I'll have three tickets.'

'I'll have one, please.'

'I'm going for the basket of fruit. There's grapes in that.'

Madeline hoped no one would win it so early on. It made a handsome table centre and would bring in the money. Once the best prizes had gone the interest would fall away.

Louise passed the stall and Madeline thought how happy she looked. As always it brought a lump to her throat to see her daughter in a happy frame of mind. Perhaps at last she was over the childish tantrums and the mood swings from joy to deep gloom. I wish you could see her, Roland, she thought. He would have been delighted to see his little girl, and the way she was struggling into adulthood. Already Madeline could see what a pleasant companion she would be and what a splendid wife she would make one day. How on earth had she ever thought a boy would be ideal? Not that she didn't still hanker after a son, but it was too late. If only Oscar had been able to give her a child . . . but that was now water under the bridge. She had promised herself never to dwell on that side of her marriage. He hadn't wanted or needed her that way, neither had he wanted any children of his own.

When the flow of visitors eager for a tombola ticket dried

up momentarily, Madeline took a look round the garden which was now thronged with people in their summer best, all determined to enjoy the occasion. Children wandered by with toffee apples, men doffed their straw boaters to passing ladies, women chattered in groups, exchanging gossip and admiring each other's clothes.

Suddenly a familiar figure emerged from the surrounding people and she caught her breath. It was Daniel Grant. He was hurrying towards her, glancing nervously around him and she was struck not only by his manner but by his expression.

'Mr Grant!' she exclaimed as he arrived at the stall. 'Is everything all right? You look troubled.' She hoped her own feelings were not written for all to see on her face. 'You must buy a tombola ticket.'

'What? A tombola . . . Oh! Yes. With pleasure.' He fished in his jacket pocket and held out sixpence.

As Madeline tore off the tickets, he said, 'I must talk to you alone. It's really quite important . . .'

'Alone? Oh, no! I don't see how we could . . .'

'It really is important. I don't want Louise to know about it. Could we perhaps . . .?'

A large woman in a black straw hat appeared at his elbow and said, 'Three, please.'

For a moment Madeline stared at her, her mind reeling, unable to take in what the woman was saying. He wanted to talk about something Louise mustn't know about?

'Three! Tickets!' The woman waved an impatient hand in front of Madeline's face.

With a hasty apology, she accepted the coins and handed over the tickets. Lowering her voice, she turned back to Daniel. 'What on earth has happened? It's not Louise's progress, is it? She thought she was doing quite well.'

The woman unfolded the first ticket and said, 'Twenty-three!' and searched the prizes for a matching number. 'There we are!' she cried in triumph, seizing a bottle of bath crystals. 'I'm always lucky, I am. My mother used to say I was born under a lucky star.' She laughed unfolding the second ticket.

Madeline wished her to the ends of the earth, but she kept a smile fixed on her face. 'Well done!'

79

'Seventy-eight. Now let me see . . .'

Madeline and Daniel waited while she hunted among the prizes.

The woman shrugged. 'Not that time. Well, here goes again . . . Fourteen! Now that sounds a bit lucky to me . . .' She snatched up a jar of honey. 'Fourteen. I win again.' She laughed, flushed with her success. 'I must go and tell my daughter.'

As she bustled away Madeline repeated, 'It's not Louise, is it?' She failed to see what else could be upsetting him.

'In a way . . . Look, I may be partly to blame for this but . . . I think Louise is getting rather too fond of me.'

'She likes you, I know. Isn't that a good thing?'

'Like, yes. But . . . I fear she's getting *too* fond of me. A little too . . . familiar, if you'll pardon the word.' He glanced round anxiously. 'She frequently compares me to your first husband, drawing favourable comparisons.'

'Is that all? Oh, you had me worried for a moment.' Madeline drew a relieved breath. 'Poor Mr Grant! I'm sure there's nothing for you to worry about . Louise is inclined to romanticize everything, but there's no harm in it.'

He appeared unconvinced. 'Are you sure? I would hate anything to . . .'

A lad of ten or eleven held out threepence. 'It ought to be a penny each or four for threepence,' he declared. 'Then there's more incentive for people to spend more. That's what my father says and he's an accounts manager for the railway company. He knows everything there is to know about money. He's a financial wizard, if you know what that means.'

Distracted, Madeline tried to hide her surprise. She said, 'Well, that may be true, but I'm afraid this tombola is three tickets for threepence.'

The boy adjusted his spectacles while he thought about it, his face creased with a fierce frown. He had an earnest expression – he was probably the school swot. Madeline wavered. Never having had a son, she had a weakness for small boys and this lad was no exception. Bright but odd. She wondered how like his father he was, then, not for the first time, wondered what sort of son Roland would have given her. Unbidden, she recalled the few photographs she had seen of

Roland as a boy. Tousle-haired with large eyes and a shy expression. A sweet-faced youth of sixteen when they had first met. She was fifteen when her straw hat blew away while she was watching the tennis in the park. She had given it up for lost, but Roland had rushed after it.

The boy was still trying. 'Suppose I say I'll spend twopence if your sell me two tickets, but I'll spend threepence if you give me four.'

With an effort Madeline returned to the present and regarded her young challenger thoughtfully. Beneath the grown up manner she sensed vulnerability. His way through life would not be easy, she concluded. But how could she give him a discount? He would boast about it to his friends, if he had any, and then she would be in trouble.

Slowly she shook her head. 'I'm sorry,' she said.

'Then what about six tickets for fivepence?'

Daniel muttered, 'Heavens preserve us!'

A woman hurried up. 'Oh, dear! He's not arguing for a special price, is he? Take no notice. I blame his father. He encourages him in all this nonsense.'

'It's not nonsense, Mama.'

She rolled her eyes at Madeline. 'He's going to drive his wife mad one day.' She turned to him. 'Now do you want tickets or don't you, Donald? They're a penny each.'

He fixed Madeline with a stern look and said, 'One, please.'

He unfolded number sixty-six and won a marcasite brooch in the shape of a lizard. Madeline groaned inwardly. He was probably hoping for the jar of sweets or the iced cake. She hoped he wasn't going to argue for a refund. He held out his hand for it, then to her surprise turned with a beaming smile and presented it to his mother. 'You have it, Mama. It will look nice on your velvet jacket.'

Madeline watched them go. As she turned back to Daniel Grant, two young men approached. They were Albert and Stanley and Madeline introduced them.

To her dismay the two seemed less than pleased to meet him, mumbled their excuses and hurried away in search of Agatha and Louise.

'Well, they didn't spend much,' Madeline joked. 'The dark haired one is Louise's first admirer!'

81

Daniel said, 'I should have realized. I should have seen it coming, but she is so like you. I've brought this on myself . . .'

'Mr Grant!' an excited voice called.

His face fell as Louise herself came hurrying up to them. 'You came after all! You said you wouldn't. You said you had another engagement.' She grinned. 'But it doesn't matter. You're here. I want you to meet Agatha. She's dying to meet you.' She turned to Madeline. 'Have you sold many tickets, Mama? I have – and I shall sell some more to Mr Grant.' She turned to him. 'You will buy some raffle tickets, won't you? The money's for a very good cause. You might win a weekend at a very smart hotel in Brighton.'

He looked trapped, Madeline thought, but fished obediently in his pocket for some change. When the transaction was over, Louise said, 'Do come and meet my friend Agatha. It won't take a moment.'

Madeline said, 'Stanley and Albert came looking for you, Louise. Why don't you go and find them and then later . . .'

Louise flashed her a steely glance 'Because I want Mr Grant to meet Agatha *now*. We won't be long.' She began to walk away, turned and paused, waiting for him to follow, her growing impatience obvious.

He hesitated and shrugged. To Madeline he said, 'I shall have to give in gracefully!'

Madeline watched them go, aware of a small knot of unease within her, but a small queue was forming for tombola tickets and she put the matter out of her mind.

'So you see, Oscar, I really wasn't paying too much attention.' It was Monday morning and the postman had brought a disturbing letter. 'It wasn't a good time for him to try and talk to me and people kept interrupting and then Louise came up to us and whisked him away. I didn't see him again. I suppose he went home.'

'And now this!' He held up the letter and she nodded.

Oscar sighed. 'We mustn't get this out of proportion, dear. Read it again.'

Madeline obeyed.

82

My dear Mr and Mrs Swain,

I regret to inform you that a family matter has arisen recently which requires my personal attention so that I am forced to cancel my lessons for the next two weeks. When I more fully understand the nature of the crisis I shall write again. My apologies for this unexpected interruption to your daughter's tuition, but it is unavoidable.

Yours faithfully,

Daniel Grant

'I simply don't believe this,' she told him, her voice high with agitation. 'Why didn't he tell me when we met on Saturday? Why make such a mystery about it? This is all to do with Louise. I'm sure of it. On Saturday he seemed to be suggesting that she had . . . had become too fond of him and was trying to turn him into some kind of father figure.'

'A middle-aged artist?'

'That's what Roland would have been by now if he'd lived.'

'Ah! I see. But she's never given *us* any hint of such a notion, has she?'

'Not to my recollection.' Madeline was feeling increasingly guilty. She remembered some of Daniel's words that she could not repeat to Oscar. He had hinted that, because of his attraction to her, he had paid Louise more attention than was suitable. How could she tell Oscar that? Madeline blamed herself and the idea that she might have been unwittingly responsible for Louise's situation made her hot and then cold. She also held Daniel partly to blame and angry words formed in her mind with which to accuse him. Only he was not available. He had removed himself from the arena.

The only person who was not to blame was Louise, but she was the one who was going to be most hurt by it. Madeline's mind raced and she felt dizzy with the mixture of fear and guilt which filled her. She was also deceiving Oscar by not telling him the whole story, but to do so would hurt him immeasurably. She was caught in a trap of her own making, she thought unhappily, and cursed her stupidity.

Oscar patted her hand. 'Don't look so worried, dear. We can sort it out . . . And Louise hasn't seen the letter yet?'

'I dared not show her. She was sulking all day yesterday because Mr Grant left the fair early and because he didn't make any effort to make friends with Agatha or the two boys. When I tried to cheer her up she flounced off with Middy and stayed out way past tea time and then refused to eat anything at all saying she has quite lost her appetite.'

He raised his eyebrows. 'And she hated the whole world?'

Madeline smiled faintly. 'Not in so many words, Oscar, but yes. Poor Louise.'

'Did she hate Mr Grant also?'

Madeline shrugged. 'She was still sunk in gloom this morning so I didn't mention the letter. I wanted to talk to you first. You know how she is.'

'Will she believe his excuse?'

'I wish I knew . . . And what happens at the end of the two weeks? Will he ever continue the lessons?' Her eyes widened as another thought struck her. 'And what will Gertrude have to say? She won't be at all happy.'

Oscar frowned. 'I think poor Mr Grant is trying to create a cooling down period. Perhaps he is right. Louise will be disappointed, but she has young Stanley and this might give them a chance to get to know one another better.' He gave Madeline what was meant to be a reassuring look. 'Let's take it one day at a time, my dear. Mention the letter quite casually as if it is of no great significance and see how she reacts. She might surprise us.'

Madeline looked up hopefully. 'You think we are panicking unnecessarily? Oh, Oscar, I do hope you're right!'

Soon after three Louise came down from her room, unhappiness etched into every line of her face. She threw herself into an armchair and picked up Middy. She hugged him so tightly he whined and wriggled to be free and she finally pushed him down. 'Silly dog!' Madeline steeled herself for the moment she dreaded.

'Some not very good news,' she said tentatively. 'We had

a note from Mr Grant this morning. He has some kind of family problem and has to cancel your lessons for a . . .'

Louise sat up abruptly. 'What? Cancelled my lessons? Oh, no! He can't do that, can he? Grandmama has paid for them in advance. How could he . . .?'

'He can, Louise, and he has. It is only temporary. Aren't you at all concerned for him? It must be something serious. Maybe a relative is sick – or has died.'

'But if he cancels the lessons . . .' She glared at Madeline. 'Nothing could be that bad!' Her eyes filled with tears. 'He's doing it on purpose to . . . to upset me! I know he is. What a mean, petty thing to do.'

'Louise, dear, what are you talking about? He has no doubt cancelled his other lessons. He may have to go away. You really mustn't assume that he means it personally.'

Louise dabbed furiously at her eyes. 'But he does. That's just the point. He doesn't want to see me.' She glared furiously at Madeline. 'You forget, I know him better than you do, Mama. I've spent more time with him than you have and I know how his mind works.' She swallowed hard. 'Oh, what a selfish pig! I expected better of him and that's the truth.' For a moment she struggled with her tears but finally regained control.

Madeline watched her, fearing to say the wrong thing. The truth was that she could now see the reason for the letter. Daniel Grant had encouraged her to like him and Louise had imagined something more to his attentions than kindness. This could be very difficult, she realized with a sinking heart.

She said, 'Why don't you spend the time painting and sketching so that when you go back . . .'

'Did he say how long for? The lessons, I mean? When do they start again?'

'Only two weeks, but I daresay it depends on . . .' She faltered to a stop as Louise's expression grew cold.

'Then I won't go back. I'll cancel *all* the lessons. That will teach him to . . . to ruin my career. We'll find another artist. I'll write to Grandmama at once and tell her.' A faint colour had returned to her face and now her eyes shone with anger. 'Just because he didn't like my friends and they didn't like him.' She put a hand to her heart and took a deep breath.

'Agatha said he was too old and Stanley said he looked boring.'

'Too old? How can he be too old? He could be sixty and still an excellent teacher. You said he was the same age as your father would have been and you liked that.'

Louise's lips tightened ominously. 'I don't expect you to understand,' she snapped. 'You never do. Nor does Papa!'

Madeline's patience was wearing thin. She loved her daughter dearly, but there were times when she wanted to shake her. 'I think you're overreacting, dear,' she said firmly. 'Two weeks will soon pass and you could prepare some work for your folder to show Mr Grant when the lessons resume. When you have calmed down you'll see that this is nothing to get upset about. Write a short note to him saying you hope his problems are soon over and you look forward to . . .'

Louise glared at her, her face reddening. 'Don't tell me what to do, Mama. I'm not a child. I *shan't* write to him. I shall ignore him totally. As if I care! I have better things to do with my time than sit around painting and sketching. Agatha is as free as a bird. She doesn't have to try and improve. Because *she* doesn't have any talent!' She jumped to her feet. 'And Stanley has no right to criticize Mr Grant. If you must know, *he* is as dull as ditchwater. I'm going out.'

She rushed out of the room, along the passage and out of the front door. It banged behind her. Madeline sighed. Knowing her daughter as well as she did, this was the reaction she had expected. She looked down at Middy whose ears had gone down guiltily.

'It's not your fault, Middy!' she told him.

He whined unhappily and wagged his tail uncertainly.

Madeline bent to stroke him. 'Poor little Middy. Are we both out of favour, do you think?' she said. 'Never mind. Come into the kitchen and I'll find you a biscuit.' Then at least one of us will feel a little happier, she thought.

Six

L ouise returned several hours later with a pale, grim face. 'He's not there!' she declared, before Madeline could speak. 'The landlady answered the door and asked if I was Miss Legrand and said he's left a message that he would be in touch when he returns.' Her voice shook slightly.

Madeline's heart thumped uncomfortably. Louise had gone to Daniel Grant's lodgings. What on earth would she have said if he *had* been there? 'Well, that is what he told us in his letter,' she said mildly.

'I don't believe he's gone anywhere. That stupid letter was a . . . an excuse. He's avoiding me.' She bit her lip.

Madeline took a deep breath. 'Why should he do that, Louise? You haven't quarrelled, have you?'

Louise stared straight into her eyes as the seconds ticked by. At last she took a deep breath. 'You might as well know, Mama. I'm in love with him. I know you and Papa will try and tell me I'm too young, but I know how I feel.' She sat down heavily. 'I told him because I thought it would make him happy but it didn't.'

'Oh, Louise! My dearest girl.' Madeline's heart ached for her. 'Maybe he doesn't feel the same about you. You wouldn't like him to . . . to pretend, would you?'

'Certainly not! But he does love me, Mama. He does! I can tell. He's afraid to admit it. I thought if I could see into his eyes as I said it . . .' Her eyes were dark with misery. 'He's just a coward!'

Madeline's throat was dry with nervousness. She realized how delicately she must tread if she was not to alienate her daughter further and make matters worse. She must pick her words with tremendous care. 'But there is no hurry, Louise, is there? Another year or so. If you still love him then you can talk to him again. If he truly does love you . . .'

'I keep telling you that he does!'

'Then he may think he will ruin your life if he admits his feelings at this stage. He may realize that when you are forty he will be . . .'

Louise's eyes flashed dangerously. 'Don't try telling me that! He'll be nearly sixty, but what difference will that make? Papa is much older than you, but nobody warned you against him.'

'But that was different. I wasn't eighteen! I was old enough to know what . . .' She stopped abruptly.

'Old enough to know what you wanted! That's what you were going to say! Well, I *am* old enough. Anyway, by the time I'm forty we'll have a home and a family and no one will notice the difference in our ages. I want to marry him, Mama. I *do*! I shall never, *never* love anyone else. If we can't be married I shall live a lonely life . . . and so will he. Oh, Mama. I want to make him happy. I want to give him some children before he gets too old to enjoy them.'

'Louise!' She tried to breathe but her throat was tight. 'Look dear, not all men want a family.'

Louise's face crumpled and Madeline wanted to cry with her. Why was love so difficult to deal with and, at times, so hard to bear?

Louise whispered, 'O-oh, Daniel! *Daniel!*' She burst into tears and Madeline moved to put her arms round her, only to be pushed violently away. 'Stay away from me! You don't love me or you would understand. You'd offer to talk to him.' This idea put a stop to the tears as she seized hopefully at the prospect of a possible solution. 'You could persuade him, Mama. If you write to him and point out how mature I am for my age. He'd believe you.' She swallowed and stared hopefully at her mother.

'I don't know, Louise . . . Maybe you should wait a while . . . I will have to talk to Oscar and see what he says.'

Fresh tears gathered in Louise's eyes. 'I *knew* you would say that. You always hide behind Papa.'

Unhappily, Madeline watched her daughter struggle with her dilemma. Poor Louise wanted to be angry with her parents, but she knew that she needed them to convince Daniel Grant of the rightness of their love. Madeline's own feelings began to intrude. Had she misjudged Daniel Grant? Had he overstepped the mark where Louise was concerned? Had he encouraged her in any way or had her daughter imagined it all? Was he simply a man who flirted with women? He had flirted with *her* she recalled guiltily, and she had been flattered. How easy it would be for Louise to feel the same way – and misinterpret it.

Louise was staring at her hopefully. 'Will you talk to Papa for me? Will you ask him to . . . to give his blessing?'

'Please Louise, don't set your heart on this. More than anything Oscar and I want your happiness, but if Mr Grant doesn't want to remarry nothing we can say to him will change his mind.'

Madeline regarded her daughter despairingly. Louise was a very young eighteen, but she would never recognize the fact. She was hopelessly in love and that, in Louise's view, changed everything about the world and everyone in it.

Middy ventured out of his basket, padded over to his mistress and whined for some attention. When it failed to materialize, he sat down on Louise's feet and prepared to wait.

Abruptly Louise's new found hope seemed to fade and she began to sob silently.

'Don't cry, dearest,' Madeline begged. 'This may seem terrible at the moment, but things have a way of working out. Be patient and try to think of Mr Grant's feelings. He may feel that he's encouraged you, or taken advantage of your youth. A quiet talk when he comes back . . .'

Louise sniffed then blew her nose. 'He's there. I know he is. I looked up and his window was open.'

'Probably the landlady is airing the room. You mustn't jump to conclusions.'

Louise gave her a defiant look. 'Once he leaned right over me, pretending to see my painting better. Once he pushed back a lock of hair from my forehead. If he isn't in love with me, Mama, he wouldn't do things like that. He was trying to let me know that he loves me. Wouldn't it be rather improper otherwise? Either he loves me or he is behaving improperly.' Her expression hardened. 'If he didn't do those things from love then . . . then we should call in the police and have him arrested.'

'Louise! What are you saying? He isn't just your teacher. He knows you as a friend. He knows us as a family. I'm sure he didn't mean . . .' She faltered.

Stunned by Louise's interpretation of these innocent gestures, Madeline tried to reason with her angry daughter. 'I'm sure they were simply friendly gestures. . . I mean, perhaps you are reading more into them.' She passed a trembling hand over her forehead as she recognized the depth of Louise's hurt. She felt she had been rejected and wanted to hit back. But accusing him of improper behaviour? 'As for the police – really Louise. I know you're upset, but we both surely know that Mr Grant intended nothing untoward. He's a kindly man and he sees you as one of his young pupils. I'm sure he doesn't see you as a grown woman.' Terrified, she saw the situation spiralling out of control. 'I'm glad your father cannot hear you say such things. Mr Grant is not that kind of man. You said yourself he was fatherly. Perhaps he was feeling fatherly. Perhaps he was trying to be like Roland.'

'So . . .!' She tossed her head. 'Roland loved me. Does that mean Mr Grant loves me?'

'But only as a father figure.'

Madeline's panic grew until she felt faint and the first doubt entered her mind. Was it possible that Louise was right and that Daniel Grant *had* fallen in love with her? If so it was entirely unpredictable, but such things could and sometimes did happen. If so, was that good or bad? If by some trick of fate they *were* in love and Louise was prepared to wait for another year, would it prove a wise match? Too late she realized how desperate Daniel had appeared when he tried to speak with her at the summer fair. He had wanted to warn her and probably consult with her as to what to do to avoid a disaster. Madeline tried to recall his exact words. Something about him having given Louise the wrong impression. Yes, that was it. And something about Louise being too familiar with him. If only they could have talked together this might not be happening. Think, Madeline, she urged herself. Say something to diffuse this situation before it is totally out of control.

But Louise was obviously regretting her outburst. The anger was fading from her eyes, leaving her with a look of such deep grief that once more Madeline tried to hold her but was gently repulsed. She said, 'I'm sorry, Mama. I know he isn't a bad man. I didn't mean that about the police, but I know he loves me and if he does then he can't blame me for falling in love with *him*!'

If he does? Was there a doubt, after all, in Louise's mind? The silence lengthened. Madeline said, 'I will talk to your father, Louise. If you will just calm down and be patient while we decide what is best.'

'We should all talk – all four of us,' Louise suggested. 'As soon as Mr Grant returns . . . or dares to show his face.' She sighed deeply and her slim shoulders sagged, wearied by all the emotions. 'I'm sorry I called him a coward. I expect he thinks it's for the best, but he's wrong. I'm not a child. I'm a woman and I don't want to marry a young man and I never will. It is either Mr Grant or nobody, Mama. You only have to give permission for me to marry and . . .'

'He hasn't proposed to you, has he?' Madeline, shocked, stared at her in horror.

'Not exactly. But he will. He must. I'll make him propose!' She stood up, looking tired and unhappy. 'I shall die if he doesn't want to marry me.'

'Don't say such dreadful things, Louise,' cried Madeline. 'You know you don't mean it and it frightens me. It's tempting fate to talk so casually of death.'

Louise shrugged. 'At least that would be an end to it all.' With a defiant glance at her mother, Louise ran from the room and was gone before Madeline could gather her wits together.

To Madeline's surprise, she did not stampede up the stairs but went quietly. For a while Madeline sat stock still, badly shaken by the speed of events. She breathed deeply to calm herself, trying to think of ways to soften the blow when she consulted Oscar. The doctor had warned against worrying him and she knew she mustn't upset him, but she felt unable to deal with the situation without his support. Also he would want to know what was happening.

'Oh, Louise!' she whispered. 'My poor little Louise.'

*   *   *

The following morning, Madeline came back from her shopping with a determined spring in her step. From her basket, she unpacked a bag of sugar, a pound of butter and a box of porridge oats. She had spoken to Oscar the preceding evening and he had taken it better than she had expected. Louise was a normal, excitable young woman, he advised with unexpected perception, and it was normal for her to dramatize her life. He agreed that when Daniel Grant wrote to say he was resuming the lessons, they should invite him to discuss Louise's attachment to him. Madeline had gone to bed feeling relieved and had promised herself she would try to carry on as usual and not let the matter destroy her peace of mind. Perhaps Oscar was right and she had allowed Louise to upset her needlessly. Their daughter, he assured her, was much too sensible to do anything rash, even if she *was* in love – which he doubted. Probably nothing more than an infatuation. Madeline hoped he was right.

She glanced up and smiled as Sarah came in from the backyard where she had been hanging out the washing. 'Did the butcher bring the meat, Sarah?' she asked. 'He was very late last week.'

'He did, madam, but he had no lamb's liver so sent pig's instead. I said I thought you would be happy with that.' She stowed the washing basket in the corner and began to fuss unnecessarily with her hair.

A bad sign, usually, thought Madeline, and braced herself for unwelcome news about Bert.

Sarah turned to face her, her hands clenched together. 'It's about my husband,' she said. 'He's still hanging around, asking questions and suchlike. I saw him yesterday and he . . . he looks terrible, madam.'

'Oh, Sarah! Won't you reconsider . . .?' she began.

'No ! I won't, begging your pardon. I can't face the thought of . . . of sharing a bed with him.'

'What about separate beds,' she suggested. 'If Bert was washed and shaved and fed you might recognize the man you once admired.'

Sarah closed her eyes. 'I'd like to think I could, madam, but if I found I couldn't . . . well, how could I turn him out *then*?' She opened her eyes again. 'If he tidies himself up, gets himself a job and a room and makes an effort without relying on me, I'll think again. But I was wanting to tell you, and I don't want you to take this the wrong way, that I think I should give notice. It's my fault he hangs around here and causes you such grief. I worry all the time in case he comes again and does one of you some mischief. If he was drunk, for instance.'

'Give in your notice?' Madeline made no attempt to hide her dismay. 'Oh, but we couldn't let you go, Sarah. You've been with us for years. What would we do without you? Please think again.'

'Well, you're most kind to say that, madam, but in your heart you must be blaming me for all the trouble.'

'But we came to no harm. Let's leave it for a few weeks while I think it over. I do think what he needs first is a job. That way he can regain some self-respect. I might be able to think of someone who needs a gardener or a handyman. Could he become a window cleaner, do you think? There must be a way, but he's going to need some help.'

Madeline felt she was being less than resourceful in the matter, but the problem between Louise and Daniel Grant was still filling her mind and she had given Bert very little attention.

Sarah said, 'Well, if you insist, madam. We'll give it a while, but I'm not entirely happy about things. Still, beggars can't be choosers! A bit of honest work might do wonders for him. Might set him on the right road again.'

Might even stop him from burgling, thought Madeline, aware how easy it would be for Bert to return to theft in order to survive. Perhaps Ernestine Brockwith could find him some work – but could she lie to Ernestine? If not, she would have to admit that Bert had been to prison and that would almost certainly ruin his chances. What chance did he have with a criminal record? Her earlier good intentions were already being eroded. Still, at least Sarah seemed to be softening towards her husband which was promising. She decided to make some scones for tea. Baking always cheered her.

Ten days later, just as Madeline was beginning to think they were dealing with their problems, bad news arrived from

Paris in the shape of André. The young artist, thin and reedy with straight blond hair that repeatedly fell into his brown eyes, arrived on the doorstep with the precise information which Madeline had been dreading. Gertrude had taken a turn for the worse in the shape of a slight seizure which had dulled her speech and left her unable to walk far. The letter André brought begged her to come to Paris before Gertrude's unhappy situation robbed her of any wish to go on living. This time Oscar reluctantly agreed that Madeline should go, only imploring her not to stay too long and to be back within a week.

'Should I bring Gertrude with me, if she is able to be moved?' Madeline asked. Given a choice, she would prefer to have Gertrude as a guest in Kent than stay with her in Paris.

'It might be for the best,' Oscar agreed with a sigh. 'I doubt at her age, she is going to get much better and I wouldn't wish you to make that journey more than once. I shall be fine with Sarah and Louise.'

Secretly Madeline thought that for Louise, having to care for her father might take her mind off the debacle with Daniel Grant. Since the summer fair, and the letter from Daniel, Louise had definitely languished, mooning about the house, wrapped in self-pity. Without meaning to be unkind, Madeline thought it might do her good to think about someone else for a change.

So the following day Madeline and André set off from Folkestone to Boulogne. The sea was relatively calm, but poor André was seasick and worrying about him distracted Madeline's thoughts from the depth of dark water below the ship. From time to time she imagined just how fragile the vessel was and how easily disaster could strike. She considered underwater wrecks, large rocks, a freak wave and many other horrors that could send them gliding slowly down to the sea bed before help from any quarter could arrive. It was not the thought of drowning that most terrified her, but the idea of being dead and unable to help those she loved.

André spent most of the journey at the ship's rail, throwing up the contents of his stomach and, in spite of her good intentions, Madeline realized there was little she could do to help him. The trip eventually came to an end and as she staggered down the gangway behind an ashen-faced André, she felt a certain pride in the fact that she had done it. She had made the crossing she had dreaded all her life and had lived to tell the tale. It gave her new confidence.

When they finally mounted the narrow stairs of the Parisian flat and entered Gertrude's bedroom, she welcomed them with a sob of delight that made Madeline feel that her efforts had been worthwhile.

'And poor André , too!' she told Gertrude, extracting herself gently from her embrace. 'How I admire him. He knows he will be ill, but he goes ahead. That is real devotion, Gertrude.'

André, having satisfactorily delivered Madeline to her mother-in-law, removed himself to his own home and left the two women together. Gertrude was in a sorry state and deeply depressed, but she brightened as Madeline revealed her plan to take her back to England. They would consult the doctor, Madeline insisted, and also the shipping line. There was obviously provision for invalids who wished to travel, she told Gertrude, and they would explore all the possibilities. For the moment Madeline felt she had done all that was required of her and she settled to sleep on the chaise longue, happy in the mistaken belief that now all would be well.

On the following Monday, back in England, neighbour Dorothy Carter was lying awake with indigestion. She blamed the large portion of steak and kidney pie she had eaten for supper. It was always indigestible when cold, but that was how she liked it best and she frequently ignored her husband when he warned her against taking so much.

'Eyes bigger than your belly!' was her husband's favourite expression. Today, however, he hadn't said a word as she crunched her way through the thick flaky pastry because he was three streets away, visiting his father. John Carter was a widower and lonely with it and it was his birthday so his son had gone round there to help him celebrate and, as usual, would stay overnight. It was a bit of company for the old man and Mrs Carter was quite willing to be left alone. She and her father-in-law had never seen eye-to-eye and they had tacitly agreed many years earlier that the two men would be better off without her there. They liked to talk politics and cricket and walk over to the nearby pub for a couple of pints of best beer.

It was quiet without Adam, but Dorothy didn't mind. She did a little knitting, read her magazine and talked to the cat. Later she would make herself a cup of cocoa and maybe have three biscuits with it instead of two.

Now, however, she sat up in bed and listened with narrowed eyes to the noise that was going on next door. A crash followed by a high-pitched voice. It couldn't be Mrs Swain, she decided, because she had gone over to France leaving her husband and her daughter, Louise, to fend for themselves. Not that Dorothy entirely approved. A girl like that being left to her own devices. Goodness knows what she might get up to!

Was it that awful man Bert, she wondered. Had he come back to plague them? If only Adam was not with his father, he would soon deal with the wretch. But he was out of contact and Dorothy felt she couldn't leave the daughter to deal with such an unpleasant man on her own. She would have to go round and find out what was happening.

'Never a dull moment!' she muttered to herself.

Tutting, she climbed out of bed and wrapped herself in her dressing gown and slid her feet into her slippers. She crossed to the wall adjoining the Swain's house and pressed her ear against it. The walls, she had learned, were thin enough to hear through. Never much, just snippets here and there, but intriguing snippets. Not that she often indulged her little vice because her husband disapproved. Eaves-droppers never hear good of themselves, Adam was fond of telling her. Tonight, however, she heard nothing that would explain the disturbance. Nothing at all, in fact. Straightening up with a sigh, she hurried downstairs and out of the house and, to her alarm, found the Swains' front door wide open. The house lights were on and she ventured a few steps inside.

She called, 'Miss Legrand! Is everything all right?'

There was a moment's silence and then Louise appeared at the top of the stairs. 'Oh, Mrs Carter! I'm so glad to see you. It's Papa! Come in!'

She sounded a little hysterical and Mrs Carter's anxiety grew.

'It's Papa! He's had another attack. Come up, please. I don't know what to do to help him.' Louise was already halfway down the stairs, reaching out for Mrs Carter's hand.

She was in her nightdress and her feet were bare. Her face was white and as she clutched Mrs Carter's wrist, her hand was trembling.

In the bedroom Mr Swain lay on the floor, his lips blue, his body crumpled with pain.

Louise said, 'I've sent for an ambulance and I left the door open but I'm wondering if they got lost. It seems ages ago.' She stared at Mrs Carter, her eyes wide and fearful, her lips trembling, every scrap of colour gone from her cheeks, For all the world like a lost child, thought Mrs Carter, amazed at the change in her. Normally Mrs Swain's daughter was a rather over-confident young woman. Too big for her boots was how Adam described her. Not that they didn't like her, but she was very modern and thought she knew it all. But Dorothy felt the adults should take the blame for that. Not having any children of her own, she and Adam were both inclined to think themselves experts on the subject.

But now all Louise's confidence had vanished and Dorothy felt sorry for her.

'The ambulance will be on its way, dear. Don't you fret yourself.' She knelt carefully beside Mr Swain and said loudly, 'Can you hear me, Mr Swain? You're not to worry. The ambulance is coming and they'll get you into hospital. They'll give you something for the pain, Mr Swain.'

Briefly he opened his eyes and tried to speak, but it was more a grunt of pain than anything intelligible.

Louise hovered beside them, one hand clutching her nightgown. 'Is he going to die? Oh, please God, don't let him die. If only Mama was here!'

She looked, thought Mrs Carter, as though she would faint at any moment. 'You sit down, dear,' she told her. 'I can see to everything until they get here.'

At that moment they heard the clatter of hoofs as the ambulance arrived. Dorothy hurried downstairs and met a young constable coming up.

She turned and brought him into the bedroom and briefly gave him the information he needed for his report. The ambulance men brought up a stretcher and quickly rolled Mr Swain on to it and carefully hoisted the stretcher between them.

Dorothy said, 'Mind how you go with him on those stairs!' and earned herself a scornful glance from one of them.

'Sorry,' she mumbled. No doubt they dealt with cases like this all the time.

They told her which hospital they were taking their patient to and skillfully manoeuvred the invalid down the stairs and out into the ambulance where the horse-driven van waited. When the ambulance had rattled its way into the night, Dorothy went back inside to find Miss Legrand talking to the police constable.

'I thought I heard Papa's bell,' she was saying, 'but then it stopped and I wasn't sure. I was only half awake. Then there was a dull thud. A crash . . . and I ran in and he was curled up on the floor groaning in pain! I think he had dropped the bell and tried to reach down for it and overbalanced and fell on to the floor.'

The poor young woman had wrapped her arms around herself for either warmth or comfort and her teeth were chattering with shock.

'I didn't know what to do. I should have found out how to help him. What to give him. I should have done *something*!' Her voice trembled.

The constable looked up from his notebook. 'Nothing else you could have done, miss, except get help and you did that.' He sounded as if he had used the same phrase many times. 'No sense in blaming yourself.' He closed his notebook and stowed it away in his breast pocket. With a nod to Dorothy, he said, 'That's about it, then, miss. You'd best get back to bed before you catch cold.' Turning to Dorothy, he said, 'Good thing you were on hand to help out. It seems the wife is in Paris.'

The way he said 'Paris' made it sound like a distinct dereliction of duty and Dorothy felt obliged to put him right by explaining that Mrs Swain had a relative there who was also in need of nursing.

'Lordy! That's rotten luck!' He had the decency to look abashed.

Dorothy turned to Louise. 'A warm drink! That's what you need, dear. You get up to bed and I'll bring you up some cocoa and sit with you for a while. You've had a bad shock.'

The policeman took the hint and clattered away down the stairs.

When the front door closed behind him, Louise stood up. 'You're very kind, Mrs Carter. I'm afraid I panicked. I think they thought I was mad.'

'So that's what I heard! I thought that awful man was here again, looking for your housekeeper. But you get back to your bed, dear. I'll pop home, then come back with the cocoa. And don't worry about your father. My uncle had four heart attacks before the fifth one finished him off!'

As she hurried back to her own home she felt thrilled to have been useful. What a lot she would have to tell her husband when he came back.

Visiting hours were not very long, so the following day Louise arrived precisely on time, leaving a note for Sarah to explain the situation. She had walked to the hospital, having too little money of her own and not wishing to trouble the Carters again. She found her father in a vast ward, in a bed beside one of the large windows. She had never been in a hospital before and was awed by the scale of it and depressed by the forty or more sick people who lay or sat up in the neat beds. Some of the patients were hidden by curtains on rails and from behind these she heard anxious voices – some low and quavering, others loud in complaint. It was a ward for men and these came in all shapes and sizes although Louise tried not to look at them directly. Fat, thin, young, old. Some were coughing, others moaning quietly, another rambled deliriously. Nurses in starched uniforms and crisp white head-dresses flitted to and fro on shoes that squeaked on the highly polished floor. Apparently focused on their work, they showed no interest in the visitors and Louise was aware of an atmosphere of quiet efficiency.

As she looked for her father, she noticed that other visitors carried flowers or fruit and that she had brought nothing. She had slept badly and had been too distraught to make any breakfast for herself. The visit was already becoming an ordeal. She forced a bright smile on her face, however, when she caught sight of Oscar sitting propped up in his bed, looking frail and somehow shrunken. An image of him that first day flashed into her mind. She remembered the power of the cold green water as it sucked her feet from beneath her and she recalled her terror. Struggling for air, she took in water as she was swept under. When, by some miracle, she had surfaced, she saw a strange gentleman walking towards her through the water and then he had snatched her from certain death. For her, Oscar had always been a heroic figure and now she was startled to see him so reduced in power and substance. At home in his own bed, he had seemed secure. Here, in this impersonal environment, surrounded by strangers, Oscar seemed horribly vulnerable.

'I forgot the flowers, Papa. I'm so sorry.' She leaned forward to kiss his cheek but immediately drew back. He smelled different, she thought. Perhaps it was the hospital soap – or was it fear?

'My dear little Louise!' His voice was little more than a whisper. 'I'm so sorry that you were frightened last night. If only Madeline had been at home you would have been spared all that worry.'

She sat down gingerly on the bedside chair and wondered what to say. What *did* one talk about to the sick, she wondered. Something bracing? 'You look better already, Papa!' she said. 'I hope the doctors and nurses are looking after you.'

'Oh, they are, Louise. Splendid, all of them. I'm in very good hands.' His own hands clasped and unclasped nervously. 'I want you to promise me that you won't breathe a word of this to your mother. She has enough to worry about with Gertrude and she cannot help me. She will only fret and that isn't necessary.'

Louise felt a sinking feeling in her stomach. She had

assumed that her mother would rush back to take charge of things. The idea of being alone with such a secret appalled her. 'But Papa! She will never forgive me if I keep her in the dark. I know it. I must let her know you are in hospital but . . . I could pretend it is less serious than it is.'

'No, Louise,' Oscar insisted. 'I won't have her troubled by this. And anyway, it *isn't* serious. I am already recovered and may well be discharged tomorrow. I shall certainly be fit and well and *home* by the time Madeline and Gertrude come back.'

He looked at her with growing agitation and Louise remembered that he was not supposed to be upset in any way. Reluctantly she promised to keep his secret – but with a proviso. 'If you are still here in three days' time then I must tell her, Papa. If she comes home and you are not there it will be a most dreadful shock for her.'

'Very well, then, dear. Three days.' The little exchange seemed to have exhausted him and he closed his eyes. With his eyes closed he looked even frailer.

'Papa! Are you in pain? Shall I call a nurse?'

He opened his eyes again. 'I'm in no pain, Louise. They have given me something to help me relax and it has made me sleepy. That's all. But it is so good to see you. You were wonderful last night. So sensible. I was very proud of you. My lovely daughter.' He smiled but almost at once his eyes closed again.

A nurse materialized beside her. 'Miss Legrand? The doctor would like a word with you. Perhaps you should let your stepfather resume his sleep. He insisted that we wake him in time for visiting hour.'

Louise leaned forward to kiss her father. 'Goodbye, Papa. I shall come again tomorrow.'

The nurse said, 'He needs his sleep, Miss Legrand.' She led the way out of the ward and along the corridor into a small room where an elderly man was seated at a large desk.

The nurse said, 'This is Miss Legrand.' To Louise she said, 'Mr Macdonald is our heart specialist.'

He looked up. 'Sit down Miss Legrand. I thought you should know that your stepfather's attack last night was quite severe, but because he reached us so promptly we are hopeful of a recovery. He is in very good hands.' He frowned. 'I had hoped to speak to his wife . . .'

Louise explained her mother's absence.

'Ah! Well, you must tell her we are very hopeful. His general health is good – a strong constitution, as we doctors like to say. He will fight back, Miss Legrand. What he most needs is rest. If you wish to visit, come only once a day, in the morning, for no more than ten minutes. Tomorrow, bring in his pyjamas, soap, flannel etc. We will do the rest.'

'Thank you.'

The nurse had reappeared. 'Mrs Barrett is here to see you, doctor,' she said.

He frowned. 'Barrett? Remind me, please.'

'The son's broken his leg.'

'Ah, yes!'

Louise rose to her feet, repeated her thanks and left. As she made her way out of the hospital she decided that she would find some money somewhere in the house or else borrow some from the Carters. Tomorrow she would buy her father some flowers. Walking home, she wondered whether she had done the right thing in promising to keep her mother in ignorance of his heart attack and decided she would ask the doctor's advice on her next visit. As she arrived back at the house she felt slightly less anxious and went in to the kitchen to give Sarah a progress report on her father's health.

In the small Paris flat, Madeline consulted Gertrude's calendar with a growing sense of desperation.

'Wednesday the seventh of September.' She stared out of the window, across the ancient lichened rooftops and then down on to the tree-lined street below. André had arrived earlier and was chatting with Gertrude and Madeline tried not to feel resentful, but the feeling of exclusion did nothing to soften her general unhappiness. The one thing she had not expected was this overpowering sense of homesickness. It had crept up on her and she was now quite unable to shake it off. She woke up each morning, opened her eyes and was immediately plunged into desperation. Home was where she belonged, where she felt secure, where her small world was under her control – or felt as though it was.

102

Madeline knew Paris was the sort of place that inspired artists from all over the world. She knew from Gertrude that the French food was highly regarded and André had boasted that French wines were superior to any others. She understood that the town was full of art treasures and wonderful architecture and that the Seine was romantic by moonlight. So why had she not ventured out to explore the city? Why did she waste her time thinking of England? She was *homesick*. The word mocked her. She was homesick for her family, for her home, for Hastings and Kent and all things English – particularly the language. The foreign conversations around her when she ventured out to shop made her feel like an alien and she hated the sense of not belonging. Perversely, she could find nothing in France to thrill her and longed quite desperately to be gone.

'Just let me return safely,' she whispered, 'and I will never complain again about my lot. And I shall never leave England again.'

With a heavy heart, she thought about her home, her husband and daughter. How were they managing without her, she wondered uneasily. Had Daniel written about the lessons? Was Oscar as well as could be expected? He would never be able to cope if Louise did anything foolish . . . and what had happened about the unfortunate Bert? There was so much she needed to know.

She returned to her makeshift bed, stripped the pillow and blanket from the chaise longue and stuffed them into the bottom of the already crowded corner cupboard. She had already helped Gertrude to wash and brush her hair. Seeing her mother-in-law in her natural state, without the clothes, the powder and perfume, and with her hair unstyled, Madeline had realized that Gertrude was older than she had claimed. There was no way, now, that Madeline could consider returning to England without her. Gertrude must come and live with them. The problem was how to get her from her flat in Paris to the house in Kent. Madeline had no idea how these things were managed, but she was going to have to find out. That meant contacting the company that ran the ferries to and fro across the Channel. She would talk to André about it. The young man seemed remarkably confident.

Her other problem was money and she was running out of it. There must be a way to transfer money from England . . . or maybe she could borrow from Gertrude and repay her when they reached England. She sighed and ran a hand through her hair. Then there was the sale of the Paris flat. How was that to be achieved? Presumably an estate agent, or the French equivalent, would have someone with a glimmer of English. She had no French whatsoever. Or André might translate for them.

Oh, Oscar, she thought. I need you so much, but I know I have to manage this alone.

At least when they returned home, she would be able to ask Oscar's advice on everything pertaining to the Paris flat. Although it was tiny and reached by all those narrow stairs, someone would presumably buy it. The money would see Gertrude through the rest of her days.

The bedroom door opened and André came out.

'Gertrude,' he said, in his heavily accented English. 'She eez better today, no?'

Madeline smiled. 'I think so, André, yes.' She was lying out of kindness.

He said firmly, 'I 'ope you will not take her to England? She wishes stay here in Paris.'

'I don't know, André. Maybe.'

Madeline hid her confusion. To her, Gertrude had insisted that she would be happy in England with Louise and Madeline – all that remained of her family. Obviously she was telling André a different story. Possibly she wanted to save him from the hurt of believing that he was not important to her. But suppose, instead, she was confiding in André that she really didn't want to leave her home and end her days in England, far away from her friends.

André said, 'I make 'er breakfast, no? Coffee and croissants.'

Croissants? Guiltily she admitted, 'I haven't been shopping yet.'

He beamed. 'I go.'

He darted off on his errand before she could answer and, as she heard him clatter down the stairs, she shook her head in amazement. He was genuinely devoted to Gertrude. Madeline was astonished at the love her mother-in-law

104

inspired in her young admirers. Anton had brought her violets and another young man had brought an egg custard he had made especially for her. 'To tempt the appetite,' he had told Madeline with a shy smile. If Gertrude had all these young men dancing in attendance now, she must have been dazzlingly attractive in her youth. What the French called a *femme fatale*! She tried to imagine what Gertrude had been like as a young woman of Louise's age. Possibly very like Louise, she thought with a wry smile. Was Louise going to break hearts wherever she went?

That question brought all her other worries crowding back into her mind.

While Madeline was dealing with her problems in Paris, back in England Sarah was putting a pie in the oven.

'So how was your father yesterday?' she asked Louise. 'Getting on, is he?'

Louise looked up. She was kneeling on the floor, trying to persuade Middy to roll over – a trick she was teaching him in an attempt to surprise her mother when she returned. Middy was ignoring her efforts and Louise gave an exasperated sigh. 'He wants to please me,' she told Sarah, 'but he doesn't seem to understand. In the dog book it says—'

'He's probably too young, dear. He's still a puppy, isn't he? How does he seem in himself?'

'The vet says he may not be that young. He may be fully grown. We don't know much about him, but the vet . . .'

Sarah tutted. 'Your *father*, Louise! I'm asking you about your father, not the dog. How is Mr Swain doing? Did you see the doctor again?'

'Oh! I'm sorry. Papa's very well, I think. That is, he looks about the same, but it's hard to tell. He needs a lot of rest and sleep so I can't spend much time with him. Only ten minutes. The nurse said yesterday that I should talk to the doctor again today.'

Sarah closed the oven door, and straightened up, frowning. 'I do think you should tell your mother, Louise. If she arrives home and he isn't here . . .' She shrugged.

Louise gave Middy a biscuit. 'Good boy! You tried very hard, didn't you, my precious!' She stood up. 'I keep hoping

105

he'll be well enough to come home and we can tell her then and she won't have to worry. She's so far away . . . and Papa insisted.' She opened the back door and tossed Middy's ball outside and laughed as the little dog streaked after it. 'Oh, by the way, this letter came for you. By hand. I found it on the mat when I came down this morning.'

She fetched it from behind the teapot on the dresser and handed it over.

Sarah took it gingerly. 'I hope it's not from him!' she said.

She sat down and opened the envelope, but didn't take out the folded sheet inside. 'He used to write a lovely letter,' she said. 'When we were courting, that is. Not long letters but . . . nice wording. I kept them all. Tied up with ribbon. I valued them, you see. All the sweet things he said, and writing didn't come easy to him. I hope you get lots of love letters, dear. If you do, you'll know how I felt about them. Sometimes, if we had a bit of a quarrel – and you do when you're married – I'd secretly read them again to remember how much he thought of me. Then I'd feel happier towards him.'

'Why don't you read them now? It might make you . . . able to forgive him.'

Sarah's eyes clouded with regret. 'I burned them all after I knew what he'd become. When the police came . . . You can't imagine anything so dreadful. I hope you never go through anything like that, Louise. That feeling of disappointment . . . all the deceit! It never goes away.'

Louise opened her mouth to reply but changed her mind.

'I threw them into the fire,' Sarah told her, 'and cried my heart out! He wrote to me from prison, but I never read a word of them. Straight into the fire!'

Louise regarded her helplessly. What should she say? Was there anything that she could suggest that would help? Despite her reservations about the man, she felt some sympathy for him. It was a romantic situation and it touched her young heart. She wanted to believe in a happy ending. Bert obviously still loved his wife, but Sarah refused to respond. Rather like Daniel, Louise thought, having still not heard from him. She had slipped several letters through his door, but they had gone unanswered. She had even enquired about him to his landlady.

'He's not here, Miss Legrand,' she'd been told.

'But he is coming back, isn't he?'

'Coming back?'

'Well, he's away, isn't he, on family business?'

'Oh, yes! See what you mean.' She'd given Louise an odd look. 'Yes, he'll be back. He pays his rent in advance.'

Louise had hesitated. 'Is he really away? I mean, he's not just saying that.' Her eyes had strayed upwards to his window which stood open.

'If he says he's away, he's away. Now, excuse me, but I've got work to do!'

Louise had said, 'So he hasn't read my letters yet?'

The landlady had hesitated fatally. 'I couldn't say. Nothing to do with me. I must get on.' And she had closed the door in Louise's face.

Louise sighed with frustration as she remembered. With her mother away and her father in hospital, this was the perfect time for her to meet and talk with Daniel.

She looked at Sarah. 'I'll take Middy for a walk, then you can read your letter in peace.'

When she returned, twenty minutes later, Sarah's eyes were red. At first Sarah said nothing. She was busy cleaning the inside of the kitchen window, but then she glanced up briefly. 'He says he's got a job and he's coming here today and asks me to meet him outside. Wants to take me for a bite to eat.'

'Oh, Sarah! He's got a job! That's wonderful news. That's . . .'

'I shan't be here, Louise, so don't get excited. And don't open the door to him. He'll only pester you with questions and, with you alone in the house, there's no knowing what may happen. With any luck he'll think the house is empty and if I don't turn up, he'll go away again. Best you don't get involved.' She gave the window a final rub with a clean duster.

Louise wondered desperately how to help Bert. How on earth could it hurt for the two of them to talk? If only she and Daniel could talk openly and freely she knew they would come to an understanding.

Sarah glanced at the clock. 'Isn't it time you were off to visit your father?'

Louise looked at the time and gave a scream of panic. She was going to be late! Without another word she snatched up her gloves, pulled on her jacket and rushed from the house.

Seven

Three days later, as Madeline put the front door key in the lock and stepped inside, her pleasure and relief at being home evaporated. She had an immediate and over-whelming sense that something was wrong. Hurrying into the house she was aware of an unfamiliar silence. No sounds, no sign of activity, no smell of cooking.

She hurried back to the cab driver who was waiting to help her with Gertrude. 'One moment, please,' she said and went back into the house. She called out, 'Oscar! Louise! We're home!' but there was no reply. Panic flared. Unless . . . maybe Oscar was asleep. But the dog would have barked . . . unless Louise was walking him in the park.

Don't be silly, she told herself.

No sign of Sarah although the kitchen was neat as a pin. Upstairs she threw open Oscar's bedroom door and found herself staring at an empty, but neatly made bed.

'Oh, my God!' she whispered.

Louise's room was also unnaturally tidy. For a moment she clung to the door handle, her body ice-cold and trembling, then she forced herself to retrace her steps. As if in a trance she stepped out on to the pavement.

The driver said, 'Ready, are we, missus?'

'Er . . . No . . . I mean yes!' She stared at him, trying to collect her thoughts. This couldn't be happening!

He frowned 'Something wrong? You look like you seen a ghost.'

'They've gone!' she said. 'There's nobody here.' She looked up at Gertrude who was waiting impatiently for the long and arduous journey to be at an end. 'They've gone, Gertrude. Oh, God. Something terrible's happened. I know it!'

She swayed and almost fell, but the cab driver caught her in time. 'Now you take it easy, missus,' he advised. 'We'll get the other lady inside and then you'll see what's what. Probably nothing. Probably . . .' He scratched his head unable to think of a reason why a person's family should disappear. 'Well, I dunno.'

Gertrude cried, 'What are you talking about, Madeline? Help me down, for heaven's sake!'

Madeline leaned heavily against the wheel of the cab. 'Oscar must be in the hospital!'

Only half aware of what she was doing, she helped the driver with Gertrude, and between them they carried her into the silent house and sat her in a chair in the sitting room. Madeline paid the driver and he made a hasty exit before he could be drawn into whatever was happening inside the house.

Gertrude wrapped her shawl closer. 'Where is everybody?' she demanded. 'Didn't they know we were coming today?'

Slowly Madeline sat down opposite her. 'That's what I'm saying. There's nobody here. Not even Oscar!'

It was Gertrude's turn to stare. Her mouth dropped open as her eyes widened incredulously. 'Oscar's not here? Oh, Madeline! You don't mean . . .?'

'He must be in the hospital! But why didn't Louise tell me?'

'Maybe it has only just happened. Look, dear, why not make us a pot of tea to settle our nerves and then you can go to the hospital and talk to him?' Gertrude was beginning to feel some of Madeline's apprehension. 'Maybe Louise is with him. Visiting time, perhaps.'

'Then where's Middy?' Still in a daze Madeline walked through into the kitchen and filled the kettle. For the first time she noticed a letter propped on the dresser and snatched it up eagerly. She hurried back to Gertrude. 'A letter!' she said, tearing the envelope open.

'So the mystery is solved!' Gertrude smiled with relief. 'I knew it was nothing to worry about. Is the kettle on?'

Madeline nodded and unfolded the letter. 'It's from Sarah,' she said, puzzled. She began to read aloud.

Dear Mrs Swain,

    I call in each day to see if you are back. Nothing
else to do here since Louise went off – I don't know
where . . .

Gertrude cried, 'Went off? What does she mean?'

Madeline sat down again, her thoughts in a whirl. 'Louise
has . . . Oh, God! Where has she gone? Gertrude!' Her
voice rose. 'Went off? *Since Louise went off?* I can't believe
this.'

'Read on, dear. She might explain.'

    She left no message, but left the dog behind. I have
Middy with me until you return . . .

The two women stared fearfully at each other.

Madeline said, 'Louise went without Middy? But . . .
Louise was devoted to the dog. It doesn't make any sense.'

Gertrude said, 'Does she mention Oscar?'

'Oh, yes, let me see.'

    . . . until you return, whenever that will be. Poor Mr
Swain was taken ill again . . .

'Oh, no!' Madeline turned to Gertrude. 'He's had another
attack! I must go to him.'

    He's in the hospital where Louise says he is making
good progress. He begged her not to tell you because
he knew you would worry, you being so far away and
in a foreign country.
    Bert found a job and I have taken your advice and
will give him one more chance. I hope your mother-
in-law is better and that you had a safe journey home.
    Yours obediently,
    Sarah Gravely

Madeline stood up. 'Good progress. That's something.'
Her first instinct was to hurry round to the hospital but she
had Gertrude to think about and her missing daughter.

111

Hesitating, she reminded herself that Oscar was in good hands. Her daughter was heaven knows where! 'Oh, Gertrude, what is Louise up to? I should never have left them. I should have known something would happen the moment I turned my back.'

'Why don't you talk to that friend of hers? Agatha. She might know more. Girls confide in their friends.'

Madeline let out a long breath. 'Yes, yes! I could do that. Maybe she's staying with them. Perhaps with Oscar in the hospital she was lonely or nervous and . . . Yes, that's probably what's happened.' She placed a hand over her heart, weak with relief at having found a possible explanation that was not alarming in any way. 'I'll make you some tea while you settle in and then I'll go straight round to the hospital.' She brightened. 'It may be that I'll find Louise there. She wouldn't miss visiting times. She's so very fond of Oscar.'

She left the room with a lighter step and returned a few moments later with a tray of tea and a plate of biscuits. 'So typical of Oscar not to want to worry me. I certainly *would* have worried if I'd known he was ill enough to be in hospital. Poor man. He'll be longing to come home. He detests hospitals. He finds it difficult to sleep with all the toing and froing that goes on.' She glanced surreptitiously at the clock. She was anxious to talk with Oscar but would give Gertrude five more minutes before she deserted her.

Gertrude sipped her tea thankfully. 'Well, Madeline, here we are, safe and sound. What do you think now about sea travel? Are you reconciled to the idea?'

'No! A loud "No", Gertrude!' Madeline's laugh was a little shaky, but she was recovering from her fright and glad for the not-so-subtle change of subject. 'I never want to cross the Channel again. I never want to go abroad again. Does that answer your question?'

They both laughed.

Gertrude said, 'Sarah will be glad to get back to work. But fancy her relenting over Bert! From what you say she was so adamant that she would never even speak to him again. I thought her very hard-hearted. Men are silly creatures at the best of times and . . .'

'Gertrude!' Madeline felt bound to protest. 'How can you

say that? Look at Anton and André and the others – all falling over themselves to help you. They aren't at all silly.'

Gertrude shrugged in the way that Madeline always considered Gallic. 'Men are the weaker sex. I've known that for a long time . . .' She frowned. 'Mmm. These biscuits are a little stale.'

Ten minutes later, with Madeline's help, Gertrude had managed to climb the stairs and was comfortably ensconced in the spare room, snuggling down between the sheets and looking forward to a long sleep. The journey had been tiring for her, Madeline reflected, regarding her fondly, but she had not complained once and on occasions had helped Madeline to deal with whatever problem had confronted them.

'You sleep, Gertrude,' she told her. 'I'll do a bit of shopping on my way back from the hospital. A bit of stewing beef, perhaps. I'll make a nice stew with dumplings. We all need something comforting to help us recover from the last twenty-four hours.' As she hesitated at the door, she said, 'Shall I leave a note for Louise? Asking her not to wake you?'

'No, dear. I'll be pleased to see her. I can always sleep tonight.'

The nurse at the reception desk had a queue of people waiting for her attention and Madeline decided not to wait. She would find the men's ward and talk to the ward sister. If the doctor was available she would have a word with him also. She asked for directions and made her way up the stairs and along several corridors. She guessed it was visiting time by the number of people going in the same direction. She pushed open the door and saw that the room was larger than she had expected. In the middle of the room there was a large desk where the Sister sat, poring over a pile of files, presumably updating them. There was a subdued murmur of voices as the visitors made conversation with the patients.

A young nurse bustled forward. 'Can I help?' she asked. 'Who is it you are here to see?'

'Mr Oscar Swain. I've been abroad and only just returned so I'm . . .'

'Oscar Swain?' She frowned. 'Are you sure you're in the right ward?'

113

'He had a heart attack. I thought this was the ward where
. . .' She was searching the beds for a sign of Louise and
Oscar without success.

The nurse said, 'I've been off sick for a few weeks so I'm
not entirely familiar with all the patients. I'll ask Sister. Just
a moment.'

She bent over the desk and spoke to the Sister who looked
up. She glanced at Madeline and then rose to her feet, looking
slightly agitated. The nurse hurried away leaving Madeline
with the Sister.

'Mrs Swain? The doctor has been wanting to talk with
you. He wanted to pass on a message to your daughter, but
she stopped visiting. We didn't know how to reach her. If
you would come with me, please.' She turned away and led
Madeline from the room. Madeline felt slightly uneasy. If
Oscar wasn't in this ward then he must be in a private ward
and that meant he was worse than she expected. She said,
'I don't understand why my daughter should stop visiting.'

She was shown into a small room where she was introduced to a small elderly man.

Mr Macdonald said, 'Do sit down, Mrs Swain. I understand you've been abroad.'

Madeline nodded. 'I didn't see my husband in the ward.
Is he worse? Was it a bad attack?'

He swallowed and for a moment fiddled with papers on
the desk. When he looked up Madeline had a flash of unwelcome intuition.

'I'm afraid you must brace yourself for bad news, Mrs
Swain. Very bad news. Your . . .'

'Oh, no!' She half rose from the chair.

'I'm sorry to tell you that in spite of all we did for him,
Mr Swain died yesterday. He had a third attack. Very severe.
We did everything we could.'

At that moment a nurse appeared with a cup of tea and
put in on the desk in front of Madeline. She stared at it uncom-
prehendingly as her mind grappled with the doctor's words.

'He . . . he *died*? Oh, no! I mean I . . . Oh, Oscar!'

Mr Macdonald nodded. 'I'm so very sorry, Mrs Swain.
We wanted to tell your daughter, but we didn't see her again.
There was no one we could notify. We've been very worried.'

Struggling with the shock of Oscar's death, Madeline also registered the fact that Louise had stopped visiting. 'So my daughter doesn't know . . . about her father's death?'

'I'm afraid not.' He lowered his voice respectfully. 'Your husband's body is in our mortuary. The death certificate is ready. All that remains is for you to identify him and to make arrangements with an undertaker . . . Mrs Swain, do please take a few sips of your tea. A warm sweet drink is very helpful at times of crisis.'

Times of crisis! *Oscar was dead and Louise had disappeared.* Crisis seemed too small a word. Madeline stared down at the tea in disbelief. How could all this have come about, she wondered helplessly. One moment she was returning in triumph with Gertrude, expecting a family reunion, the next she was plunged into the midst of tragedy and doubt. And where was Louise? Why had she stopped visiting?

Mr McDonald leaned forward. 'I'll find someone to help you sort out the paperwork, Mrs Swain. But now you must please excuse me. We are somewhat short of staff today and I'm needed in three places at once.' He stood up and held out his hand.

Madeline shook it distractedly. She said, 'But what has happened to my daughter?'

He shook his head. 'I wish I could be more help, but that is a family matter, Mrs Swain. It's possible that she left a message with your husband, not expecting him to die. But if your daughter has . . . disappeared for some other reason, that would be a matter for the police. They will help you.'

Seeing her eyes widen he added hastily, 'But I'm sure you will discover there is a much simpler explanation. Disappearances are rarely as bad as they seem at first and you have had a great shock today. Sit here and drink your tea and I will send Mrs Douglas up to see you. She is very experienced in these times of family tragedy.'

Obediently Madeline picked up the cup and saucer and held it to her trembling lips. Her mind was refusing to function properly and she felt very cold. All she could think about was Oscar lying somewhere within the bowels of the hospital, covered, no doubt, with a white sheet. Had they performed a post-mortem? Had he been cut open and sewn up again? The thought appalled her and she shuddered. She would never again see her husband alive, breathing, speaking, smiling . . .

'Oscar, *my love*!' she whispered. At least she would see him one more time – it would be a comfort to whisper a last goodbye.

The door opened and a small plump woman entered, carrying a new looking file.

'Mrs Swain? I'm Mrs Douglas. I'm here to help you through the maze of forms that always accompany a death. I won't ask you to fill them in, but will ask you questions and fill them in for you.' She gave her a look of encouragement.

Madeline said, 'I'd like to see my husband alone first. Is that possible? I'd like to . . . to say goodbye in private.'

'I'm sure we can allow that later.'

Allow it? Allow it? Madeline felt an unexpected anger fill her. Why, because Oscar was dead, should someone else decide whether or not she should see him? She glared at Mrs Douglas, but common sense told her that she was not to blame for the rules and regulations.

'Your husband's name and date of birth, please, Mrs Swain.'

Madeline answered automatically. She was trying to imagine herself in the police station describing Louise and declaring that she was missing. Lost. How could she have mislaid her daughter? It was ridiculous. There was no way Louise was 'missing'. Madeline decided that the moment she had finished with Mrs Douglas's forms and she had seen Oscar, she would set about finding her daughter. She would go to see Agatha. Her daughter's closest friend would probably know where she was. Yes. of course she would.

Mrs Douglas said, 'May I have your full address, please.'

Madeline gave it and the woman began to fill in the form in agonizingly careful writing, dotting 'i's and crossing 't's. Numb with shock and grief, Madeline found the process slightly hypnotic.

Mrs Douglas looked up at last. 'And which undertaker will be organizing the funeral?'

Madeline shrugged. At the back of her mind she was aware of a growing certainty which she didn't want to acknowledge.

'I can give you the names of three undertakers who regularly deal with deaths from this hospital . . .'

Was Louise's absence anything to do with Daniel Grant? There! She had thought the unthinkable. She nodded.

'So here is the death certificate. You will need that for the undertakers.'

Madeline took the paper, folded it and put it into her purse.

'They will help you with such things as flowers, the service, the invitations . . .' The voice droned on.

Suppose Louise was not with Agatha? Suppose she *was* with Daniel Grant? Could she, Madeline, just walk in and demand her return? She grew hot at the very idea. Oh, Oscar! How can I get through this without you?

'The body will be held at the funeral home unless you wish otherwise,' Mrs Douglas said gently. 'Some people prefer to keep the body of the deceased at their house, to be collected on the day of the funeral by the undertaker.'

Madeline was becoming irritated by the woman's determined cheerfulness. She stood up. 'I have to find my daughter,' she announced and without another word walked out of the room and out of the hospital. Oscar is dead, she thought. His funeral can wait. He would want me to find our daughter.

Agatha's mother opened the door. She brightened when she saw who it was, but something in Madeline's expression alerted her to the fact that all was not well. Without a word she held open the door and Madeline went into the comfortable sitting room and sat down without waiting for an invitation. It was not that she lacked manners, but the fact that she could barely stand on her trembling legs.

'What's the matter, Mrs Swain? You look quite pale.'

'Is Agatha here? I'd like to speak with her.'

'I'm afraid not. She's out with Albert.'

Briefly Madeline explained that while she had been abroad,

looking after a sick relative, Louise had apparently disappeared.

'Disappeared?' Mrs Phillips stared at her open mouthed. 'Good Lord! Run away, do you mean? Something of that sort?'

'Not exactly, but she isn't at home and my housekeeper hasn't seen her for days. And . . . And I've had some dreadful news. About my husband. He's dead. He had another heart attack and went into hospital and then had a third attack.' Fresh tears filled her eyes.

'Mr Swain's dead! Oh, you poor soul!' Her eyes widened. 'Everything's happening at once! You must be desperately worried! But do you think it's the shock of her father dying that's upset your daughter? If my Lawrence was to die, Agatha would be beside herself.'

'I don't think she knows. She stopped visiting him.' Madeline struggled to regain her breath. Her chest felt tight and a headache was threatening. She said, 'I thought perhaps she was staying with you. That maybe she had turned to you for help.'

Mrs Phillips shook her head. 'I'm afraid not. Agatha did say she went to the house a few times and found nobody there. Poor Mr Swain. You must let us know when the funeral will be held. We'd like to pay our last respects.'

'Of course I will. Do you perhaps know when Agatha last saw Louise? Does Agatha know anything about Louise's whereabouts? I have to find her.'

'Well, of course you do! If it were Agatha I'd be beside myself with worry. But you've already had such a shock! You poor thing. What about a small brandy? It's good for shock.'

Madeline gave no answer, but the well-intentioned woman poured her a small glass of brandy.

'Thank you.' Madeline sipped it half-heartedly.

Mrs Phillips watched her anxiously. 'I do hope she's come to no harm. You hear such terrible things. And poor Mr Swain. Agatha was very fond of him.' She shrugged. 'If there's anything we can do . . .'

'Thank you. I think . . . I have to go.' She handed back the remains of the brandy. Standing up, she moved like a sleepwalker to the front door.

By the time Mrs Phillips had risen from her chair and followed her to the front door, Madeline had opened the front door and was walking away without a goodbye.

'Well! Whoever would have thought it?' Mrs Phillips muttered to no one in particular. 'Mind you, that Louise was always a bit on the wild side.'

She remembered Louise, aged about ten, climbing up into a tree because a boy at school had dared her to do it. When she was about twenty feet from the ground she froze, giddy and sick. Afraid to go up or down. They had had to fetch the school caretaker who produced a ladder and brought her down, white-faced and shivering. A mention of the rescue appeared briefly in the local newspaper and Agatha had been green with envy.

A very difficult girl, Mrs Phillips thought. Willful. That's the word for Louise.

Thank heavens, she thought, that Agatha was more down-to-earth. She had her feet on the ground and Albert was also sensible. He would make a most suitable husband. She had no worries on that score. As she watched Mrs Swain make her way unsteadily along the road, she pitied her.

Madeline was exhausted, mentally and physically. She gave up the idea of finding Louise and somehow managed to get home. Closing the door behind her, she realized she had forgotten to do any shopping and wondered what she and Gertrude would have to eat for their supper. She crept upstairs and satisfied herself that Gertrude was still sleeping. Then she went into Oscar's room and threw herself on to the bed. She buried her face in his pillow and sobbed. Half an hour later she was still there when she heard the front door open. She sat up. Her heart was beating in her chest and hope flared instantly. Louise was home! She stumbled to the door and called, 'Louise! Is that you?'

Sarah answered. 'Oh! You're home! Heaven be praised!'

Downstairs the two women clutched each other like long lost friends. Sarah had Middy on his lead and the little dog went mad with joy as Madeline bent to pet him. Fresh tears fell as she wondered if Middy would ever see his young mistress again.

119

'Now don't take on so, my dear,' Sarah told her. 'I'm sure she's with friends. You know how she is. I made a big stew and I've brought it round for your supper knowing you'd be too tired after your journey. It's cold but you can heat it up again. Hardly *pot au feu* but . . .'

Madeline explained that she had no idea where Louise was and that Oscar was dead. That brought tears to the house-keeper's eyes and for a while both women were racked with grief and neither could help the other. Then, little by little, the story about Louise emerged.

'She was here one minute and gone the next,' Sarah told her. 'I thought she'd be back so I walked the dog. When she didn't appear I thought it best I took him home with me. By that time, of course, Bert had turned up.'

'Turned up? How do you mean?'

'I did wonder whether he'd scared Louise away. The thing was, I was supposed to meet him here, according to his letter, but I didn't. He sent me a letter, you see, saying he'd got a job. I was still dubious and I decided I wouldn't meet him – but later on I changed my mind. He says he was here waiting when Louise came home.'

'Just the two of them? Oh!' Madeline covered her mouth with her hand, imagining a confrontation.

Sarah went on. 'Bert says Louise was very nice to him at first – remember how she tried to persuade me to give him another chance? She's so soft-hearted, that girl.'

'We all did.' Madeline now regretted meddling.

'But then, when it was obvious I wasn't going to turn up, she asked him to leave and he wouldn't.'

'He refused to leave! My God!'

'Bert says things got a bit heated . . .' Her eyes widened as Madeline's expression changed. 'Oh, no! Nothing like that!' she said quickly. 'He swore on the bible he'd never laid a finger on her. But he was adamant he wasn't leaving until he had spoken to me. So she suddenly runs out of the house, leaving the dog and . . . and never came back.'

Madeline was once again cold with fear, her mind a riot of hateful possibilities. 'I hope you're sure about that,' she stammered. 'That Bert didn't lay a finger on her, because if she isn't here by the morning I'm going to the police and if

Bert was the last person to see her . . . alive . . . He'll have to explain his actions to them.'

The two women stared at each other, each crushed by the awful prospect of police involvement and all that would mean.

Sarah said, 'He wouldn't hurt a hair of her head! So don't you dare go blaming him for this.'

'I'm not blaming anyone . . . yet. That's for the police to decide.'

Sarah was breathing heavily and her face reddened with anger. 'It's more likely to be that Mr Grant, her teacher,' she said spitefully. 'Oh, yes! Louise dropped more than one hint about him. Fancied him. That's what I reckoned. And spending all that time alone with him . . . doing so-called lessons! Pity she ever started those if you want my opinion.'

Her eyes blazed and Madeline had never seen her so angry or so hostile but, of course, Sarah was giving Bert another chance so it was understandable that she was going to defend him. Madeline had spent so long persuading the house-keeper to give her husband a second chance that she could hardly complain now that she had done so. But Sarah herself had said she would never trust him again. Why should Madeline?

She took a deep breath. 'I'm sorry, Sarah! I take back those hasty words about your husband. I'm sure he's not involved. I hope you'll forgive me.'

Sarah's face suddenly crumpled. 'And I'm sorry. It's none of my business, your daughter and her art lessons. I spoke out of turn. It's just that she did go on about him – him being so like her father, so she said. I did think it a bit odd, to tell you the truth.'

Madeline allowed herself to admit that at some uncon-scious level, she had been thinking along the same lines herself although she didn't share the awful possibility with Sarah. Another idea now entered her head. Suppose Louise had run to Daniel for help when Bert refused to leave the house. After all, with her father in hospital, she could hardly have stayed in the house alone with a strange man. But if she *had* turned to Daniel for help, why hadn't he contacted her or Sarah or Oscar to say so? Something must have happened to make that unwise . . . or impossible.

Just then, Gertrude called from upstairs and Madeline swallowed her anger and fear and went up to her. On the way she promised herself that if Daniel was involved in any way with Louise's disappearance, she would not blame Gertrude. Partly because Gertrude had acted in good faith, and in Louise's best interests, in arranging the art lessons. Partly because, at present, Gertrude was the only family she had left and they were going to need each other.

Supper that evening was a subdued affair. Madeline and Gertrude ate the savoury stew gratefully, but although it satisfied their hunger, it did nothing to ease their anxiety and grief. Gertrude had made a promising recovery from the minor stroke. Her words were slightly blurred but understandable so they were able to converse normally. Her mobility was still impaired and she could only move up and down stairs with difficulty. In her own flat, her life would have been difficult for the foreseeable future and she was quite reconciled now to the idea of spending the rest of her days with Madeline. She was particularly pleased that she was able to offer some support and encouragement in the present crisis. They ate their supper in Gertrude's bedroom, but Madeline promised that she would not be 'banished' there, she would come downstairs for part of each day so that she could give her legs some exercise and hopefully regain her strength. She was determined not to become bedridden.

That night, when Madeline had left her feeling as comfortable as possible, she retired to her own bedroom, exhausted and sick at heart. Try as she could to sleep, she stayed wide awake with her thoughts growing blacker as the minutes became hours. She wept for Oscar, prayed for his soul and thought back over the years to all the happy times they had shared. What would he advise, she wondered, if he were alive now. She was sure he would know what to do and his support would reassure her. She had relied on him in so many ways. Without him, she felt lost.

She thought about Bert and Louise and dare not put her fear into words. Fighting off the nightmare scenario that he may have harmed her, she turned her mind to Daniel. If

Louise was with him, she would surely be safe. He would never dream of hurting her, would he? Had they all been deceived by him? First thing tomorrow she would go round to the gallery to see if he was there and if not, to ask after his whereabouts – and whether or not anyone had seen Louise. If she learned nothing she would go to his flat and see if Louise was with him. If they were not there, she could talk to his landlady. She had to have as much information as possible before she went to the police in case they insisted that Louise was old enough to know her own mind and they were reluctant to institute a search. They would no doubt tell her that daughters were always running off and she must wait a while, to see if she returned voluntarily, before they took any action.

But suppose none of these theories was the right one. Suppose something quite unconnected had happened? She might have been run over and in hospital with amnesia. In the morning, if she didn't get news of her daughter, she would enquire in all the hospitals. She might have been kidnapped! Or murdered!

Downstairs, Middy howled and then barked. Poor thing, she thought. He, too, had lost someone he loved and would never understand why. Didn't dogs pine if they lost their owners? She sighed, recalling how she had said, 'No dogs in the bedroom' when Louise had begged for just that. Suddenly she threw back the bedspread and made her way downstairs. When she entered the kitchen Middy hurled himself into her arms and whined softly.

'I know, Middy! I know you miss her. We all do. You can come upstairs with me.' She picked up his basket with her free hand and carried basket and dog up the stairs, careful not to wake Gertrude who was snoring quietly. She put the basket beside the bed and put Middy in it. He lay there obediently for a few minutes, then jumped on to the bed and snuggled down beside her. It was such a comfort to lay her hand across his small warm body so she allowed him to remain, but, although he slept, Madeline remained wide awake.

Louise, where are you, she wondered anxiously, and her sobs broke out again in earnest. For the first time she saw her own future stretching away through the empty years and was filled with self-pity. She had lost Oscar and possibly Louise. Without those she loved her life could never be the same. It could never be worth living.

Eight

As soon as Sarah arrived the next morning, Madeline sent her out with a shopping list. Gertrude had had her breakfast and was settled in bed with her book. Madeline had had very little sleep and when she looked in the mirror she was appalled at what she saw, but, disregarding her appearance, she found a taxicab and set off at once for Daniel Grant's gallery, aware that it was Sunday but hoping to find him there. She had to start somewhere and she felt sure that if he was responsible in any way for Louise's disappearance she would read it in his eyes. If only she could find him.

When they arrived, she asked the taxi driver to wait for her. To her relief Miss Maddock was inside and opened to Madeline's agitated knocking.

'Mrs Swain! I'm afraid we're not officially open. I'm . . .' She faltered as she took in Madeline's reddened eyes, pale face and slightly tousled appearance.

Before she could ask the inevitable question, Madeline spoke. 'I want a word with Mr Grant. Is he going to be in today?'

At once a guarded look came into her eyes. 'I'm not sure,' she said carefully. 'He's been very busy lately and we haven't seen much of him. Can I give him a message?'

They moved inside and Madeline saw that the exhibition had not been changed. Her heart sank. If Daniel was not around then where was he? And was he with Louise?

She said crisply, 'I have to see him . . . before I contact the police. My daughter Louise – I think you may remember her. She is one of his students . . .'

'I remember Louise, yes.' She looked genuinely puzzled. 'You mentioned the police. Is something wrong?'

125

'Yes. Very wrong. My daughter is missing. I have just returned from abroad and I'm looking for her. Trying to trace her movements while I've been out of the country. Has she been into the gallery?'

There was a short silence. Miss Maddock was obviously trying to decide how she should answer. Finally she said, 'No, I haven't seen her.'

'And when did you last see Mr Grant? Is he also missing?'

'I . . . I don't think that's any of your business.'

'On the contrary, it most certainly *is* my business, Miss Maddock! They may be together!'

'Together? Oh, but surely . . . That is . . .'

'Miss Maddock, if you don't answer me, yours will be one of the names I pass on to the police.' Madeline gave her an icy look.

'Oh! . . . I'll just check in the diary.' Miss Maddock tried to hide her fears as she rooted in the top drawer of her desk and produced a diary. 'When did I last see him?' She riffled through the pages, obviously flustered. 'That would have been the seventh. Today's the eleventh so that was four days ago. He was here most of the morning and . . . Well, I did think he seemed very distracted, but I didn't say anything. He didn't say he was going away but he didn't come in the next day and I haven't seen him since. I assumed he was ill – or had been called away suddenly. I have the key so I've just tried to carry on. What exactly . . .?'

Madeline regarded her thoughtfully. She believed her. She didn't look as though she was reciting a prepared speech. 'Thank you. May I ask that, if my daughter *should* come in at any time, you will tell her I'm looking for her and . . . and would like her to get in touch.'

'Certainly. I think that would be all right. Perhaps you'd give me your address.'

Madeline gave it to her and watched her write it in the back of the diary.

A man came into the gallery with a framed picture under his arm.

Miss Maddock said, 'I'm so sorry Mr Warner. We aren't officially open. I'm simply checking that the gallery is all right because . . . because Mr Grant has been away for a few days and hasn't returned. I know he's interested in your painting. Will you call in again next week when we're open?'

'Will he be here?'

'I expect so.'

Madeline slipped out without saying goodbye. Already she was practicing what she would say to the police. She could feel the chances of finding Louise receding into the distance. There was an empty feeling inside her and a growing hopelessness. She had set out earlier determined not to give way to her fears, but it was already becoming difficult not to think the worst.

Before she could break down, she turned and climbed back into the taxi. She gave the driver directions to Daniel's lodgings and fretted while he slowly removed the horse's nosebag and hung it beneath the cab. How, she thought, could she ever have trusted Daniel, let alone feel anything for him? It must be Daniel who held the answer to Louise's disappearance and the answer was going to be unpalatable. Even unbearable!

Number 16, Arnold Avenue was not in the smartest part of town, but nor was it in the seedy area. The house was neat enough and the small front garden consisted of a large pebbled area bordered with dusty primulas. She rang the bell which was answered by a thin woman in a wraparound apron.

'Well?' she demanded, glancing suspiciously from Madeline to the cab behind her.

Madeline began to explain that she was trying to find out what had happened to her missing daughter. At first the woman showed no interest, but suddenly her eyes gleamed. 'You'd better come in,' she said. 'Don't want the neighbours listening to every word!'

As she led the way into a cramped parlour she announced herself as Mrs Wickham. When they were both seated, she said, 'I never should have let him use the studio for his lessons, but he offered to pay me extra so I gave in. Tramp, tramp up the stairs every day, wearing out the carpet. Not worth the hassle, believe you me.'

Madeline said, 'I had to go to Paris to care for a sick relative and when I came back my daughter, Louise, was . . .'

'Louise! Yes, that was her name. Little hussy!' Her expression had changed. 'I'm sorry, but that's what I call it when

127

a young woman comes dashing round in the evening to call on her teacher and is still here in the morning.'

Madeline felt a great faintness sweep over her and clung to the padded arms of the chair she was sitting in. Her worst fears were materializing. 'In the morning?' she echoed faintly.

Folding her arms, Mrs Wickham nodded. 'This is a decent neighbourhood and I made it quite clear when he first took the rooms. No women after hours. I wanted no funny business. The thing is there's a large window in the room that makes it suitable for the artists to work. The light's good, you see. He was so keen to have it and I took a bit of a shine to him at first. He seemed so genuine.' She shook her head. 'So that was your daughter! Well, I never! My heart bleeds for you. I had two daughters of my own and you always dread that sort of thing.'

That sort of thing. Madeline could only nod.

'She came banging on the door, white as a sheet, and saying there was some man in her house and he wouldn't get out. Something to do with her housekeeper. She was almost in tears so I called him down. I must say he didn't seem at all pleased to see her and I reminded him she had to be gone by nine. He understood, all right. As it happened I had promised to sit with the lady next door – ' she jerked her thumb – 'because it was her husband's night out and, her being an invalid, I do sometimes help out.'

Madeline forced herself to sit upright in the chair and pay attention.

She said, 'There was an intruder in our house and my husband was in hospital so Louise was all alone.'

'She did say that. She certainly looked scared, I'll say that, but they went upstairs meek as two lambs. I should have checked what they were up to, but by the time I got back his lights were out so I knew he'd gone to bed and thought no more of it.'

'Mrs Wickham, did he often have young women in his flat after nine o'clock?' She held her breath as she waited for the answer.

'Never. I'll grant him that much. Only during the day when he was giving lessons. Young men, too, of course, but only during the day and they were no trouble. Not noisy. Nothing like that. Anyway, next morning I heard voices and barged right in and there they were. Not in bed or anything, I didn't catch them in bed together, but eating breakfast. *Breakfast!* They looked sort of . . . How can I put it? As if they shared a secret. She looked very flushed but happy. Her eyes were sparkling. He looked nervous. Very subdued, he was.'

'Oh!' Madeline groaned. She put her head in her hand and thanked God that Oscar would never know. When she managed to raise her head, she said, 'Do you have any idea where they are now? Assuming they're together.'

Mrs Wickham was now softening a little. 'I'm afraid I don't,' she said. 'To be frank with you I was so angry I told them both to get out and not come back. I told Mr Grant he should have known better than to compromise a young woman. They both began talking at once, trying to excuse what had happened, but I wasn't having it. I told him he'd got a week's rent left – he paid monthly – but he could forgo that in lieu, if you see what I mean. I was punishing him.' She rolled her eyes. 'Then she started crying, good and proper, and apologizing to him, like it was all her fault.'

Madeline felt her own tears prickling, but blinked them back. She must not get emotional, she reminded herself. No hysterics.

Mrs Wickham went on. 'A bit late for that, I told her. Crying over spilt milk!' She sighed. 'Maybe I was a bit harsh, but I never could abide that sort of behaviour. And what were my neighbours thinking, I wondered. Nothing good! And I've my good name to think about.'

'I think it was an emergency,' Madeline said, more to herself. 'I shall have to report her missing, Mrs Wickham, and I'm afraid the police will probably want to talk to you.'

'The police!' She was shocked. 'I've never had to speak to them so they needn't come bothering me.' She stood up, her mood darkening. 'You'll have to go now. I can't help you. He packed his things and they both went staggering away down the road. Lord only knows where they went. The police can ask until the cows come home, but I can't tell them any more than I've told you. I don't blame you, but daughters can be a handful. You need eyes in the back of your head.'

Madeline found herself back on the pavement. As she headed for the taxicab, Mrs Wickham called after her. 'He has a gallery somewhere in the town. You could maybe try there.'

Madeline didn't even turn round, but she raised a hand by way of a thank you and heard the front door slam. She had run out of options, she thought despairingly. Now she would have to put the matter in the hands of the police.

That evening she brought Gertrude downstairs before she complained about being stuck in her room. Although it was a slow business managing the stairs, Madeline knew that Gertrude felt better for having a change of scenery. It was, she realized, important that Gertrude was not allowed to become an invalid. They sat together at the dining-room table while Middy watched from her favourite place in front of the cold grate.

'It's as if he knows it will one day offer warmth,' Gertrude said.

Somehow, Middy, a link with their missing girl, was closer to their hearts and was being spoiled in various ways. All Madeline's rules about pets had flown out of the window, but she was too unhappy to care.

After they had discussed the unsatisfactory ending to Madeline's day of investigation, she confessed to a deep sense of failure.

Madeline pushed her plate away, the food unfinished. 'I am beginning to have a very bad feeling about this, Gertrude. I know I have to inform the police tomorrow in case . . . in case something has happened.'

Gertrude swallowed a forkful of mashed potato. '*Mais non!*' she exclaimed. 'I feel the opposite. We must *think* good thoughts. Positive thoughts.'

Her words still came slowly, but Madeline thought she noticed a small improvement.

Gertrude continued. 'Soon, I think, she will be back with us. Very sorry for herself and very contrite, but she will be back, Madeline. I feel it here!' She placed a hand over her heart. She eased the last scrap of pork from her chop and ate it with relish.

Madeline watched her with amazement and admiration. How could she be so confident, she wondered, in the midst of so much doubt and anxiety.

'I envy you, Gertrude,' she told her. 'I wish I could believe it will end well, but . . .'

'Believing will make it so! I know. I have been in this world of ours for much longer than you, my dear. You must have faith. Later you must go to church and pray for her.'

She placed her knife and fork together on the empty plate. 'And you should eat more,' she scolded. 'You are going to need all your strength for the coming days.'

Madeline nodded dully. She wished she could rally her defences, but her heart was leaden with grief and shock and even to move through the day required a tremendous effort. She said, 'I have to think about the funeral.'

'There is no need. While you were out I have been doing just that!'

Madeline stared at her.

'I have thought about the service and have thought of two nice hymns, but you can change them if you wish. Did Oscar ever talk about hymns? Do you know what he would like us to sing?'

'No. He never spoke of death.' Although he must have considered it, she thought, wondering why he had never shared such thoughts. Probably didn't want to call attention to the difference in their ages. He was always so considerate. She swallowed hard, blinking back tears. Had she ever really known him? Did anyone really know anyone else? The thought depressed her and she hastily turned her attention to the funeral.

Gertrude said, 'No doubt you will know a local undertaker. I couldn't help you there, but for the flowers – the family wreath, that is – I thought blue and purple irises and white carnations. Unless Oscar had favourite flowers . . .'

'He liked roses.'

Although they had only a small garden, Oscar had liked to dabble with window boxes and plants in pots and when his heart trouble became serious, and he was confined to bed, he missed the gardening. Therapeutic, he had called it. Communing with nature. She had teased him about it.

She said, 'Maybe some white roses instead of the carnations.'

Gertrude nodded. She was watching Madeline surreptitiously. 'Whatever you wish, dear. I'm only trying to help. You have so much on your mind and I have so little to do.'

Madeline said, 'Something terrible has happened to her. I know it.' Her voice strained with the effort of sounding normal. 'If anyone has laid a finger on her, I swear I'll kill whoever it is!'

Gertrude regarded her with alarm. 'Don't talk like that, Madeline! What has got into you? How would killing someone make the situation any better?'

'I'd feel better!'

'You'd be the prime suspect and you'd rot in jail. Would that really make you feel better?'

The silence lengthened. Then Madeline said, 'We'll have to send out cards to all the people who knew him. I'll make a list.'

Gertrude smiled. 'I've started it already, dear. I sat in bed this afternoon and felt so useless. I had to do something.'

'You're wonderful! I don't how I would have coped without you.'

Gertrude fixed agonized eyes on Madeline. 'You don't blame me, do you, Madeline? I know that if it wasn't for me, Louise would never have met Daniel Grant. If all this is my fault . . . I don't know how I could live with it!'

'No, dearest. How could this be your fault? We both thought the lessons were a marvellous idea. Oscar was also thrilled. Oh!' The mention of his name made her swallow hard and briefly she covered her mouth with her hand. 'It has nothing to do with anyone but Louise and Mr Grant and I don't even want to blame them until we have Louise safe at home and hear the full story. Things may not look so bad then. Please don't give it another thought, Gertrude. Now, the list for the invitations.'

When they had finished Madeline sat back with a sigh. 'I must go to the police tomorrow. Do you agree, Gertrude?'

Gertrude nodded. 'I do. The sooner the better. But bear in mind that at any moment she might turn up . . . or the postman might bring a letter from her. But by all means set the ball rolling. If she *has been* . . . if she'd had any kind of accident, the police will find out. They'll have access to information from all the hospitals. We really mustn't expect the worst, Madeline. It is so negative.' She frowned. 'If she has run off with Mr Grant, which looks possible, she will quickly come to her senses and get in touch. She won't want us to worry. We must be patient.'

Madeline nodded, afraid to speak because, to her great dismay, she felt her fear giving way to a deep anger. If Daniel had hurt her beautiful daughter . . . it could not have been Burt . . . she would make sure they suffered the torments of hell for their sins. For the first time she thought about the worst possibilities. Had Louise been abducted? Murdered? Raped and left to die somewhere? How, she wondered bitterly, could Gertrude remain so positive? Or was it just a front?

She helped her mother-in-law back to bed, then went downstairs and slipped on Middy's lead. She instantly remembered her meeting with Daniel when Middy fought with the black poodle. It seemed so long ago that meeting in the park. She decided to take Middy to the park as usual, refusing to be cowed by events. As they walked she retraced that morning in her mind, searching for possible clues to what would happen later. Was there any way she might have foreseen what that meeting would lead to?

She had been so impressed by Daniel then. Almost attracted to him. No, she corrected herself. She had been *very* attracted to him. It had been a fairly mild flirtation, but at the time she had been excited by the knowledge that she was still attractive to other men. Was that so dreadful? she asked herself. Could she have guessed that a few compliments would have led to this day? How could she have known then that it would end so disastrously?

'Think sensibly, Madeline,' she told herself sharply. 'No one could have expected Louise to fall in love with a man old enough to be her father.'

It was dusk when they reached the park and she took off Middy's lead. If Daniel was to suddenly materialize in front of her, she felt she would scratch his eyes out. She now knew that Daniel, and not Bert, had been the last man to see Louise

133

before she disappeared. The police would have to be told. They would have to know everything.

She arrived at the police station just after ten o'clock the next morning and asked to see a senior police officer. She had waited for the postman in the hope that Louise had written to her, but he had brought nothing but a monthly bill from the grocer.

A police sergeant named Boxley showed her into a scruffy office. There was small window, but it was closed. The air was full of stale pipe smoke and the three narrow shelves groaned under the weight of dozens of files in cardboard folders. The sergeant whistled tunelessly under his breath as he moved a pile of folders from a chair.

They both sat down and Madeline began her account of Louise's disappearance. He made notes, frowning as she spoke, and twice interrupted her account while he sharpened his pencil stub. Madeline was not reassured by his appearance. He was a large red-faced man, with a uniform that was one size too small. He continually ran his finger round the inside of his tunic collar and seemed to be sweating. When she finally stammered to a close he laid down the pen and rubbed his nose.

'Sounds like an affair of the heart, doesn't it?' He stared at the fingernails on his left hand. 'Young girl infatuated with an older man. Happens all the time!'

'But not exactly like this, surely. Not in the same circumstances. Surely you treat these cases seriously, Sergeant Boxley?' Already her confidence in him was badly dented. 'My daughter is only eighteen, just a child really, and if she has been led astray by this man . . .'

'Of course we treat them seriously, Mrs Swain, but from the landlady's account it doesn't sound as if she was dragged off against her will.' He regarded her wearily. 'When they were turfed out by the landlady she could have run home or gone to a neighbour for help. But no! She went off with him, carrying some of his luggage, as cool as a cucumber. Doesn't sound as if she was coerced, does it? This should reassure you.'

Madeline considered his words. 'Then why hasn't she been in touch? She would surely want to know how her stepfather

134

was. She doesn't know he's dead. She was very fond of him. It doesn't sound at all like her.'

He raised his heavy shoulders in a cumbersome shrug. 'She might know. Might have been in touch with the hospital. Would they think to tell you if she had. She may know about his death. It may have upset her even more. She might be feeling hysterical, not to say grief-stricken, and this man might be helping her through it. Who knows?'

'I . . . I don't know.' *Was it possible?* 'Maybe I should contact the hospital again.'

'Now don't go rushing round to the hospital, Mrs Swain. That's our job now. You've put the matter in our hands. It's called routine enquiries and we're rather good at them.' He rubbed his nose again, then searched his pockets fruitlessly for a handkerchief and sniffed instead. 'What sort of girl is she? Quiet? Sensible? Trusting? Or a bit on the wild side?'

Madeline hesitated. 'Trusting, not always sensible and she is sometimes unpredictable. A bit headstrong at times but her heart's in the right place. But she'd want to be at the funeral, I know, but how can I let her know where and when?'

The idea of Louise already knowing about Oscar's death had never occurred to her. She was ashamed to think that she had misjudged Sergeant Boxley.

He said, 'Why not put a note of the death in the obituary column of the local *Gazette*? She might see it, especially if she was wondering but afraid to ask the hospital. Make sure to put the time and place of the funeral. It might tempt her out of the shadows, so to speak.'

'I will. And thank you for the suggestion.'

'We'll speak again with everyone concerned. You'd be surprised what people remember when faced with a dark blue uniform. I'll send one of my constables to talk with your neighbours, too. Don't you worry, Mrs Swain. I doubt if your daughter is being held against her will. I also doubt if they have gone far. We shall have to find out if he has any relatives where they might go . . . and we'll check our books and see if either of the men has a criminal record.'

Madeline felt her face flush. 'Oh! I wasn't going to tell you. Bert Gravely has been in prison. I wasn't going to mention it because he's done his time and been punished

135

and I thought he deserved a fresh start. Maybe that was naïve of me. Am I in trouble?'

'It was naive but it doesn't matter. You didn't actually *lie* to the police. It was a sin of omission but could hardly be regarded as wasting police time or misleading us or interfering with our enquiries.'

'Oh, dear! I didn't think. I'm truly sorry, Sergeant. I didn't mean to make your job any more difficult than it is.'

He stood up. 'Don't give it another thought, Mrs Swain. We'll be in touch whenever we have any news. And if anything else happens we should know about, pop in and tell us.'

Murmuring her thanks, Madeline fled the station and hurried away with mixed feelings. She was annoyed with herself for her stupidity, but she was also slightly more positive than before the interview. Sergeant Boxley did seem to know what he was doing. Seeing Louise at the funeral was a distinct possibility. She made her way back to Gertrude with a heart that was, if not exactly happy, measurably more hopeful.

Three days later, true to his promise, Sergeant Boxley called in to give them an update on the investigation. Just a quick visit, he warned her. He had a meeting with senior officers in half an hour which concerned a murder – a young man, he added hastily before she could ask. Without bothering to sit down or even accept the offer of a cup of tea and a biscuit, he flipped open his notebook and began to read.

'Grant . . . let's see now . . . Yes. You'll be glad to hear that Grant has no previous convictions whatsoever.' He glanced up. 'So I don't think your daughter is in any danger from that direction. Make your mind easy on that score.'

Madeline, her hands clasped nervously, nodded and he continued.

'Carter . . . your next door neighbour . . . no previous convictions, but that's no surprise. Mrs Carter heard the argument before she heard your daughter run out of the house. She caught some of the words. Says the walls are very thin! Said she heard your daughter say, "You have to go," and "You can't stay here." Also something to the effect that his wife wasn't coming to meet him and she insisted that he leave the house. He didn't leave. They were shouting and then she heard the front door go and ran to the window, thinking it was him leaving but saw Louise and went to the front door and called her, but she didn't turn round.'

Madeline could imagine Louise's fear when she realized that Bert refused to leave.

The sergeant said, 'The question is, why did she let him in? He could have waited outside.'

Madeline shrugged. 'She is very soft-hearted. She always felt that his wife should give him a second chance. I expect she was trying to help him.'

'Most unwise, but, then, you can't tell youngsters anything. I've got a lad of my own about the same age. Knows it all!' He flipped on through the pages, whistling tunelessly as he did so. 'Ah! Here we are! Our Miss Maddock at the gallery. A little more forthcoming. Seems she'd suspected that your daughter was attracted to Grant. Says she could read it in her face whenever the two of them were together. Seems your daughter was in the habit of popping into the gallery with her dog.' He raised his eyebrows. 'Did you know that?'

Madeline's lips tightened unhappily. 'She told us she walked the dog in the park.'

He shrugged. 'Maddock says that Grant sometimes spoke about her mother – that's you – and seemed to like the family and was once invited to Sunday lunch.' He turned a page and turned it back. 'Doesn't seem to have mentioned your husband.'

Madeline went hot and cold. This sergeant was very shrewd. She stammered, 'He hardly knew my husband because he is bedridden. I told you about his heart condition.'

'Ah, yes! And he has since passed on. Of course. That explains that. Was there anything between you and Grant, Mrs Swain? I do need to know everything.'

'Nothing! Nothing at all! Except . . . he did pay me a compliment when we first met, but as soon as he knew I was married . . . that was the end of it.'

'No secret meetings?' He turned over more pages before she could answer. 'Now we come to Agatha Phillips. Phillips says . . . Let me see now . . . Yes. She understood you had met in the park on one occasion.'

Madeline was horrified at the direction the conversation was going. 'We did meet accidentally. He was coming to Sunday lunch and Louise and Gertrude, my first mother-in-law, were making *pot au feu* for lunch and I was banished from the kitchen and took the dog for a walk. Middy got himself into a fight and Mr Grant appeared and separated the dogs. It was quite accidental, I can assure you.'

'Why was he in the park?'

'He'd come early and had time to kill.' Even to her own ears it sounded weak. But that was what had happened, she reminded herself. The meeting *had* been accidental.

'So your daughter accepted that. She wasn't jealous?'

'Jealous of what?'

'If she was already in love with him . . .'

'This was early on. She hardly knew him!' She was sounding flustered and hoped he didn't notice her confusion. 'We thought we should meet him since we were going to entrust Louise to him for the lessons.'

He held up a hand. 'I'm just wondering if Louise thought he was getting fond of you and saw you as a threat. Might have accounted for her rash behaviour. We have to look at everything in detail, Mrs Swain. We have to consider every possibility.' He smiled.

She said, 'We all liked him. We were all . . . fooled by him.'

'Fooled?' He gave her a quizzical look. 'He sounds a decent man. Maybe he was put in such a position by your daughter . . . that he had no choice but to allow her to stay the night. And maybe it was all perfectly innocent.' He shrugged. 'Or started that way. Who knows? In my line of work you come across all sorts of situations. People are not machines, Mrs Swain. We men are strange creatures. Most kindly men can be moved by a woman in distress. Especially an attractive young woman who is in love with him!' He flicked through more pages. 'I spoke to the landlady – now where is that? Ah, yes.' He studied his notes, frowned, glanced round, found a nearby chair and sat down. 'It's taking a bit longer than I expected,' he explained. 'I'm going to be late

138

for my meeting, but it won't be the first time or the last!' He read from the notebook. 'Mrs Swain, the landlady told me that she heard your daughter and Grant arguing and that she crept up the stairs to listen. According to her, Grant said, "You can't sleep here!" Several times it was said. He said he would take her home and make sure the house was empty. She replied that if he wouldn't let her stay it meant he didn't love her and if that were the case . . . she would rather die!'

'Oh, God!' Madeline felt a wave of faintness.

The sergeant watched her closely. 'Does that sound the sort of thing your daughter might say in those circumstances or is the landlady lying for some reason that escapes me?'

Madeline felt as though she had been struck a physical blow. It did sound like Louise in one of her more hysterical moments. She fought back a desire to deny it, but then shook her head. It sounded as though Daniel had tried to be sensible and Louise had made it impossible. If so, she had caused him to lose his lodgings. She covered her face with her hands and the sergeant waited.

At last she looked up. 'It does, Sergeant. Louise was very young for her age in many ways which is why we would never have given her permission to marry until she was twenty-one. She knew that was how we felt.'

'You do see where this is leading, Mrs Swain.' His voice was gentler now. 'If your daughter wanted to marry him and was suddenly presented with an opportunity to do just that, she may have taken it in the full knowledge of what it entailed. Mr Grant may be guilty of nothing more than a weakness. Faced with her tears he gave in. He took the risk and they have been thrown together by the landlady's ultimatum.'

'If only I hadn't gone to Paris! I should have been here!' Madeline cried in anguish.

'Or if your husband hadn't been in hospital.' He leaned forward. 'Things happen, Mrs Swain. Usually, in my experience, it is a series of unfortunate accidents which, taken one at a time, are perfectly innocent. Put them together and . . . chaos. Disaster! Call it what you will. No point in blaming. It's happened.'

'So what happens now? Will you still look for her?'

139

He shrugged. 'My men have been alerted, but it's no longer a question of possible foul play. We won't be hunting down Grant, if that's what you're wondering. Your daughter, it seems, is alive and well and with the man she loves. The rest is up to her. She'll get in touch. They always do.' He stood up. 'If you hear anything at all from her or from him, you must let us know at once.'

'So . . . we just wait?'

'I'm afraid so.'

As soon as he had gone Madeline went upstairs to tell Gertrude but found her sleeping. Returning downstairs, she made a cup of tea and sipped it slowly. She felt sick and empty. The police sergeant's words had shaken her. Gone was the idea that she had clung to – that Louise would somehow be miraculously returned to her and that life would return to something like normality. She had a growing conviction that that was not going to happen. She had lost Oscar and now she had lost Louise. But at least Louise was alive.

Write to me, Louise, she prayed. Write and tell me you are safe and well and happy. I forgive you for everything! Write to me or to Gertrude. Say you still love us, as much as we love you! She closed her eyes and Roland's bright image came unbidden to her. 'Oh, Roland! What can I say? I don't know how or where I went wrong but our lovely daughter has ruined her life. Can you find it in your heart to forgive me?'

Nine

Oscar's funeral was due to start at half past two the following Monday. Agatha arrived early at the church feeling distinctly nervous. She had wanted Albert to accompany her, but he was at work, unable to ask for a day off to attend a funeral for a non-relative. She stood in the church entrance at quarter past two, unwilling to go in alone in case Louise's mother was there. Peeping into the church, which was bright with sunlight and sweet with the smell of fresh flowers and lavender polish, she found it empty of people except for an elderly lady who was apparently practicing the hymns for the coming service.

'Oh, Mr Swain!' She stared at the coffin. Highly polished and with antique handles it added to her disquiet, resting majestically upon the trestle and surmounted by a wreath of blue and white flowers. 'I'm so sorry.'

She bent her head and crossed herself, feeling horribly like an intruder. From the room on her left she could hear someone moving about and assumed it was the vicar, putting on his robes. Hastily she glanced around, wondering where to sit so that she would not be noticed. Behind one of the columns, she thought. That way she need not speak with Mrs Swain until after the service. Tiptoeing out of the church she drew a deep breath and headed for three large Cyprus trees which would offer her some concealment.

The letter was weighing on her mind. She patted her pocket to make sure she still had it with her. To lose it would be rather disastrous, she reflected. It had come that morning from Louise and the contents had thrown her into a flurry of apprehension. A letter from Louise! A secret, *private* letter. That was how Louise had described it. Agatha felt burdened by the knowledge that she had ignored her best friend's frantic plea – that she show the letter to no one! Agatha, however, had strong memories of her recent talk with Sergeant Boxley. Any new information must be placed at his disposal. That's what he had said and she had seen by the look in his eyes that he meant it. At first she considered burning the letter and telling no one. Then she had decided to show her mother but only if she promised not to tell the police. Her mother, having read it, was equally worried by the contents and showed it to her husband.

'Leave me out of it!' he had insisted. 'It's a woman's thing! You know best, dear.'

Hardly helpful, Agatha thought with a sigh, but she knew what he meant. Eventually her mother had decided that Agatha should pass the letter to Louise's mother and let *her* make the decision about the contents.

From her place in the shadow of the trees, Agatha watched the first mourners arrive and failed to recognize any of them. She thought about Louise who, from the tone of the letter, had no idea her stepfather was dead. How could she? From all accounts she hadn't visited the hospital towards the end. One day she would find out and be utterly distraught.

'Oh, Louise!' she murmured. 'You think you're so happy, but everything is going wrong for everyone else. Why did you do it? It won't last. It *can't* last. Poor Stanley! He thought you were wonderful. When he finds out, it will break his heart.'

At last she saw Mrs Swain making her way slowly along the church path towards the porch. She looked somehow smaller and less confident than she used to look and Agatha sympathized with her. She could easily imagine how her own mother would be feeling in similar circumstances. She waited until all the mourners appeared to be inside the church and then slipped inside and sat right at the back.

The service was a sombre affair and did nothing to lessen Agatha's anxiety. When it was over she was the last to hurry outside. As she joined the group beside the grave, Mrs Swain caught sight of her and smiled faintly. The letter seemed to burn inside Agatha's pocket and she wished that her friend had not chosen to pour out her heart in such an emotional way. She sighed as she watched the first handful of earth tossed on to the gleaming casket. At least Mr Swain would never know the contents of his stepdaughter's letter. Louise could never hurt her stepfather.

As the vicar's closing words ended, Louise's mother made her way towards Agatha.

'How kind of you to come, Agatha,' she said. 'I know my husband would have been pleased to know that you cared. I hope you'll come back to the house. We have . . .'

'Oh, no!' cried Agatha, panicking. 'I just came to . . . My mother thought you should . . .' She drew the letter from her pocket and thrust it into Mrs Swain's hand. 'Mama thought you should see this. I didn't want to hand it over to the police sergeant. We . . . we didn't know what to do so . . . Well, here it is. It's from Louise. I'm so sorry.'

Madeline returned to the house where Sarah and Gertrude had put together various cold meats and salad. There was wine, beer, tea and a large trifle. Nearly twenty people squeezed into the dining room and the conversation soon changed from discreet murmurings of regret to a more sociable recounting of happier times. Through it all Madeline kept the letter a secret. She wanted to read it alone when everyone had gone home. Her emotions swung from fierce hope to deep apprehension. She had been dismayed by Agatha's words and her obvious unhappiness. At least it was a letter – even though Louise had chosen to confide in Agatha instead of her own mother. That knowledge hurt her more than she could admit even to herself.

When the front door had closed on the last guest and Sarah had finished washing up and gone home, Madeline was wondering how to break the news to Gertrude. A bad shock would do her no good, but she was Louise's grandmother and would not want to be shielded from the news, whatever it was. They sat together at the table in an exhausted silence, but before she could decide how to introduce the subject, Gertrude reached across from her chair and touched her hand.

'I saw Agatha give you a letter,' she told Madeline gently. 'Is it from our girl?'

Madeline nodded, unable to reply for the tightness in her throat.

'I can bear it, Madeline. We'll do it together, if you like.'

Madeline lifted her head slowly. 'Why Agatha? Don't we deserve some consideration? Doesn't she know how desperate we are for news of her?'

Gertrude swallowed hard. 'Shall I read it? Would that be easier for you?'

After a moment's hesitation, Madeline handed over the letter and watched her mother-in-law draw out the letter and unfold it.

Gertrude said, 'Pages and pages of it!' She put on her spectacles and studied the first few lines in silence. Then she drew a long breath and began to read aloud.

> Dearest Aggie,
>
> I just have to tell someone how happy I am and it has to be you because I dare not write to Mama or Papa. I must be in their black books – the blackest of the black – but you can tell them that I am safe and well so they will not worry about me. The truth is that I am with the man I adore and love with all my heart and am deliriously happy. Dan is so sweet and takes such good care of me . . .

Gertrude looked up. 'That's good to know, Madeline. We must take heart from this letter. Louise is alive and well and safe . . . and happy!' She shrugged her thin shoulders.

Stricken, Madeline said, 'Dare not write to us? Does she see us as monsters?'

'She doesn't mean it that way,' Gertrude replied, rather unconvincingly. 'You know how young people are towards their parents. They never see that you are doing or saying things in their best interests. Roland was the same. He had so much artistic talent and yet at one time he wanted to enlist in the army – simply because his best friend was joining up! He'd have regretted it for the rest of his life, but at the time he thought it would be a great adventure. I talked him out of it – and a good thing too.'

'Did he ever thank you for it?'

'Never. I didn't expect him to. He wouldn't speak to me for ages, but he eventually recovered his senses.'

'What happened to his friend?'

'He broke a leg in a training accident and was invalided out.' She shook her head. 'Shall I go on?'

Madeline nodded.

> He tries to pretend that my feelings for him will cool as time goes on and that I must then return to my home, but I know it will never happen. I will always love him and when I am twenty-one we will marry. It was so romantic, the night we were first together, when I had to leave home because of Bert. He didn't threaten me exactly, but he was growing angrier by the minute because Sarah had failed to keep the appointment he had made. At first I was sorry for Bert but then didn't quite trust him enough to stay all night alone in the house with him. But that's what brought me and Dan together, so in a funny way I shall always be grateful to Bert.

The two women regarded each other incredulously.

Madeline said, 'I'd like to strangle him!'

Gertrude tutted. 'Maybe you should let Sarah go,' she suggested. 'She will always be an uncomfortable reminder.'

'Read on, please. I have to know the worst.'

> . . . Married life in the bedroom is very strange, but nice . . .

'Married life!' Madeline cried, 'Oh, no! I've been hoping against hope that he would never go that far!'

'He's a man, Madeline. He's only human. Louise is a very attractive . . .'

'Child!' she cried angrily. 'She's still a *child*, Gertrude! How could you defend him? What is to become of her now?'

> We didn't mean it to happen – at least he didn't want it. But things somehow happened. I was hysterical and in tears and he put his arms round me to comfort me. He gave me a small glass of brandy to calm me and I

made him drink some too. He put me to bed on the
sofa, but in the night I went into his room . . .

Madeline gave a little cry. 'Oh, Louise! I thank God that
Oscar is not alive.'

Gertrude said, 'It seems our little Louise made all the
running, though.' She stared at the letter, stunned by the
disclosures. Then she continued, her voice trembling slightly.

. . . I can't go on, but it was so wonderful. When you
and Albert marry you will understand.

Madeline said bitterly, 'I will never understand how he
could take advantage of her . . .'

Gertrude gave her a stern look. 'Face facts, Madeline. I
think Louise provoked it. I know you are Louise's mother,
but you must be fair. She's my granddaughter, but I think
she was partly to blame even if you don't want to admit
it.'

Madeline jumped to her feet. 'Oh, God! I can't bear this.
If only Oscar were still alive. He would know how to deal
with this . . . this terrible mess.' She turned away towards the
window and began to cry fierce anguished sobs. Suddenly
she turned back, snatched the letter from Gertrude's hand
and ran upstairs with it. Once in her room, she sat on the
edge of the bed and forced herself to read the rest of it.

I am trusting you, Aggie, to show this letter to no
one. Not your parents and definitely not Mama or Papa
in case they notify the police who might try and trace
us by the postmark. I am not telling you my address
because then you cannot be persuaded to betray us.
Being sent away from Dan's lodgings was so humili-
ating. He was so upset and I did feel guilty because it
was all my fault, but that is all in the past and he has
forgiven me.

We will eventually find a way to marry, hopefully
before we have our first child. No, no sign of that yet,
but I would be delighted if it happened. In the meantime we each wear a wedding ring because we don't

want to scandalize anyone or start unpleasant gossip. Dan's not so enthusiastic about a child, but I know when a baby comes along he will be a wonderful father.

A friend of his has told him about a gallery in America where he might sell some of his pictures so we will shortly say goodbye to England and try our luck abroad. I wish I could believe that Mama and Papa would be willing to forgive and understand that what happened was meant to be, but they won't think that way so it is better not to meet. It would only lead to a quarrel and I will not put Dan through such an ordeal. I have upset his life enough already. Please keep all this to yourself. I will write again one day. Love to you and Albert and please tell Stanley how sorry I am for hurting him.

Your loving friend,
Louise XXXXXXXX

Madeline crumpled the pages in her hand, then pressed them to her lips. This then was the end of everything. The end of all their hopes for her daughter's future happiness. America! It was so far away. Almost another world. Would they go? Would they prosper? Would she ever know?

She heard Gertrude's slow steps on the stairs and a tap on the door brought her in with a cup of tea.

'Plenty of sugar in it!' said Gertrude. 'And a spoonful of brandy. Drink it, Madeline.'

Madeline thrust the letter into Gertrude's spare hand and took the tea. 'We've lost her, Gertrude. The Louise we knew has gone forever.' She breathed deeply, trying to lessen the growing sense of confusion and weakness.

In silence Gertrude sat down on the bedside chair, smoothed the ruined pages and began to read. When she had finished she looked up. 'Could you forgive her? Would you allow them to marry?'

'Not willingly but I would. She talks so blithely about a child. What is she thinking of? It's quite beyond me.'

'But you and Roland married in haste. With two such parents, no wonder she has a wild streak.'

'I knew you'd say that. They say history repeats itself. But

147

America! Will we ever see her again, Gertrude? I have this terrible emptiness in my heart. I worry I shall never set eyes on her again!' She stared dry eyed at her mother-in-law. 'There's just the two of us now.'

Gertrude swallowed. 'Will you inform the police? Will you show them the letter?'

'I think I must. It's only right they should know. The case is as good as closed, but I feel I should tell them about the letter – or at least tell them we know where she is and that she is well and happy.' She frowned suddenly. 'We do know that, don't we? She wouldn't write like that if she were having any doubts. Would she, Gertrude?'

Gertrude shook her head. 'That is the letter of a happy Louise,' she said firmly.

'If anything goes wrong between them . . . she would come home, wouldn't she? She'd know we'd welcome her with open arms.'

'Of course she would.'

Madeline sighed. 'I don't know what to pray for,' she confessed. 'If she's unhappy we'll get her back. If she's happy . . . we may never see her again.'

The following day, when Madeline had steeled herself to give Sarah notice, she was robbed of the opportunity when Sarah herself raised the subject.

'I think it only fair to tell you that I shall be leaving when I've worked my two weeks' notice,' she announced.

Madeline said 'Oh! I see. Actually I was going to talk to you about the matter since . . .'

Sarah removed her hat and coat and tied on her apron. 'It's Bert's idea. He doesn't want me working for you anymore so . . . there we are!'

Illogically, Madeline felt aggrieved by Bert's decision. 'Did he give any reason why you should give in your notice?' she asked coldly. 'Have we mistreated you in any way?'

''Course not, Mrs Swain. But you must agree the last few weeks have hardly been easy with you thinking ill of Bert because of what happened.' She began to sweep crumbs from the breakfast table into her hand, but her tone was challenging.

'You mean, refusing to leave the house so that Louise was terrified and . . .'

'And ran round to her gentleman friend! Yes, that's what I mean. Why didn't she go next door to Mrs Carter? That's what I ask myself. But dear me, no! She has to make out she's terrified of poor Bert and makes that the excuse to . . . to throw herself at her art tutor.'

Suspecting that she had gone too far she straightened up and glared at Madeline who was already regretting her hasty words. Sarah was in no way to blame . . . except that if she had given Bert a second chance when he first asked for it instead of prevaricating, things would have been very different.

'I used to think you were fond of Louise.'

'I'm not denying that, Mrs Swain, but then she was just a child. Now she's a woman, apparently, and a very troublesome one at that! Look at the heartache she's caused. Everyone's upset including me. Nothing's the same. Bert's being very understanding. He wants me to stay home for a few months and rest and get myself together. He's got himself a respectable job in a warehouse with the possibility of something better in six months' time. He's going straight and I for one . . .'

'Let's hope he means it!' The words snapped out and Madeline was secretly appalled. Why was she taking this attitude? Why not let Sarah go without any needless recriminations or bitterness? That is what she had intended. Somehow the conversation had turned sour and she felt herself to be to blame.

Two spots of angry colour burned in Sarah's cheeks. 'That's typical!' she cried. 'That's how everyone treats a man who's been in prison. No mercy. No willingness to forget the past. No wonder they find it difficult to make a fresh start. I thought better of you, Mrs Swain.' She gave up the pretence of working and stood with her hands on her hips, her breath coming in shallow gasps as her resentment grew. 'Know what my neighbour said yesterday? That they're moving . . . to a better neighbourhood! D'you know how long they've lived in that house? Eleven years. Oh, it was all right while Bert was locked up. Now he's back we're

149

not good enough.' She swallowed hard and Madeline saw that she was trying not to cry.

'Sarah, I'm . . . I'm sorry,' she began. 'I think we've both said enough.'

'We certainly have!' She snatched at the strings of her apron and pulled it off. She began putting on her coat, thrusting her arms into the sleeves and struggling with the buttons. 'Well, I'm off. You can save your breath, I'll never set foot in this place again and don't bother to send round what I'm owed. We don't want your money!'

'Sarah, please . . .' Madeline stammered. 'There's no need to . . . I mean we shouldn't part like this. We . . .'

Sarah paused at the kitchen door, her purse clutched fiercely in her hands. 'And just so you know, when Bert was left here alone . . . Well, that's when he decided to smarten himself up. He slept in your husband's bed! In your husband's clean pyjamas! And in the morning he shaved himself with Mr Swain's razor and dabbed on . . .' Her voice shook. 'And dabbed on some of his hair oil. Then he brushed his shabby suit with Mr Swain's clothes brush. And he "borrowed" one of Mr Swain's ties. That's how he made himself look so presentable. When I saw him I was properly taken aback. He'd tried so hard to impress me and he looked so smart. So I thought yes, I will give him another chance. All thanks to Mr Swain, if you look at it like that. He did want me to give Bert a second chance. So I did!'

Speechless, Madeline could only stare at her. He had slept in Oscar's bed! Oh, God! It was unforgivable. Stole his tie!

'Bert looked quite respectable and that's how I see him now.' She tossed her head. 'No thanks to you, though! You've damned him without a thought and I'm done with the lot of you!' She turned and rushed along the passage, let herself out and slammed the door so hard that all the cups rattled on the hooks on the dresser.

Madeline sat down, weak at the knees and sore at heart. Was this how it was going to be, she wondered shakily. One blow after another. First Oscar, then Louise, now Sarah. She questioned whether it was her fault, shaken by the thought that she had inadvertently created the chaos. If so, where had she gone wrong? What had she done? And what else could go wrong? Too drained even to cry she placed her elbows on the table and rested her head in her hands. Was life going to be worth living?

For six unhappy weeks Gertrude and Madeline tried to comfort and support each other without success. October came and went, the days shortened and the weather grew sharp, adding to their depression. The days were too long and empty, the nights were an agony of restless sleep and dark nightmares. They didn't eat properly since neither was inspired to cook suffering from a loss of appetite. Madeline had made no effort to replace Sarah and the house looked, and was, sadly neglected. Madeline threw herself into her charity work with a feverish intensity in an effort to keep her thoughts at bay, but emotionally she was still in turmoil and was soon hovering on the edge of a nervous breakdown. Gertrude insisted that they call in the doctor.

'You have little energy to spare,' he told Madeline, 'and you must give up these extra activities. Look after yourself instead. It is not being selfish,' he said, as she began to protest. 'It is common sense. You have no reserves and are making yourself ill.'

Madeline agreed unwillingly, but only because she knew he was right.

No medicine could cure what ailed Madeline, he told Gertrude. Guilt and grief were a potent combination for disaster. He told Madeline that Gertrude's natural resilience was severely strained.

'But she seems to be making progress,' Madeline protested, shocked.

'Physically she is improving, but she is too proud to show her innermost feelings. Inside she is suffering.'

There were no letters from Louise and they had no idea whether or not she and Daniel were still in England. Each day was a prolonged fight against depression which dogged both Madeline and Gertrude. They put up a suitable headstone for Oscar, and Madeline visited it regularly to lay fresh flowers and to talk to her dead husband. Agatha called in occasionally and Madeline looked forward to her visits though Agatha never had news for her.

'I thought she would write to me,' she confessed. 'But she hasn't. I suppose she is too busy with her new life. Mama says I have to forget her and look forward to my own future.'

Sometimes Albert came with her on the visits, but on those occasions Madeline was forcibly reminded of the sort of life she had expected for her own daughter. Middy also pined and for several weeks refused to eat much, but Madeline and Gertrude spoiled him simply because they had no one else on whom to lavish their affection and he eventually returned to his own sunny self.

On Thursday, the first of December, on a raw and misty morning, there was a knock at the door which sent Middy flying up the hall, barking furiously. Madeline, alone in the house, made her way to the front door with a rapidly beating heart. This was what she had imagined so many times in the stillness of a sleepless night. She had never given up hope that Louise would return, even if she brought Daniel and was on her way somewhere else. She had rehearsed many times how she would greet Louise and what she would say, not to mention the promises she would extract. 'Just keep in touch, darling. Please. A letter or a postcard. Is that too much to ask?' And of Daniel she would ask only that he loved and cared for her and kept her from harm. She had promised herself that she would not break down in tears, but that she would be cheerful and accepting of the situation without a word of reproach. She prayed nightly and whenever someone came to the door she believed her prayers had been answered.

'Louise,' she whispered as she rushed along the hall. 'Please let it be you!'

But already the outline against the glass panel was wrong and the knowledge brought tears to her eyes. Tears which she resolutely blinked back. A young man stood on the doorstep. Straight fair hair fell untidily over his eyes. He clutched a worn carpet bag and looked grey and ill. At first Madeline failed to recognize him.

Disappointment sharpened her voice. 'Yes. What is it?'

'André,' he reminded her. 'I'm André .'

Ah! Gertrude's young admirer! He didn't smile and she realized he had probably just made another bad sea crossing. She knew how badly it affected him.

152

'Come in,' she said, opening the door wider. 'How wonderful to see you.'

He stepped inside, dropped the carpet bag and bent to fondle the dog.

Madeline picked up the bag and led him into the kitchen where she had just boiled a kettle of water. André stood in the doorway, looking dazed but determined.

'Where ees she?' he asked.

'Louise? Oh, she . . .' Her throat tightened. Maybe he didn't know that she had gone.

'*Non*. Gertrude. Where ees she? I must talk to her.'

'Gertrude? Oh! Gertrude has gone for a walk in the park. She doesn't take the dog in case he pulls her over. She is getting stronger every day. She'll be back soon. Do sit down, André. It's good to see you again.'

She hurried around the kitchen, collecting cups and saucers, milk and sugar. 'We have no biscuits, I'm afraid,' she said. 'I'll make some later.' It felt surprisingly good to have someone to fuss over.

He watched her, his eyes dull with fatigue. 'I have to come,' he told her. 'I have to see for myself that Gertrude is happy. I have to be certain she wishes to stay here. She writes to ask me to sell the apartment for her, but how can she bear it? To leave her beloved Paris. This cannot be good for her. It cannot be right.'

Madeline sat down and poured tea. 'You must talk to her when she returns. Did you know, André , that Louise has . . .?' The words stuck in her throat and her hand shook, spilling tea on to the tray.

André said, 'I know. I am truly sorry. But she will come back, no?'

'I . . . expect so. Yes. Maybe.' She handed a cup of tea to her visitor. 'Gertrude is making good progress, André . You will see for yourself. And she likes being here.'

'In England? I think not. How you say it . . . Paris is in her blood.'

Madeline changed the subject. 'Where are you staying, André ? We have room for you here.'

'Thank you. I think I shall stay here for a few days so I can care for her. For both of you. You need someone.

153

Gertrude is very frail. She eats like a little bird. You are both sad and sadness eats into the soul. I will cook for you. I make a big thick *cassoulet* with duck meat and beans . . . and I will make fish soup.' He rolled his eyes and some of his weariness left him. 'Do you like fish soup?' He was sitting up now, watching eagerly for signs that he had inspired some interest. 'And I'm forgetting *pot au feu . . .*'

She nodded, at once touched and overwhelmed by his enthusiasm. 'That sounds wonderful, André, but . . .'

There was a sound at the front door and Middy raced off again. André followed and when Gertrude stepped into the hall she was almost bowled over by her welcome. Half an hour later they were all still talking with great animation. Madeline made some lemon biscuits and a sponge. Later that evening, André, finding the cupboard rather bare, made them a large, fluffy omelette and smothered it with grated cheese. He produced a bottle of wine from his carpet bag and they shared the simple meal cheerfully.

When Madeline went to bed that night she had a faint smile on her face and a growing suspicion that life probably could, and should, hold more for them. She felt strangely comforted. It seemed that with André's arrival, they had possibly survived their very darkest moments.

Three weeks later a letter arrived from Daniel. Madeline read it several times and then took it to Gertrude, in the kitchen with André.

'Read it out,' she suggested. 'We don't have any secrets from André.'

Gertrude obeyed, with much head shaking and occasional murmurs of dismay.

> Dear Mrs Swain,
>
> I have struggled for many weeks to write this letter. I am sure I will never be able to explain what happened that night when a very troubled Louise came to me for help. At the time it seemed a disastrous encounter and we both took fright and left town. Louise was terrified that you would find her and take her back where she belonged. However, our rashness has proved less disas-

trous than might have been expected because we are both very happy. Louise has changed over the past months from an anxious student to a radiant young woman although I cannot persuade her to write to you herself. Hopefully as time passes she will change her mind. I wish you could see how happy she is. It would set your mind at rest.

We were both distressed to hear from Miss Maddock at the gallery (which has now been sold) that your husband has died. Poor Louise was beside herself with grief. She blamed herself for not continuing her visits to the hospital, but I have convinced her that neither you nor your husband would want her to torment herself in this way and that all either of you ever wanted was her happiness.

A friend of my uncle's has offered me a partnership in his gallery in New York and by the time you read this we will be on our way to what I hope will be a happy new life. I will add his address to this letter in the hope that you will find it in your heart to forgive us and will write back.

My sincere best wishes to you and again my deep regret and a rather forlorn hope of forgiveness.

Yours sincerely,
Daniel Grant

Gertrude finished reading it and they regarded each other hopefully.

Madeline said, 'Contact at last!' Her voice was husky as she fought back a rush of emotion. 'New York! It sounds . . .' Her voice trailed off.

'Very exciting?' Gertrude suggested, but her expression belied the words. She bit her lip unhappily.

'I was going to say New York sounds a long way away!' She held out her hand for the letter. 'It's been . . . a bit of a shock, to say the least. She's happy . . .'

'But?'

'We shall never see *our* Louise again.' Madeline put a hand to her mouth to hide her agitation. 'I mean we shall never see our *girl* again. It will be a different Louise.'

155

Gertrude hesitated, then shrugged. 'She had to grow up sometime, Madeline. It's just been rather sudden.'

'I thought we'd watch her grow up.'

'Perhaps she was growing up, but we didn't recognize the signs.' They were both silent, deep in thought before Gertrude said, 'I think Daniel Grant should have apologized for what happened. He was older and should have been more careful. I do still blame him, Madeline.'

Madeline sighed. 'But the sergeant was right. There was no need for Louise to go to Daniel's lodgings. She could have gone next door to the Carters. It makes more sense. I don't know. I want to be fair but . . . But what does it matter now?'

Gertrude shook her head again. 'He doesn't mention marriage.'

'But surely . . . I wonder what the American law says about under age females? They might need our permission. We'd have to give it. At least we can write to them and tell them that.'

They were both silent. André glanced across at them from the vegetables he was preparing. He was still with them and, to their relief, showed no sign of returning to Paris. Madeline thought of him secretly as their mother hen because he chivvied them and coaxed them out of their most despairing moments and nourished their bodies with his inspired cooking.

He said, 'My brother, 'e run away from home when he ees fifteen.' They regarded him eagerly.

Madeline said, 'And did he come back?'

'*Non!*'

Gertrude frowned. 'Not at all?'

'He never comes back.'

Startled, Madeline asked, 'So what happened to him?'

'We don't know.' He rolled his eyes. 'How you say . . . Water under the bridge!' He tossed the carrots into a deep pie dish and began to drain some beans that he had soaked overnight.

Gertrude said, 'At least we know.' She steepled her fingers thoughtfully. 'We have to accept that she might be . . . even more changed when we see her.'

'I was thinking the same thing.' Madeline replied. She

156

took a deep breath. She had been thinking the unthinkable. 'She might be . . . expecting a child.'

André laughed. 'That would be fun, no?'

The two women exchanged shocked glances.

Gertrude said, 'She's much too young.'

Madeline nodded. 'Much too young.'

André said, 'But a grandchild – and a great-grandchild for you, Gertrude. *Fantastique!*'

Middy rose from his basket and stretched his legs. He moved to sit quietly beside André, watching his every move, hoping for a titbit. André tossed him a bean which he gulped down before realizing that he didn't like it. He gave André a reproachful look and then padded to Madeline and slumped on to her feet with his nose between his paws.

Madeline eased her stiff shoulders. It was wonderful to hear news of Louise, but now she had something else to worry about. Would Louise persuade Daniel that a baby would complete their happiness? Either way she, Madeline, was helpless to intervene and it was a disturbing feeling. Caring for a child brought with it the need to control and monitor the situations for the child and after eighteen years it had become second nature. Losing this control left her feeling useless and bereft of the responsibility. How would Louise cope with motherhood, she wondered. The prospect had been of no significance until now. Did Daniel want a family? Would a child come between them? It took young mothers so much time and energy to look after a baby there was sometimes less time for the husband and that was dangerous. Did Louise have any idea what a child might do to their relationship? She remembered how her own relationship with Roland had come perilously near to breakdown. Only Gertrude's wise counsel had saved the marriage. If Louise needed wise counsel, who would she turn to, all those miles away in New York?

As though reading her thoughts Gertrude leaned across and patted her arm. 'You know what they say, my dear,' she said. 'People have to make their own mistakes and learn by them. Louise has made her bed and she must lie in it!'

Madeline's stomach churned at Gertrude's words. 'You think she has made a mistake? It couldn't be a . . . a love match?' She realized that she was clinging to the hope that since her daughter had followed her heart, all would be well.

Gertrude hesitated. 'I do think she was wrong to catapult Daniel Grant into a situation he did not seek, but it's done and can't be undone. Maybe they will survive. Stranger things have happened.' She shrugged lightly. 'Would you and Roland have survived? We shall never know.'

Madeline regarded her unhappily. 'If only there was something we could do!'

'We can pray, my dear.'

Ten

Christmas came and went and André was still with them. Gertrude and Madeline talked about it and decided to ask him whether he wanted to stay in England or was planning to return. They were shocked when he immediately burst into tears and begged to be allowed to stay with them.

'Gertrude needs me,' he insisted, turning to her. 'While you live, I want to be near you. I have nobody. You are my family.'

Later that evening while he was walking Middy, Gertrude finally explained his devotion.

'He is such a tender plant,' she said. 'He had a bullying father and a very cowed mother. The two boys had a difficult time and when his brother ran away to escape the father, André was left alone with them. One day he tried to intervene when his parents quarrelled and the father turned on him and beat him unconscious.'

'Good heavens!' Madeline was horrified. 'He did that to his own son?'

'He was very drunk. He put André in the hospital with serious bruising and a broken rib, not to mention two missing teeth. Poor André is such a gentle soul. He was terrified to go back. He wanted his mother to leave his father, but she refused. The usual thing. She had no income and no chance of employment. I found André in the park one day. He was sitting on a bench, sobbing. I took him home and comforted him and offered him my chaise longue.' She smiled. 'He stayed for months. He's difficult to dislodge!'

Madeline laughed. 'But what would we have done without him? He's been good for us. More like a son than a lodger or friend.'

'One day he showed me some sketches and I thought he showed some promise. I paid for his lessons for a year and a half and he improved a little. By this time I had found him a room nearby and, of course, he came every day. He had no one else. Too shy to make friends and with no family to speak of. He met his mother secretly but was no longer allowed back to his home.'

'How old was he?'

She considered. 'By then he was about eighteen.'

'The same age as Louise.'

For a few moments they thought about him in silence.

Madeline said, 'Perhaps we could introduce him to the new people at Daniel's gallery. He needs to think about his future and a career. How old is he now?'

'Probably about twenty–four, although he looks younger . . . But first he must go back to Paris and sell the apartment for me. We are going to need something to live on, Madeline. I don't like to ask how you are placed financially . . .?'

'I don't mind at all. I spoke with the bank manager some time ago and Oscar has left me provided for as long as I'm not too extravagant – and don't live too long!'

Gertrude raised her eyebrows. 'Can one live too long? I hope to go on forever! But as for André, if he wants to stay here as a . . . a paying guest – would you agree?'

'Yes,' she said quickly. 'But only a little and only if he can afford it. I can't imagine life without him now.'

Three months passed and spring beckoned. On Thursday the 30th of March, when the worst of the snow had been scraped away and the snowdrops began to appear, the news came that both Madeline and Gertrude had been longing for. A letter from Louise. It told them that she was expecting a baby in July.

> I know we have had some sad and difficult times, Mama, and I know I behaved badly but Dan is sure I am forgiven and I do want to make a fresh start and think we should be friends again. I want you to share our happiness that we are starting a family. It is what I want more than anything in the world and Dan says

if it will make me happy he is happy too. He is the dearest man, Mama, and is doing very well with his pictures and making a lot of money . . .

Madeline cried, 'A baby! And she is so far away! Still, at least they can afford a good doctor.'

'A doctor? She isn't ill, dear, she's expecting a child. You should know. All perfectly natural. I hope they won't waste hard earned money on doctors!'

Madeline regarded her doubtfully. 'Sometimes things go wrong with a pregnancy.'

'Not with our girl! She's perfectly healthy. Stop worrying and enjoy the news, Madeline.'

Madeline read on.

> Dan's gallery is thriving so we are able to move to a larger apartment before the baby arrives. His partner is nice, too. His name is Stuart Hine and his paintings are mainly based around the events of the Civil War. They are in great demand in the north but not so popular in the south. Stuart Hine is almost famous. He has a son called Robert and the family originated in Scotland. Robert is not at all artistic, but Stuart is resigned to the disappointment!

It was a long rambling letter. Robert, it seemed, was good with horses and had a share in his uncle's stud farm just outside New York; Louise and Daniel had been invited to visit when the weather improved. Louise had made a new friend by the name of Stella who lived in a nearby apartment and was training to be a concert pianist, but they nonetheless managed to spend a lot of time together shopping. Louise had had her hair cut and was told by everyone that it suited her. The letter ended with kind regards to all and kisses for Madeline and Gertrude. No mention of poor Middy.

The letter was read and reread with delight. Even André was pleased that Louise had written. He saw the effect the contents had on Madeline and Gertrude and was happy for them. 'I shall be an honorary uncle, *n'est ce pas*?' he joked.

At first, Madeline's joy at hearing from her daughter outweighed anything else, but after several readings she began to feel uneasy. She began to find the letter unsatisfactory in several ways. There seemed to be very little about the coming child – none of the usual information that preceded the birth of a child. Nothing about their preferred gender. Did they want a boy or a girl? There was no mention of names and no talk at all about preparing a nursery. Louise didn't even refer to her health. Was she suffering morning sickness? Was her weight a problem? Was the doctor happy with her progress? There wasn't even a definite date for the baby to arrive, simply July. It struck Madeline as odd that Daniel was hardly mentioned but the Hine family featured strongly. There was also no reference to art lessons so perhaps Louise had abandoned the idea of following in Roland's footsteps.

Had Gertrude noticed the omissions, she wondered uneasily. If she had, presumably she was hoping that Madeline had not been equally perceptive. She decided that perhaps she was being paranoid and ought to keep her doubts to herself. But there was another matter that she must confront. She cornered Gertrude one afternoon as they put fresh linen on the beds.

'I think I must write giving permission for Louise to marry,' Madeline announced. 'Now that they are expecting a child they must be married for the baby's sake.'

Gertrude smoothed the sheet and tucked it in. 'You're right,' she said. 'The relationship is obviously going to last. I did wonder at the beginning if Louise would come rushing home, having thought better of the escapade. Thank heavens she is wearing a wedding ring. If the child is beginning to show . . .'

'Do you think they would come back here to be married? It would so perfect if they did.'

Gertrude stuffed a pillow into a clean pillowcase. 'It would be expensive . . . and do you think the journey would be good for her in her condition. It's a long sea journey from New York to Liverpool. We could suggest it, I suppose.'

'But then Louise will think we're starting to interfere.' Madeline frowned. 'I'm going to write to her tonight. Will you want to send your letter with mine?'

162

'Why not?'

Downstairs the front door opened and closed. As they finished the bed they heard André's voice.

'Very bad dog! Go in your basket and stay there!'

He looked up as they entered the kitchen. 'I am very unhappy with 'im. I let 'im off as usual but 'e runs off and gets into a . . . How you say? A *scuffle!* Yes. With a large poodle! The owner, 'e blames Middy. I am not so near to see what 'appens. What could I say?' He glared at Middy who began to wag his tail, but then the dog obviously thought better of the idea and lowered his ears instead. 'Bad boy!'

Madeline said, 'Do you think he ever thinks about Louise? Do dogs remember the people they love?'

André was not to be sidetracked. 'Next time 'e stay on the lead.'

Gertrude said, 'We were wondering if they would agree to be married in England instead of New York. Here in St Mark's Bay.'

'Aha!' He brightened at once. 'A wedding! I shall make a cake. With icing and gold ribbons.'

He opened the oven door and studied a ham which was slowly roasting. Shutting the door he said, 'I met Agatha in the park with 'er cousin, Victoria. A nice young woman.'

Madeline stared at him. 'I didn't know she had a cousin. Pretty name, Victoria.'

'It seems they were born on the same day but five years apart. Victoria is older. They 'ave been friends all their lives.'

Gertrude, still busy with thoughts about Louise, said, 'If they stayed on in England the baby could be born here and christened before they go back!'

Madeline said, 'If they go back!' and raised her eyebrows.

Gertrude raised a warning hand. 'Stop there, Madeline. We mustn't ask too much of them. If they have a new, successful life in New York it would be unfair to put pressure on them to return here. It would be wonderful, I grant you, but hardly fair.'

Madeline sighed. 'I know you're right, dear. I'm just dreaming dreams! What I most hope is that they are both happy, that Daniel is doing well, that the baby is healthy, that . . .'

André laughed. 'A very long list!'

'Don't tell me! I'm a thoroughly selfish mother.'

Gertrude looked at her gently. 'As soon as Louise is a mother she will understand you better.'

Madeline nodded. 'How I long for that day.'

They had to wait until August for the long awaited news. Louise had given birth to a baby boy who had been registered in the name of Daniel Oscar Legrand. Over the past months there had been an occasional letter. Three from Daniel and two from Louise and both Gertrude and Madeline had written many times. Madeline had become increasingly worried by Louise's scrawled offerings which were written as joint letters addressed to Mama and Grandmama. When she confided her doubts to her mother-in-law, Gertrude said crisply, 'Let's be thankful for any letters, my dear. Her life is obviously very full. We are simply echoes from her past.'

In spite of Madeline's early insistence that she was willing to give her permission for them to marry, Louise didn't once refer to the offer which would have resulted in the legitimizing of the little boy.

Daniel wrote to thank her for her offer, but he said that Louise had set her mind against it. He had hoped to change her mind one day but was not at all hopeful.

Time passed slowly. One of André's paintings was accepted by the gallery but did not sell, much to his disappointment. Gertrude's health continued to worry Madeline, although she refused point blank to visit the doctor. She was pale and seemed to have no appetite. She was troubled by a cough and tired easily and on some days Madeline or André had to coax and almost bully her out of bed and down the stairs. Not only was Madeline fearful that Gertrude would become bedridden, but she needed her company. When Madeline secretly consulted the doctor, he said, 'What can you expect from a lady of her age?' which Madeline found unhelpful.

She herself was basically in good health, but her sleep was often disturbed by nightmares and she found it increasingly difficult to relax during the day. She took up tapestry work, but although she found it satisfying, nothing could fill the gap left by her daughter.

On a cold day towards the end of November, André was trying to persuade them to have a party on Christmas Eve for which he would prepare all sorts of elegant food. 'And we will 'ave a tree and decorate it! And party games too.'

Madeline was not responding well to the idea. 'Parties are for children,' she told him. Christmas, for her, involved Louise. She thought with a desperate longing of all the Christmases past when the young Louise had still believed in Father Christmas. The excitement when the tree was brought in; the letter which Louise wrote to Father Christmas and posted up the chimney; the choice of a new party dress and velvet slippers, and the thrill when the carol singers arrived outside their door. She remembered the secret shopping trip when they'd found a perfect present for Oscar, hanging up Louise's red stocking on Christmas Eve, and Christmas mornings, which had always started so early, with Louise's delighted discovery of her filled stocking. Did Louise recall any of these glorious moments, she wondered, or had they all faded from her memory.

'For only children? *Mais non!*' cried André, his face alight with excitement. 'I know many games. You will have charades! And there will be *les petits cadeaux*!'

Gertrude translated. 'Small gifts.' André's enthusiasm was bringing a gleam to her own eyes. 'What do you say? It would be fun, Madeline. Something to look forward to.'

'But who will we invite?' Madeline was wavering. It would be the second Christmas without Louise, a fact nobody had dared say. The first had been miserable and best forgotten. She had been dreading another Christmas. Had André realized? He was a sensitive young man. This might be his way of helping them through the festive season. 'We don't have a very large circle of friends.'

She didn't express her deeper thoughts. What did they have to celebrate? It would be so different if Louise were still with them.

Undeterred, André produced a list he had prepared for such a moment and handed it to Gertrude who was nearest.

'We invite the Carters from next door and Miss Maddock

165

and 'er fiancé from the gallery. I am sure Agatha would like to come with Albert and 'er cousin and maybe 'er parents.' He looked at Madeline. 'We could include your Sarah and . . .'

'No!' cried Madeline. 'He caused us so much grief! I blame him for Louise's defection. And he slept in Oscar's bed just days before his death. He used his things.' André was staring at her in alarm. She went on, greatly agitated. 'It was unforgivable. No, I can't abide the thought of either of them in this house again. Hasn't he caused us enough trouble? Don't ever mention either of them to me again!' She fled from the room, unsuccessfully trying to hide her tears.

She heard André say, 'What 'ave I said?'

Outside in the passage, Madeline rested her head against the wall, a hand clamped over her mouth. She heard Gertrude explaining what had happened before André's arrival in England and he was obviously mortified. 'But,' Gertrude continued hastily, 'I like the idea of a party. It's just what we need. I'll talk her into it, André.'

'But I must apologize to 'er. Poor soul!'

'You had no idea, André. How could you? Mrs Swain will understand. She'll recover. It was the shock, that's all.'

Madeline pushed herself away from the wall and went up to her bedroom.

Within minutes there was a knock at the front door. Middy sprang into action. Madeline heard André hurry along the passage. 'Middy! Stop that noise!' She heard him open the door. There was a muted exchange and then he called to Gertrude.

'He say 'e ees Mr Grant.'

Madeline froze. Mr Grant? Daniel was here? Then maybe Louise was with him! She leaped from the bed and rushed downstairs, almost colliding with André as he stood waiting for Gertrude's response.

She cried, 'I'll see to it, André.'

As soon as she saw Daniel, his expression told her instantly that there was bad news to come. He stood on the step, a small suitcase in his hand and looked thoroughly ill at ease. 'Come in! Please!' She caught hold of his sleeve. 'Come

166

along to the kitchen. We'll make you a cup of tea. Are you hungry? You must tell us everything.'

Minutes later they were all in the kitchen, seated round the table. André produced some biscuits and before anyone spoke, Daniel ate one and gulped down a cup of tea. He looked slightly disheveled and very tired. Madeline tried to imagine the long sea journey from New York to Liverpool and the subsequent buses and trains from Liverpool to St Mark's Bay. She saw, too, that his face was creased in unhappy lines, something she had not expected from Louise's last letter. Madeline stared at him speechlessly. Deeply concerned by his wretched expression, she suddenly feared what he had come to say. Gertrude sipped her tea, watching him over the rim of her teacup. The uncomfortable silence lengthened, until André could no longer bear the unhappy atmosphere.

'Should I go?' he suggested. 'Yes, I must. I'll take Middy for a walk.'

No one argued and he drew on his coat. Middy pranced around the kitchen, but at last André snapped on the dog's lead and made a discreet departure.

Madeline kept her eyes on Daniel's face. He looked years older, she thought with a shock. She stammered, 'Louise . . . She's not . . . dead, is she?'

Gertrude reached for her hand and held it tightly. Her face, too, was pale.

'Dead? Good heavens no!'

Madeline let out her breath. 'But she isn't with you? You've left her somewhere? Oh! She's not still in New York, is she?' A hard knot of disappointment formed within her at the idea that Louise was still determined to keep a distance between them and had refused to accompany Daniel to England.

Daniel drew a long breath and clasped his hands on the table. He forced himself to meet her eyes. 'This won't be easy, Mrs Swain.'

'Call me Madeline . . . and Daniel . . .' In a rush of generosity she said, 'We must forget all the . . . the regrets and mistakes of the past. Forgive and forget. Just tell us about Louise . . . and little Dan, of course.' She brightened. 'How is he?'

167

Daniel closed his eyes and the women exchanged anxious glances.

If she's not dead then she must be ill, Madeline thought. She began to tremble. If Louise was ill then she, Madeline, would go to her even if it meant the long sea journey across the Atlantic.

Daniel swallowed hard. 'I don't know how our son is because . . . Louise has taken him away from me.'

It took a moment for the words to sink in. Gertrude gave a little cry and covered her face with her hands. Madeline heard the words echoing in her head. '*Has taken him away from me* . . .' At first it hardly made any sense.

Daniel said, 'I haven't seen him for a few months now.'

Gertrude uncovered her face. 'But where has she taken him?'

He appeared not to have heard her. 'I feel such a damned fool! I should have guessed, but she was always saying how wonderful it was for Dan – to be outdoors and have so much freedom . . . Oh, God! Why didn't I follow my instincts? I did suspect but I told myself that I was imagining things. I couldn't believe it. I didn't *want* to believe it.'

Madeline sat back, shocked. 'You're telling us that she has left you.'

He nodded. 'Now I know why she didn't want to get married even after your kind letter. I wanted to go right ahead and regularize the relationship, but Louise was strangely reluctant. By that time she had decided I was not the right man for her and she wanted to be free to . . .' He couldn't go on. After a long pause he forced himself to utter the truth. 'She was falling in love with Robert Hine.'

Abruptly Gertrude stood up. 'I can't bear this!' She opened the back door, stepped out into the garden and closed the door. Through the window Madeline watched her make her way slowly to the garden seat and sink down on to it.

Daniel said, 'I'm so sorry, Madeline. So desperately sorry. I've ruined everything for all of us.' He looked at her, his eyes full of misery. 'The thing is . . . I'm still in love with her. I still want her and my son, but I don't think I shall ever get them back. I've been to a solicitor and, of course, we are not married so what rights do I have? Possibly none. Robert's young, good-looking, wealthy. She left me a note, but I tore it up. I was in rather a state. She said she was sorry but she now knows what real love is. She claims that what she felt for me was . . . infatuation!'

Madeline wanted to scream or to cry – she hardly knew. Frustration boiled within her. She had thought that they were clawing their way out of the pit of despair into which they had fallen, but now they were faced with a worsening scenario. She said, 'There must be a way. She'll realize her mistake.'

He shook his head bitterly. 'I was her mistake and I allowed her to make it.'

Madeline swallowed hard. 'I said "No regrets!", Daniel. I meant it. We've all been guilty of errors of judgement but we . . . we have to salvage something. We need to think this through.'

'I've done nothing but think all the way across,' he told her. 'I can't bear the thought that Daniel is going to grow up calling Robert Hine "Papa". It's selfish but there it is.'

'How is it selfish?'

He shrugged. 'Maybe growing up on the stud farm with young and happy parents is not so bad from Dan's viewpoint. If I regain custody of him, he'll have no mother. Would he ever forgive me for that?'

Madeline groaned. Then she caught sight of Gertrude huddled on the garden seat. 'What is she thinking of! It must be cold out there.' She hurried to the door. 'Gertrude, do please come in, dear. You'll catch your death of cold.'

Gertrude didn't argue but came inside unwillingly. Madeline put an arm round her. 'Stand by the stove and . . . here!' She pulled off her own shawl. 'Wrap this around your shoulders.'

Daniel said, 'I tried to write to you, but I could imagine your horror when you read the letter and I wanted to tell you in person. Face to face. I suppose I hoped three heads are better than one. I thought we might think of a way to . . . Oh, God! I can't bear to lose either of them.'

Gertrude huddled closer to the fire. 'Does she love him? Dan, I mean. Is she motherly, protective, capable? Is she passionately devoted to her son? Any or all of those things?

169

What I'm wondering is if she marries this Hine fellow she will doubtless have other children. She might be prepared to hand Dan back to you. You could employ a good nanny to help care for Dan and provide a woman in his life. Many children adore their nanny. Most of them, probably. Most nannies remain single and adore the children.'

'I hadn't thought that far,' he admitted. 'I am still trying to find a way to get them both back.'

'Do you think her feelings for Hine are the real thing? Is she in love with him or is this another infatuation?'

Madeline rubbed her eyes tiredly. 'Does Hine want him? Maybe he doesn't want to bring up another man's child. Dan would always remind him that you were Louise's first . . . lover. If you went straight to him with your proposition . . .'

Gertrude said, 'But that would alienate Louise. Would that be wise? How would poor Louise feel if her child was taken away?'

Madeline shook her head helplessly. She felt for Daniel but also for her daughter. How could Louise do this to Daniel after loving him so dearly? None of it made sense. Shock, disappointment and fear were draining her energy, but she tried to rally herself. They must think positively about the whole problem. Daniel was right – they must put the boy's best interests first. And Louise's second? Oh, Louise! She mourned for the daughter who was now no more. A new Louise had taken her place and they were all struggling to come to terms with her. Dramatic changes were taking place in the daughter she had loved and cherished for so many years. Was Louise truly in charge of her own destiny or was life running away from her, out of control?

'Where is it all going to end?' she whispered. It occurred to her that if she came face to face with this new Louise, she would hardly know what to say to her.

She heard Gertrude say, 'We have never even seen him. Baby Dan, I mean.'

'Oh, I'm sorry.' Daniel opened the suitcase. 'Here are a few photographs. He looks just like his mother.'

Eagerly the two women pored over the photographs of Louise's son. There was one official photograph of a very formal group. Baby Dan sitting on Louise's lap with Daniel standing proudly at Louise's side. The other three were snap-shots taken with a Brownie camera – one showed Dan in his cot, one showed him peering over Louise's shoulder and the last one showed him fast asleep in Daniel's arms.

Gertrude said, 'Oh, I must see him for myself before I die.'

Daniel said, 'Don't talk of dying.'

Madeline smiled. 'I second that! You and André are all that keep me sane.' She looked at Daniel and then Gertrude and thought, we are all struggling to retain a sense of humour against odds that never seem to be in our favour! Perhaps a good meal would restore their flagging spirits. She could think of nothing else to offer so rose briskly from her chair. 'I shall roast the chicken and we'll have mashed potatoes with gravy! For dessert we'll have a creamy rice pudding with currants and cinnamon.'

Their faces brightened a little and, determined to ease the heartache, Madeline hurried to make a start. Gertrude offered to peel the potatoes and Daniel, as the exhausted traveller, was sent into the sitting room with *The Times* and a brandy and told to relax. As if on cue, André arrived back with Middy who rushed to his bowl for a drink and greedily slurped water all over the floor.

For once Madeline couldn't be bothered to mop it up. 'Just for a change we are doing the cooking. We need something to keep our minds off certain problems. We'll tell you later. Chicken with stuffing and mash with gravy,' she told André with false cheerfulness. 'Would you be kind enough to keep Daniel company in the sitting room? He's all alone. We've given him *The Times*, but he won't find it very interesting.'

'*Bien sur!* Middy was very good,' André told them. 'No fight today. No running away . . . And I met Agatha in the park.' He hesitated, took off his jacket and turned slowly to face them. 'She was shocked. She 'ad a letter from Louise yesterday. She was married secretly a month ago – to a man named Robert 'Ine!'

The silence was tangible.

'Married!' said Madeline. 'To this other man? Oh, no! *No!*' She looked at Gertrude who was breathing heavily and had one hand over her heart.

171

'This is my fault,' Gertrude muttered brokenly. 'If only she had never met Daniel Grant. Dear Madeline – ' She sat down heavily – 'will you ever forgive me?'

'Don't talk like that, please,' Madeline said. 'I've told you before – there's nothing to forgive. We were all pleased with the idea of the lessons. No one is to blame.'

André looked from one to the other but said nothing.

Madeline looked at Gertrude. 'How will Daniel take this news? And what does it mean for baby Dan? Is he now officially Daniel Oscar Hine?'

André searched for something positive to say. 'But maybe they will be 'appy family. Maybe the little boy will be loved. Is it so terrible?'

Gertrude had recovered a little and now breathed normally. 'No, André, it will always be terrible if the boy doesn't know his real father . . . and if we never see Louise again or meet Louise's son. Who is going to break the news to Daniel? I don't think I could do it without breaking down or . . . or blaming him.'

'He already blames himself, Gertrude.' Madeline made a great effort to steady herself.

'Poor Daniel is now totally alone. I'll tell him. Perhaps you and André could manage the meal while I break the news. We shall need something to fortify us.'

André said, 'I wish I 'ad not told you this bad news.'

'We had to know sometime, André, and at least we can try and help Daniel. He will be distraught.'

She went into the sitting room with a heavy heart, searching for a gentle way of telling him that Louise was married. As soon as she entered the room he folded the paper and laid it aside. He began to speak, but Madeline held up her hand and he fell silent. She sat down in the armchair on the opposite side of the fire which was getting low. To give herself more time she picked up the tongs and added some coal.

She gave him a straight look. 'There is something you have to know, Daniel,' she told him as calmly as she could. 'Agatha has heard from Louise that . . . that some weeks ago . . . that she has married Robert Hine. I can't imagine how much that will hurt you, but . . .' Her voice cracked with the strain of

172

her own unhappiness and tears filled her eyes. 'Oh, Daniel! What did we do to bring this about?'

He had risen abruptly and now crossed to her. 'Are you sure?' he asked. 'I can't believe . . . It's so sudden. Do Robert's parents know about this? They would never wish it for their son. Marrying a woman with an illegitimate child? I can't imagine Stuart allowing it – and his wife will be most unhappy.'

'I don't think they know. Agatha says it was a secret wedding.' She pulled out a handkerchief and wiped her eyes. 'This mess is turning into a tragedy,' she whispered. 'Poor Gertrude is beside herself. She is too old for these shocks.'

He put an arm awkwardly around her and she longed to cry on his shoulder. She needed to be comforted and longed to comfort him in return but that was impossible. Sensing her nervousness, he moved away and stood staring out of the window.

'That will make it impossible to reclaim my son. I expect the marriage makes him an American citizen. Who can prove that Dan is not Robert's child?' He turned round, eyes dark with defeat. 'I wouldn't have expected this sort of behaviour from Robert. They are such a nice family. Or I thought so. His father, Stuart, is very straight and I trust him. Could she have persuaded Robert to elope, I wonder . . .'

'She persuaded *you* to run away with her!' The words were out before Madeline could stop herself.

'You're right, of course. Louise can be very persuasive . . . Oh, God! How could she do this to me? She knows how much I love him.'

Madeline was silently wondering the same thing. She was also wondering if she had ever known her daughter. She had thought they were close, but obviously Louise had been a very different person. Released from the strictures of a familiar family environment, she had changed. Or had this Louise been there all the time and she, Madeline, had never seen this side of her character? Had she ever subconsciously suspected that this manipulative woman was developing? Could that have happened?

Daniel said, 'Talk to me, Madeline. Help me. I don't know

173

what to do, but I shall have to go back. My work is there. What's left of my life is – or was – in New York.'

'You will have to see her, Daniel. Talk to her with no one else present.'

'And say what exactly? "Please leave your husband and come back to me and bring Dan with you?" He sighed. 'Robert can offer her so much more than I can. He will one day inherit the stud farm. Louise will be very, very wealthy. Dan will have everything he needs. He'll be set for life.'

'Money isn't everything,' Madeline said, clasping her hands tightly in an attempt to remain calm. 'He needs his real father!'

'He's only a baby. I doubt if he will even remember me.'

Madeline felt dizzy with the effort of trying to make sense of an impossibly complicated situation. She was looking for answers, but there seemed to be none. A sudden thought sent her into a panic. 'Suppose they come here? Suppose Louise wants to show off the baby? What shall I say? I can't have Robert Hine in my house after what he's done. He won't set a foot in this house. Oscar would never have allowed such a thing.' Her face crumpled. 'Oh, Oscar! I *need* you.'

Before she knew what was happening, Daniel's arms went round her. 'Please, please don't cry! I can't bear to think how much pain I've caused you by my actions. So many wrong decisions. Looking back I can hardly believe them all!' He held her close and it was so wonderful that Madeline wanted to surrender to the moment, but instead she drew gently back from him.

'Don't worry about me, Daniel. I'll survive this somehow, but you . . . I want to help you, but I don't know how.'

He stepped back. 'I'll do whatever I can when I get back to New York. I'll talk with Stuart. He's a very decent man. He may be willing to influence his son. I'll say I've seen you and that you and Gertrude desperately want to see the baby. Hopefully they'll visit England. Stuart does have a cousin somewhere in the west country although he did say the family have never been to England. Never been to Europe, in fact, so they might arrange a little tour . . . And Madeline – ' he took hold of her hand and she made no objection – 'if Robert is included in the package, don't turn them all away because of me. I want you to see Louise again. She may be making our lives difficult, but she still loves you. She pretends she doesn't care, but she does. And I want you to meet our little boy.' He smiled. 'He is the good thing that has come out of all this grief. I very much want you to meet your grandson.'

Eleven

The Christmas season duly arrived and to Madeline's great surprise, she enjoyed herself. The three of them made a big effort to put aside their cares and concentrate on the party. Invitations were written and sent out and most of them were accepted. Gertrude rallied marvellously, cheered along by André, and Madeline awoke each day with the intention of enjoying it as much as she could. There was no reason, she told herself, why her daughter's actions should spoil her own life and as each day passed she clung on to the hope that she might one day see Louise and Dan, with or without Robert Hine. She knew that Daniel was right about the man and determined to be courteous if he ever visited, but she would never forgive him. His disruptive influence had done immeasurable harm to what should have been Daniel and Louise's family.

When the day of the party arrived, which was Christmas Eve, she put all these unhappy thoughts aside and gave herself over to the prevailing mood of excited anticipation. The hours flew by and became a hectic blur. There was so much to think about. For Madeline, familiar only with the usual family Christmas, a party of this kind, on such a scale, was uncharted territory and she was more than willing to let André and Gertrude oversee the organization. Happy to take orders, she scurried about the house, draping strands of ivy around the pictures, arranging sprays of holly on the window sills. She polished glasses and arranged them on two large trays. André had insisted that they serve a champagne cup made from champagne, soda water, powdered sugar, pounded ice and brandy.

'One glass of this,' he assured Madeline, 'given to each guest on arrival will 'elp to create the right atmosphere.'

Gertrude explained that the exact proportions of the ingredients of the cup were André's secret. 'Better we don't know!' she said, laughing.

There would be no need for plates, André insisted, as everything edible would come in small portions.

'It's a finger buffet,' Gertrude explained. 'People help themselves to the canapés and eat them in one or two bites. You'll see.'

She seemed very much in tune with André who, an ardent party-giver, was in seventh heaven. It seemed that Gertrude had generously 'lent' her Paris flat to André each Christmas and between twenty and thirty people had somehow crammed themselves into the small space.

Today André reigned supreme in the kitchen, baking small sausages, tiny vol-au-vents and what he described as 'elegant titbits' – cheese straws, crispy anchovy fingers and salmon patties. The day before he had made a pork pate and this, he had told them, would be served on small water biscuits.

Gertrude had made ginger beer and lemonade.

'André's in his element,' Gertrude said, smiling.

'Perhaps he should have been a cook instead of an artist.'

Gertrude shook out the large tablecloth and smoothed it over the table. She paused and stared at Madeline. 'A cook?' She frowned. 'A pastry cook! I wonder if that would suit him. We must think about it.'

Madeline placed the flowers she had arranged in the centre of the table and they both stood back to admire the effect. Madeline had tied a broad red ribbon round the glass bowl and the red, blue and purple anemones made a bright splash of colour against the crisp white damask.

Gertrude said, 'If he wishes, he could train in Paris. The French are the best cooks in the world.'

Madeline didn't know if this were true, but she let it pass. 'It would be costly, wouldn't it?'

Gertrude shrugged. 'I shall pay for it myself. I was planning to leave everything to Louise, but now she no longer needs my help.'

Madeline was aware of a frisson of resentment at these words, but told herself that Gertrude was right and that she was perfectly entitled to spend her money on a more deserving cause if she wished. André had been like a son to her and maybe it was fair.

Louise had, for so long, been the centre of their universe that it was hard to think in any other way. She tried to visualize her daughter as a wealthy young mother, but that, too, was difficult. Yet she and Oscar had always hoped Louise would marry reasonably well and be provided for by her husband. Now it had happened so why did she not appreciate the fact and enjoy the rest of her life, knowing that Louise was in good hands? Obviously this Robert loved her or he would never have risked being disinherited by his parents by marrying secretly against their wishes.

Gertrude said, 'Wake up, Madeline! You're miles away. We have fifteen guests descending on us at seven and it's already half past six and we're not even dressed. At this rate we'll never be ready.'

'Sorry!' With an effort, she forced her mind back to the present. 'What shall I do next?'

'Go upstairs and change. You are the hostess and must be available to greet the guests. Make yourself look beautiful.'

'What about you?'

'I'll go up as soon as you come down again. Don't argue, dear. Shoo!'

André looked up from the stove as Gertrude entered the room. His face glistened with perspiration, but his eyes shone with excitement. 'Ten more minutes! We are nearly there. Is the dining room ready?'

'It is. And I have sent Madeline upstairs to put on her finery.' She sighed.

André said, 'You are wishing Louise could be here, no? I wish it too, but it won't be long now.'

Gertrude smiled as she sat down. 'Seven days! And Madeline knows nothing about it.'

He turned to a large jar of potted prawns and began to fill the vol-au-vents with a deft, practiced hand. 'So she 'as not guessed? Not a glimmer of an idea?'

'No. I know her, André. If she had guessed she would never be able to contain herself. No. It will be a wonderful surprise. A wonderful way to see in the New Year.'

'They will like the 'otel. It is very *impressionnant*!'

Gertrude frowned. 'In a way I wish we could tell her. She would be able to look forward to it. Happy anticipation, you know. As it is, she will hardly have time to recover from the shock before they are off again to Italy. A few short hours, André. That's all it will be.'

'Better than nothing and Louise was most insistent that her mother should not know. You have hidden the letter, I 'ope.'

'Of course, but . . .' She sighed again.

'But 'e is coming. Robert 'Ine. That worries you.' He finished filling one plate of vol-au-vents and started another.

'They look good, André. May I try one?' Her hand crept towards the plate, but he slapped her wrist playfully.

'*Non!* You must wait!'

Resigned, she continued. 'I wish it were just Louise and the baby. That would be perfect.'

'You may like 'im.' He pointed to the plate. ''Elp your-self, Gertrude. I was only joking.'

Without further prompting, Gertrude popped one of the vol-au-vents into her mouth and he waited anxiously for her verdict.

'Perfect!' she said. 'Would you like me to sample all of your . . .?' She stopped abruptly as Madeline's footsteps sounded on the stairs.

Madeline was wearing a new dress in soft green with cream lace at the neck and sleeves and wore a plain gold locket which Oscar had given her for their tenth wedding anniversary. She had swept up her hair and fastened it with a dark green barrette.

André said, '*Très belle!*'

Gertrude nodded. 'You look lovely. Now it's my turn.' She hurried up to her bedroom and changed her clothes, but before she had even applied her perfume there was a knock at the door. The party had begun.

It was an outstanding success and Madeline found herself swept up in the fun. Agatha and Albert had brought Victoria who spent much of the evening helping André and their shared whispers alerted Madeline to the fact that they were fond of each other. The Carters from next door had brought

179

a box of chocolates to finish off the feast. The champagne cup had the desired effect and, as André had predicted, the ice was soon broken. Agatha sang several songs with her mother as accompanist and Miss Maddock played her violin. Her fiancé, a little the worse for wear, recited a slightly risqué monologue, but nobody appeared to be affronted, for which poor Miss Maddock, who was some-what mortified, was obviously very relieved. The doctor had a ready supply of riddles and jokes and his quiet wife watched him from her corner and laughed in the right places.

André, in his element, flitted to and fro, organizing every-thing with a confidence which spoke of previous successful parties. They played guessing games and pen and paper games and ended up with charades. Nobody seemed to want to go home and it was after midnight when Madeline closed the door behind the last guest.

André, Madeline and Gertrude sank down into three armchairs and groaned with exhaustion. All three were beaming with satisfaction.

Gertrude said, 'That was a party to end all parties. I haven't enjoyed myself so much in years.'

Madeline said, 'All thanks to André! You were superb. The food was quite excellent. I think the crispy anchovy things were my favourite.'

'Anchovy fingers,' he corrected her. 'I liked the salmon patties. That was a new recipe and it worked well.'

Gertrude said, 'I drank too much champagne cup, but I don't regret it for a moment!'

'I thought Victoria a very nice girl. I saw her helping you carry round the canapés,' Madeline said.

André's smile broadened. 'She is sweet, *n'est ce pas*?'

Gertrude said, 'Very sweet, André. She likes you a lot, I could tell by her face. Are you looking for a wife?'

Madeline cried, 'Gertrude! You'll embarrass him.'

He rubbed his eyes tiredly. 'I do not embarrass. But yes, I will one day want a wife. And if Victoria wants an 'usband . . . and thinks I am suitable . . .' He rolled his eyes. 'Then you will 'ear wedding bells!'

'A wedding,' Gertrude echoed. 'How I love weddings. You

180

hear that, Madeline? A wedding. Do you think we shall be invited?'

'If not I shall want to know why!'

Later that night she was still exhausted but wide-awake, too excited to sleep. For the first time in months she felt relaxed and happy and she relished the sensation. She replayed the party in her mind and was certain it had been a success. So it was possible to be happy, she marvelled, when your life seems to be falling apart. It was a comforting thought. She was really lucky to have Gertrude and André with her – for the moment! It looked as though André had fallen in love with Victoria and, if so, Madeline was pleased for him. Gertrude would not live forever and he had so much love to give.

Her eyes began to close and she hoped she was falling asleep. Perhaps tonight there would be no nightmares . . .

As Christmas and the party faded into past, the weather brought very cold conditions. The streets were first white with snow and then brown with slush and getting around was difficult. Middy hated the cold and particularly objected to the snow, but, whatever the weather, André walked him in the park twice a day and managed to meet Victoria on many of these occasions. She always brought treats for the dog, who came to look forward to meeting her almost as much as André.

'Middy is much better now,' she remarked one day as they walked along the path below bare trees and a grey sky. 'He doesn't tug on his lead so much.'

'It is the training,' André explained. 'I spend much time on 'im and 'e is quick to learn.'

As if to prove them wrong Middy made an unsuccessful attempt to chase a squirrel and nearly strangled himself as Victoria held on tightly to his lead. She said, 'Poor Louise. She must miss him.'

'No! If she love 'im so much she would take him with 'er.'

'He loves you, André.'

'And you also.'

'Perhaps. He's a nice dog.'

181

As they strolled, he told her about Gertrude's offer to send him to train in Paris as a pastry cook.

Her expression changed. 'Oh! But you wouldn't, would you? I mean, aren't you going to be an artist? You sold one of your pictures.'

'But only one. The gallery turned down the next two I offer them so maybe I don't make a living out of painting and, you know, it does not trouble me. I like to cook but I never thought of it before. I am at home in Paris.'

Her footsteps faltered. 'But . . . Oh, André! I would never see you. Wouldn't you miss me?' She stopped and turned to look at him. 'I thought that you and I . . . I mean, that you might want to stay in England.'

'I wondered if you would like Paris?'

They stared at each other, unwilling to risk the next step.

André broke the silence. 'I wondered if you could live in Paris for a while. With me.'

'Oh, but . . . my parents would never . . .'

'As my wife.'

'Your wife! Oh!' Her eyes widened. 'Goodness, André!'

Middy managed to wind his lead around their legs and began to bark but neither of them noticed him. The park keeper walked past, gave them a curious glance and walked on. A small girl pushing a doll in a small pram appeared with her mother and an older boy with an iron hoop ran right past them without really seeing them.

André said softly, 'You don't have to decide now. I can wait . . . but not for long!' A tentative smile softened his face. 'If Middy would allow I could go down on one knee and . . .'

'But the ground is all wet and muddy!'

He looked around at the muddy grass, deserted swings and dripping leafless trees. 'This isn't very romantic, is it? Maybe some other time I . . .'

'No, André! I mean, this is quite perfect,' she assured him breathlessly.

'Then, dearest Victoria, I love you. Please will you marry me?'

She threw her arms around his neck and whispered, 'Yes, André, I will! With great pleasure!'

'Because . . .?' He regarded her quizzically.

'Because? Oh, I see! Because I love you more than anyone else in the whole world.'

'Then I will come to your 'ouse tomorrow and ask your father for your 'and.'

Ecstatically they clung together while Middy whined for someone to help him out of the tangle he had created for himself. Suddenly remembering his existence, they both stared down at him. He stopped whining, sat down and began to scratch behind his ear.

'Dogs!' said Victoria laughing. 'They simply don't understand romance.'

New Year's Eve arrived with gales and rain. The first thing Madeline did each morning was to re-light the fires that had not survived the night. Sometimes, the ashes were still hot and a few twists of paper and a handful of kindling wood would set them going again. On this particular morning, when she came in from the shed with the coal scuttle, she was surprised to find Gertrude in the kitchen boiling the kettle.

'I woke so early,' she explained. 'I fancied a cup of tea. Now you can join me.'

Madeline stared at her head which was a mass of curling rags. 'You've curled your hair.'

'So I have. I thought yesterday how lank it looks lately and thought I would take a bit of time over it. It cheers me up when I'm down. Hair is so important, isn't it? For one's morale, I mean.'

'I suppose it is.' She sat down. 'I think that when André finally goes back to Paris I shall get another housekeeper. I'd forgotten how heavy the coal scuttle is when it's full.'

Gertrude poured boiling water into the teapot. 'I could do something with your hair, Madeline. It might suit you to change the parting.'

Madeline gave the stove a poke, added some coal and closed the little door with a clang. 'I wonder how André's getting on over there. It all seems rather sudden. I miss him.'

'Strike while the iron is hot. They'll accept him. Georges knew my father, you know. They went to the same college. He'll take him on for my sake and then discover how good he is. It will be a good profession for him. He will teach him everything he knows and André will relish every moment.'

Madeline stirred her tea. 'I'm so pleased for André that he has Victoria. They will be good for each other. She is so excited to be going to Paris and the wedding is only a month away. You have to admire her parents. They have taken it very well. One minute you have your daughter and the next she is getting married . . . Oh, Madeline! How thoughtless of me. Please forget those careless words.'

Madeline swallowed, nodded and took a mouthful of tea. 'A new year starts tomorrow,' she said. 'I wonder what it will bring for us. For any of us!'

'Plenty of surprises, I expect. Some good, some bad.' Gertrude was trying hard to sound normal, but it was difficult. 'Don't be surprised, Madeline, when you go into the pantry. There's an iced cake there. André made it before he went to Paris. He says we must celebrate the New Year.'

'How sweet of him. But where has it been since he left?'

'Hidden in his bedroom!'

Madeline immediately crossed to the pantry and discovered André's surprise. A square cake covered with white icing and tied with a gold ribbon. For a moment her heart lurched. It resembled a wedding cake. When she returned to the table Gertrude's cup was empty and she had gone back upstairs. 'We *are* in a hurry today!' she muttered.

An hour later when the house had been tidied, Gertrude insisted on restyling Madeline's hair and made her wear the green dress she had worn for the Christmas party.

'Just because we are alone it doesn't mean we can't celebrate the New Year,' she insisted. 'We shall have our own party and we shall think on absent friends.'

After some half-hearted argument Madeline gave in. When she came down again, Gertrude was in the kitchen and she had locked herself in.

'Gertrude? What are you up to? Open this door!'

'It's a surprise! Go away. Sit in the sitting room and work on your tapestry.'

'Oh, for heavens sake!' Baffled, Madeline obediently made her way into the sitting room – and stopped dead in her tracks.

For a moment confusion swept through her. Was she losing her mind? She stared at the tableau before her. Louise sat in the armchair holding a baby, and a man Madeline had never seen before stood at the window. Shock robbed her of speech for a moment and her hand went to her heart which seemed to have stopped beating. The man turned. He was young and sturdy with wavy red hair and a freckled, good-natured face. His mouth was generous and his blue eyes regarded her steadily.

He said, 'I brought your family to see you, ma'am.' His voice was husky but pleasant. 'We all wish you a happy New Year.' His American drawl was very clear and she sensed a certain arrogance in his manner. He made no move towards her and she remained, her feet seemingly frozen to the floor.

She found it difficult to breathe. They were here. He had brought them. Robert Hine was standing in her sitting room. What was she to do? She thought of Daniel and the anguish this man had caused him. No, she corrected herself – the anguish that this man *and Louise* had caused him.

Louise said, 'This is my husband, Rob, Mama.'

A wide wedding band glinted on her left hand. At least this union had been entered into legally, Madeline reflected.

'Rob's just the dearest man! I know you two are going to get along.'

Her voice already showed the American influence. Madeline longed to say something but words failed her.

He said, 'Pleased to meet you, ma'am. This is your grandson Dan, but he's chosen this moment to fall asleep. I guess the trip has tired him.' He finally stepped towards her and shook her hand with a warm, firm grasp.

She said, 'Yes . . . Well . . . I can see that it has.' She looked at the baby. Daniel was right. He looked just like Louise at five months old. 'He's . . . Oh, he's wonderful!' she stammered, overcome with the depth of her feelings. She felt an unexpected jolt – a physical and emotional yearning to hold him in her arms.

Louise was smiling. 'I promised you a boy, Mama. Do you remember? He won't sleep for long – just a cat-nap – so make the most of it, Mama. When he wakes you can hold

185

him. Robert's brought his camera. He wants to take some photographs, then we'll send copies to you for you to keep.'

'Oh! How kind.' She stared at Louise, astonished. Her daughter had put on a little weight but it suited her. Gone was the restless child, and in her place there was this lovely young woman, a virtual stranger, dressed in an expensive and stylish travelling suit in soft grey wool. Madeline found herself wondering if they still knew each other.

She said faintly, 'I wish your father was here to see Dan.' She put out a hand and clutched the mantelpiece as a wave of weakness seized her.

'Mama! Do sit down!'

Robert was suddenly beside her as she swayed, and he helped her to a chair.

'Thank you. It's just the shock.' She sank back as Gertrude swept into the room carrying a tray holding champagne and glasses. She set them down and then looked at their visitors. She gave Louise a brisk kiss, smiled at the sleeping baby and then offered her hand to Robert.

'I'm Gertrude, Louise's grandmother,' she explained.

At once Madeline wished she had done something equally gracious. Gertrude was unflappable, she thought enviously – but then Gertrude must have known they were coming and had had a chance to decide how to behave toward Robert Hine.

Gertrude said, 'I'll bring in the cake,' and made herself scarce once more.

Louise said, 'Maybe you should hold him while he's asleep, Mama. He does wriggle so when he's awake. He's very strong for his age.' Without waiting for a reply she stood up and lowered the baby gently into Madeline's eager arms. 'And don't you dare cry, Mama!' she said, her smile softening the words.

Madeline, overjoyed to be holding her grandson in her arms at last, closed her eyes briefly in a silent prayer to thank God for the moment. He was heavier than she had expected but his head, in its white knitted bonnet, rested warmly against her arm. His tiny hands were clenched, his eyes closed in sleep, the small mouth like the proverbial rosebud. 'Has he got any hair?' she asked.

'He has now. He was born bald and wrinkled and horrible!'

She laughed. 'But within a few weeks he had changed. His hair's going to be curly and dark like Daniel's.'

She speaks of Daniel so easily, thought Madeline in surprise.

Robert said, 'Is it fine with you folks if I go for a quick walk? All that travelling has left me kind of stiff.'

Louise grinned at him. 'You're just missing your sports, darling.' She turned to Madeline. 'Robert's a keen sportsman. He rides, of course, and he just loves fishing and hunting.'

Robert said, 'Louise is going to be a good shot one day. She's learning fast. And she rides well.'

'I have my own darling horse,' she said, 'called Dandy and he's a three-year-old piebald. Robert thought he'd be a bit too much for me, but I proved him wrong, didn't I, Rob?'

'You certainly did!'

'How wonderful.' Madeline had a vision of Louise riding barebacked across the prairie, her hair streaming in the wind. She glanced down at young Dan and saw that he, too, would grow up in this wonderful environment. But would he ever know his birthright? Would he ever know England and all that it offered . . . He would be an American. *Was an American!* She would never know him. There would never be that meeting of minds that only comes when one generation is close to the next and they share the same history and values. And, worst of all, he would never know his real father.

Gertrude came in with the cake and a knife and explained that André had made it and had left it for them to celebrate the New Year.

Louise said, 'How sweet of him.'

Gertrude nodded. 'He is going to marry Agatha's cousin. He's in Paris at the moment. He's going to study as a pastry cook with an old friend of my father's.'

Louise cried, 'A wedding! Oh, how lovely! Will I be invited?'

Robert said, 'We'll be in Italy in two days time so I guess not.'

Her face fell. 'Oh, what a shame. I just love weddings.'

As Gertrude cut slices of cake, Robert did the honours with the champagne. The cork popped, but he managed to avoid spilling a drop.

187

Madeline said, 'Do you have any photographs of your wedding, Louise?'

Husband and wife exchanged a quick glance.

Louise said, 'No. We didn't bother. It was all so sudden. I was swept off my feet.'

Madeline wanted to say, 'For the second time!' but realized how unkind that would sound. She wanted desperately to enjoy their visit and to be seduced by the idea of Robert as a son-in-law, but the thought of Daniel's unhappiness made it impossible.

Gertrude said, 'What did you wear, dear?'

'Oh, yes! I nearly forgot!' Delighted by the question, Louise launched into the details, her face glowing at the memory of the occasion. It seemed that Robert had bought her a dress in oyster satin with buttoned strap shoes to match. On her head she wore a circlet of white velvet encrusted with tiny pearls. She carried a small prayer book bound in white leather and two white roses.

'No expense spared,' Robert added, amusement in his voice. 'We were in a small dusty town in the middle of nowhere with a shabby clapboard church . . .'

Louise laughed. 'Tell them about the organist, Rob.'

His face lit up with a broad grin. 'Hey! The drunken organist! How could I forget him? First he played the wrong hymn and then fell off his stool. The preacher man must have been a hundred if he was a day . . . But your lovely daughter had insisted on looking the part so we'd bought the dress and my suit in New York before we hit the highway. The word had gotten out and there was quite a crowd when we left the church. A woman threw rice . . .'

'And Rob threw candy for the children.'

While her husband was speaking, Louise had opened her soft leather handbag and produced two gift wrapped presents. The small square one was for Madeline and the long thin one was for Gertrude. 'Open them after we've gone,' she instructed. She handed them to Robert who placed them carefully on the table.

Daniel began to wake up and Madeline said it was Gertrude's turn to hold him and surrendered him reluctantly. As soon as he was on Gertrude's lap he began to wave his small fists happily. Madeline bit into the rich fruit cake and tried to enter into the spirit of the unexpected party, but she found it hard to swallow.

Louise asked about Agatha and Albert and then complained because she was going to miss another wedding. 'But I'll send her a wonderful wedding gift! Something from Harrods, perhaps.' Robert coughed and her face fell. 'Oh, no Rob! I forgot. There won't be time to go shopping. I keep forgetting we're off again tomorrow evening. First here, then Rome in Italy, then Athens, Greece . . .' She frowned. 'Where are we going after Greece, Rob?'

'I forget but it's all in the itinerary.' He swallowed his champagne and set down the glass.

Madeline said, 'If you insist on a walk, Robert, perhaps you would take Middy with you.'

Louise's eyes widened. 'Middy! Oh, heavens! I quite forgot him.' She jumped to her feet and rushed into the kitchen and they heard hysterical barking, scuffling and laughter as the two were reunited. Madeline caught Gertrude's eye. Were they both thinking the same thing, Madeline wondered – that someone had to mention Daniel. She knew she could never face him again if they did not raise the subject of the baby's real father.

Five minutes later, Robert and Middy had set out on their walk and the three women were left with the baby. Louise retired to the bedroom where she fed him and changed his nappy.

'He'll soon be on solids,' Louise told them proudly.' And he has one tooth coming through, but he doesn't make the slightest fuss about it.'

Madeline took a deep breath and glanced at Gertrude who gave a small nod. 'Louise, dear,' she began carefully. 'We saw Daniel a few weeks ago. He is very unhappy. What is going to happen, Louise? You surely cannot mean to keep the boy from him. You'll break his heart!'

Louise's expression changed. 'It really isn't your business, Mama. It's between him and me. I mean, between him and me and Robert. Rob adores him.'

'So does Daniel.'

Louise tutted irritably. 'Oh, heavens, Mama. Daniel this!

Daniel that! Why do you have to spoil everything? We've come all this way and . . .'

'But Daniel is his *father*, Louise! Nothing's going to change that.'

'Not legally because we were never married. Robert has married me and in a way that makes him Dan's father. It's not a legal adoption but as good as. It's not fair on Dan to tell him he's not Robert's son especially if we have children of our own. That would make Dan a sort of inferior son. I want him to be as much a son as the others will be.'

Gertrude said, 'You don't mean . . . You're not expecting another baby, are you?'

Louise laughed. She was recovering from the reproaches. 'Heavens no! But I expect to have more. Rob wants a large family and we can afford it. Money is no object, as they say. Dan will have brothers and sisters. He will have *everything*! You should be pleased. Both of you. Don't you want what's best for me and little Dan?'

Gertrude gave her a long look, began to speak but changed her mind, then gathered up the tray and left the room. In her absence a long silence fell. Louise handed Dan back to Madeline and stood and stretched. She crossed the room in three light steps and dropped a kiss on the top of her mother's head. Encumbered with the baby Madeline was unable to return the kiss.

Louise went on briskly. 'Anyway it's lovely to see you and Grandmama again. Maybe you'll come out to America one day and visit with us.'

'Come to America? Heavens, Louise! I don't know about that. That is, it's a kind thought and would be very exciting.' Madeline shifted the baby into a more comfortable position.

'He's getting so heavy, isn't he, Mama! But how do you think I look Mama? Doesn't Robert look after me well? Isn't that what you wanted for me? That I should marry well and be happy? I adore Robert and he is just crazy for me. The moment he set eyes on me he made up his mind. He knew his parents wouldn't approve, me being with Daniel, and he was right. So he whisked me away.' Her face lit up at the memory.

Madeline stared down into the contented face of Daniel's

child. Could she really interfere? Why should she be balancing Daniel Grant's happiness against that of her own daughter? 'Don't you love him any more? You were once . . .'

'Oh, Mama! Don't! He said you wanted to see me and Dan and we've made a special effort to call in and see you and Gertrude. I thought you'd be delighted.'

'Oh, dearest, I am! I've lived for this moment ever since you disappeared.'

'I didn't disappear, Mama! You are so dramatic! I simply moved in with Daniel. It was what he wanted. I'm sure of it. I had to encourage him. He would never have said anything because he is so much older than me. Robert is more my age.' She frowned at some unspoken thought, then brightened with an effort. 'Oh, what does it matter now? I'm so wonderfully happy!'

'It matters because you and Daniel have a child, Louise! It's so cruel to keep Dan away from him. Don't you see that? Surely you could come to some arrangement. Robert could hardly object.'

Louise had the decency to look a little crestfallen. 'I had to take the baby with me, Mama. Don't *you* see *that*? How could I leave my little boy behind? When Robert asked me to marry him, I said only if he would accept Dan. He didn't want to agree, naturally, because he just knew we would have our own family . . . but he was so in love with me, I knew he'd say yes in the end and he did. I didn't do it to hurt Daniel. I did it because I admitted my mistake and saw that my future lay with Robert and . . . and I saw that we would have a wonderful life. Surely you can see it was the grown-up thing to do.'

She looked at Madeline, her eyes full of entreaty. 'Do please say you understand, Mama.'

Madeline stared down at her hands. 'I understand that you were in love . . .' she began. 'But I keep thinking of poor Daniel.'

'But he's nothing to you and I'm your daughter! I thought I was in love with him, but it was just a girlish thing. An infatuation. I'm truly sorry that we've caused him so much pain and I've prayed and prayed for forgiveness, but would you rather I spent my whole life with the wrong man? What I feel for Robert is completely different. Surely you . . .?'

The door opened and Gertrude came back into the room and Louise turned to her eagerly. 'I was just telling Mama that what I felt for Daniel was what the magazines call "calf love".'

'Did Daniel know that?'

Louise blinked. 'I don't know. How could I tell? I was younger then.' She looked from one to the other in exasperation. 'Why can't you leave the past behind? Why don't you ask me about the future?'

Madeline and Gertrude exchanged helpless glances. Gertrude sat down and held out her arms for the baby. When she was bouncing him on her knee she said artlessly, 'So, how do you get along with Robert's parents? Daniel was telling us what a decent man Stuart Hine is.'

'Oh! Did he? Yes . . . Well, I daresay he is a decent man, in a way. I don't blame him for being upset. I mean, eloping the way we did. It was all very difficult.' Her face darkened. 'Robert was supposed to be marrying a girl called Elaine. He didn't tell me at first. She's the daughter of a friend of theirs. Childhood sweethearts. That sort of thing. Robert said it had always been assumed they would marry, but then he fell hopelessly in love with me!'

Madeline sighed deeply. She was longing to understand what had happened but dreading the details.

'And don't sigh like that, Mama, *please*! It was nobody's fault.' Louise trawled through her memories. 'Mr Hine was not very pleased. Well . . . he was furious actually and Mrs Hine cried. She was so fond of Elaine and she already thought of her as a daughter-in-law. I was the fly in the ointment, if you must know . . .' Her mouth trembled. 'It was awful. Poor Robert! They were thoroughly beastly to him – and to me.'

'To you?' Madeline instinctively sprang to her daughter's defence. 'But you didn't know about Elaine!'

Louise shrugged. 'His mother said I had broken up the most perfect match and had shown no consideration for Elaine.' She tossed her head. 'I couldn't let that pass! I asked her if she wanted her son to marry the wrong woman and regret it for the rest of his life?'

Seeing the expression on her mother's face, she set her chin defiantly. 'And don't blame me, Mama. It was Robert's decision. He was determined I should become his wife and because they wouldn't agree to the match he said we'd elope. So we did.'

Madeline kept her gaze on young Dan who was now sitting on the floor. 'So . . . they're not very pleased.' She tried to imagine the Hine's household thrown into turmoil by the events. It was like the ripples on a pond when a stone is tossed into it, she thought. She dare not meet Gertrude's eyes.

Fortunately at that moment Robert arrived back with Middy, and Louise rushed out to the kitchen to make a fuss of the dog. Robert announced that they must make tracks for the hotel shortly because they had an early start the next morning, but he would take the photographs as promised. Within minutes he had seated them in various attractive groups and had taken a dozen photographs. Gertrude, with a little instruction, took one with him in it. Madeline was reluctantly impressed by his confident, easy manner as he coaxed smiles from them and even jollied Dan out of a small tantrum before it developed into a crying fit. Madeline told herself to be grateful for small mercies. Robert would be a good husband. If Daniel had not been abandoned; if the baby had not been snatched away from his father; if Elaine had not been grief-stricken by the collapse of her own marriage plans . . . then Madeline would have approved of Robert wholeheartedly. Against her instincts, Madeline admitted to herself that she couldn't fault Robert Hine but all those other considerations *were* there. Louise had made a good marriage against a background of heartbreak.

'Robert adores photography,' Louise was saying. 'I'll see that he takes plenty of Dan and me and the house. Oh, we forgot to tell you about the house we're building. I mean, we're having built. It's a combined wedding present from Robert's three aunts. He's the only nephew and they just adore him. It means we don't have to share the big house with his parents for much longer, thank the Lord.'

Robert packed away the camera, glanced in the mirror over the mantelpiece and ran strong fingers through his hair. 'There's no time to tell them about the house, Louise. We'll send photographs when it's finished.'

Suddenly the taxi was at the door. Madeline held the baby for the last time and clung to Louise.

'Take care of yourself, Mama, and you, too, Grandmama!' Louise kissed them and Robert shook them by the hand. He looked, thought Madeline, as if he was glad to be moving on. Perhaps Louise had needed to beg him to make the journey which couldn't have been easy for him.

Hardly able to breathe, Madeline watched them climb into the taxi and caught a last glimpse of Louise as the horses responded to the flick of the driver's whip and the taxicab drew her daughter and the baby away.

Stunned, they closed the door and went back into the sitting room.

Madeline said, 'They've gone!' The tears were very close. 'Oh, God!'

Gertrude said soothingly, 'But we've seen her, dear, and we've seen the little boy. Months ago, when she disappeared and we thought she might be dead, we'd have given anything for a few hours with her. Whatever we think about Robert Hine, we have to be grateful to him. He brought them here all the way from America.'

Madeline drew a deep breath and then another. She knew that Gertrude was right. She counted to ten in an attempt to calm herself. Controlling her ragged emotions with an effort, she nodded. 'Yes. You're right and I'm an ungrateful wretch! We've seen her and she's happy and the baby's a delight.'

'And healthy and takes after Louise! So it's all good news, dear, and a wonderful start to the year.'

Madeline said, 'Why did you keep the visit so quiet? Why didn't you drop a hint?'

'I would have preferred to tell you, but Louise was adamant. She wrote telling me that they were coming and insisting that it was to be a surprise for you. Apparently she'd had a letter from Daniel telling her of his visit here and how distressed we were. André, of course, decided to make a cake.'

Madeline nodded then held out her arms. 'Happy New Year!' she said, not knowing whether to laugh or cry.

Gertrude put her arms around her and held her close. 'We must make it so!' she said.

*   *   *

194

Later that evening they unwrapped the presents. Madeline's was the white leather-bound prayer book that Louise had held at her wedding. Inside she had written – *With love to my darling Mama on the event of my wedding. Louise.* And the date. Madeline pressed it to her heart, kissed it and showed it to Gertrude.

'She has sent me the two white roses,' Gertrude whispered. They had been pressed and framed. Across the bottom of the white mount Louise had written – *From Louise to my dearest Grandmama on my wedding day.*

They looked at each other. Madeline said 'Even though she was miles away she was thinking of us.' She glanced at the prayer book. 'I shall sleep with this on the bedside table.'

Gertrude said. 'You may yet see her in America, dear. If you want anything enough you have to make it happen!'

Madeline summoned up all her courage. 'Will you come with me if I go?'

'Try and stop me. Madeline.'

Twelve

A nd the old century gave way to the new one as the bells pealed out to see in 1900. The year passed with the coming and going of letters and Madeline's mantelpiece filled up with framed photographs of Dan and his mother. The idea of travelling to America was often aired and discussed in great detail, but Gertrude's strength was failing and Madeline was afraid the sea journey would be too much for her or, worse, that she would fall ill in America. She therefore took the matter no further and there were other excitements from time to time to distract her.

André and Victoria were married in St Mark's Church at the beginning of May and both Madeline and Gertrude were invited. The sun shone and the wind dropped and the bride looked wonderful as she left the church with her beaming husband. They left for Paris the next day where André had found a small flat, but they both promised to return from time to time. Letters from André helped them keep abreast of his training as a pastry cook and they shared a feeling of pride in his success.

In July the long awaited letter from Louise told them that she was expecting Robert's first child. Madeline read it out to Gertrude who was confined to bed with a heavy cold and a chesty cough.

Dearest Mama and Grandmama,
    At last. Robert is going to be a father and Dan will be a big brother! I am hoping for a girl this time, but Rob wants his first child to be a boy. It is early days yet – the doctor has said it should be the middle of next February, probably the 14th or 15th. I know you will

196

be pleased for us. I am in fine spirits and good health. We will move into our house in three weeks time and I am busy interviewing staff . . .

'Staff?' echoed Gertrude. 'How many staff do they need?' Madeline read on.

Rob's mother insists we shall need a cook and a maid as well as a woman to do the heavy work and a man for the garden. We already have a nanny in mind, she has been recommended by a friend of mine . . .

Gertrude sat up a little straighter. 'A nanny as well? Goodness gracious! Louise will have so much time on her hands. She won't know what to do with it!'

Madeline rolled her eyes. 'All that money has gone to her head.'

. . . who will look after Dan while I concentrate on the new baby.

'Madeline stopped. 'Oh! Poor Dan!' Dismayed, she looked at Gertrude. 'Whose idea is that, I wonder?'

Gertrude brooded. 'It's a very difficult time for a toddler when the second child arrives. They often feel left out and start to feel jealous. Not that it's uncommon. It happens all the time. Still, it's their family. It's not our place to interfere. They have Robert's mother to advise them. At least the Hines are vaguely reconciled to the match now.'

. . . Rob has bought a miniature pony for Dan to ride when he is a little older. It's just the cutest thing you ever saw and we've named him Chuck. Children on a stud farm are expected to ride practically from birth here, but don't start to fret. The stable hands are falling over themselves, all offering to teach Dan to ride (He's a great favourite!) but Rob will do it personally.

197

Gertrude said, 'Have you noticed, Madeline? Louise never mentions Daniel. I wonder if she has any idea how hard the lawyers are working on his behalf. The court case is any week now if my memory serves me correctly. They must grant him visiting rights this time or I think he'll go mad.'

Madeline put down the letter. 'I keep worrying that he might do something rash.'

'Rash? Good heavens, Madeline! Daniel's not the rash type.'

'Not normally, but don't you think his letters have that desperate tone about them. I'm terrified he will do something serious and get himself into trouble.'

'You don't mean . . . kidnap the boy, surely?' Her eyes widened. 'Not Daniel!'

Madeline sighed. 'Let's pray that I'm wrong.' She picked up the letter.

> Robert sends his best regards to you both. As you see I enclose the latest photographs of us. Do take care of yourselves.
> Love from your affectionate daughter,
> Louise
> PS The scribble at the bottom of the letter is from Dan!

They scrutinized the photographs – Dan asleep in his new bed; Dan with his nanny – a buxom, rosy faced woman; Louise sitting under a large awning in the garden of the new house which they had already seen; one of Dan holding a small puppy and one of Robert astride a large black horse.

'Do you think Robert helps to train the horses?' Gertrude asked. 'Or does he just oversee staff and . . .' A fit of coughing interrupted her sentence.

Madeline glanced at her. 'I'm going to ask the doctor to call,' she told her. 'I fancy you look a little flushed. Do you feel hot at all?'

'I do at the moment, but I'm sure I'm . . .'

'I'm *not* sure, Gertrude, and I don't want to take any chances. At your . . .'

'Don't you dare say "at my age"!' Gertrude looked at her

fiercely. 'I'm a tough old bird, you know that, Madeline. A cool drink of barley water and a nap will sort me out. You'll see. If I'm no better in the morning . . .' She began to cough again.

Madeline hesitated. She knew how much Gertrude hated fuss. Almost as much as she hated doctors whom she considered to be mainly expensive charlatans. She also disliked Doctor Forbes and called him a pompous ass, though fortunately not to his face.

By the evening Gertrude seemed no worse and insisted that a doctor was not needed. She settled to sleep soon after nine and Madeline, reassured, sat reading in the armchair that Louise had occupied during her brief visit. Becoming bored by her novel, she took out the photograph album and went through it, reminding herself that Louise was now happy and settled. No need to worry on that count. It was Daniel who now caused her anxiety. His letters were few and far between and his situation had changed. Inevitably the measures he was taking to improve his access to his son had caused a rift between himself and Stuart Hine.

He had twice been allowed to visit the boy for two hours at a time, but Robert had insisted on being there with Louise, to make sure, Louise had explained, that Daniel put no pressure on her and caused her no distress. Robert also forbade Louise to discuss the question of access with Daniel, explaining that the lawyers were being paid to deal with the matter. Because Daniel and Louise had not been married, Daniel had no real claim on his son and this was acting against his demands for access. Young Dan was naturally too young to recognize his father and Louise wrote that she considered the visits a waste of time.

Meanwhile, Daniel was in the process of dissolving the gallery partnership in New York by selling his share back to Stuart Hine. With the money he was going to rent new premises and set up his own much smaller gallery in another part of the town.

Madeline sighed. She decided she might as well go to bed so once she had locked up, she went upstairs. She glanced in at Gertrude who was sleeping and went on to her own bedroom. She had intended to move back into the main bedroom, but since Bert Gravely had slept in it, she couldn't bear the thought of sleeping there. She undressed and climbed into bed, then climbed out again to open her door in case Gertrude rang her bell in the night.

It didn't ring but Madeline awoke with a start to the sound of violent coughing and quickly ran into the next room. What she saw terrified her. Gertrude was hanging over the edge of the bed, desperately struggling to draw breath.

'Gertrude! Oh, my dear!' She rushed to lift the semi-conscious woman back into bed. 'Don't worry, Gertrude. I'll fetch Doctor Forbes. You're going to be all right!' Gertrude's skin was cold and clammy and Madeline's hopes plummeted.

'I'm worried I'm going to die!' said Gertrude, between gasps for air. Her face was pale and she looked at Madeline with terrified eyes. 'I know it! I'm going to die!'

'No, you're not! What did you tell me yesterday? That you're a tough old bird! So show me!' While she chattered on she was trying to hide her own fear. It certainly looked as though Gertrude might well die from whatever afflicted her.

Dare she leave Gertrude alone while she went for the doctor? He lived three streets away. She glanced at the bedside clock. Twenty past one! Would the doctor agree to being disturbed in the middle of the night? How bitterly she regretted not persuading Oscar to have a telephone system installed. She made Gertrude comfortable and promised to hurry back.

Outside there was a clear sky and the moonlight was bright enough to see by. She set out in some trepidation for she had never before ventured out at this time of the night when all sorts of unholy creatures wandered the streets intent on malice. She thought of Bert Gravely skulking around in the shadows or forcing open the window of an innocent house-holder who slept unaware. With a shudder she turned up the collar of her coat, thankful it was a mild night. She was trembling but that, she knew, was from fear not cold. A black cat leaped past her from somewhere in a nearby hedge and she let out a scream of fear.

It seemed an age but eventually she saw the doctor's brass plate and hurried to ring the bell. An elderly woman answered.

She wore a hairnet over curlers and a dressing gown over her nightdress but her feet were bare.

'The doctor's sleeping!' she snapped. 'This had better be important!'

Madeline explained.

'Wait here. I'll tell him.'

The woman's urgent manner added to Madeline's unease and she stood on the doorstep, glancing to right and left in case anyone unsavoury should approach her. Fortunately no one did.

The next few minutes seemed an age, but at last the doctor came downstairs, snatched up his bag and let himself out of the house. His familiar portly figure was reassuring. He had been their doctor since before Louise was born and although he lacked the so-called bedside manner, he had never failed them. Together they hurried along the streets, retracing Madeline's steps and on the way she described what had happened. When they reached the house they hurried upstairs and Madeline knocked on the door.

She saw at once that Gertrude, slightly recovered, had made a big effort to appear normal. She was sitting up, apparently engrossed in a book. 'Good evening, Doctor Forbes,' she said brightly. 'There was really no need . . .'

Madeline groaned inwardly. Gertrude had obviously summoned up all her courage to convince the doctor that she was perfectly well.

He regarded her sternly. 'There is really no point in trying to hide the truth from me, Mrs Legrand. I can assure you that I shall certainly not hide the truth from *you*! From what your daughter-in-law tells me you are not at all well.' He leaned over her and took her pulse. He looked down her throat, felt the glands in her neck, then used his stethoscope to check her heart and tapped her chest. He then took her temperature and looked concerned.

'Do you have any pain in your chest, Mrs Legrand, when you cough?'

'No. None at all. At least,' she faltered, 'not very much. I am quite recovered now and not in any pain. It's just a bit of a cough brought on by this silly head cold. A summer cold is always a nuisance.'

He took out a small notebook and jotted down her replies. 'Have you woken in the night at all, perspiring heavily?'

'No I haven't except occasionally. Well . . . hardly ever.' Glancing down at her hands, she looked guilty, thought Madeline. How long had she been concealing the symptoms?

'Are you aware of any weight loss occurring over the past weeks or months?'

'Certainly not!' Gertrude gave him a frosty look.

Madeline frowned. Now that she came to think about it, Gertrude had appeared to lose a little weight, but whenever Madeline mentioned it, she had denied it vehemently.

'When did you last weigh yourself, Mrs Legrand?'

Gertrude glanced at Madeline for help, but she merely shrugged.

He said, 'I see. Have you ever suffered from an attack of bronchitis?'

Gertrude hesitated again. 'I did have a nasty bout of it when I was in my early thirties. One winter. I was laid up for about six weeks but nothing since.'

Madeline lurked in the doorway while he continued to ask his patient a string of pertinent questions. Madeline was afraid that Gertrude would be less than truthful if she felt it to be to her advantage to lie. Gertrude, like many people of her generation, dreaded being sent into hospital or a sanatorium. They tended to regard a hospital as something akin to the workhouse and were nervous about their prospects of ever coming out again.

When the doctor's examination was over he said gruffly, 'You are certainly not at all well. We will see if we can reduce some of the symptoms and make you more comfortable.'

Madeline led the way downstairs and braced herself to hear the worst.

'I fear the prognosis is not exactly promising,' he told her as they sat in the front room. 'Is there anything she has not told me?'

'She did have a mild stroke while she was in Paris, but by the time I joined her only her speech was troubling her – and the fact that she couldn't walk as well as she did earlier – but she has improved.'

He wrote out a prescription in a slow, precise hand. 'It might be very early consumption, which is now known as tuberculosis of the lungs. It *might* be nothing more than congestion of the lungs, but even that has risks. A few months in a private sanatorium might be of value but that can be costly. We shall have to wait and see.' He regarded her closely, frowning. 'Are *you* in any way indisposed, Mrs Swain? You have obviously had a bad shock.' Without waiting for an answer he continued. 'I shall also prescribe a light sleeping draught for you. You nursed your husband for a long time and it now appears that you may well be repeating your duties for your erstwhile mother-in-law. Be careful not to overtire yourself.'

Madeline promised and accompanied him to the door.

To her surprise, he paused after putting on his hat.

Madeline asked the question although she dreaded the answer. 'Doctor, she will . . . that is, can she be cured?'

'That is always possible and you should both remain hopeful, but it is early days and either of these maladies could prove fatal in such an elderly person. It would be greatly to her benefit if she could go to Switzerland where the air is less tainted than in England. The mountain air is always beneficial in these cases. I could recommend a sanatorium. Could she afford this, do you think? I don't want to raise her hopes unnecessarily, you understand. If such treatment is beyond her means I shall not mention it again.'

'I . . . I think she might be able to afford it. She has recently sold a flat in Paris, but I can't speak for her. She doesn't confide in me about money matters.'

'Perhaps you could suggest a sanatorium, pretending that I have not raised the question. Did you know that she is eighty-six years old? She is very vulnerable.'

'Eighty-six! No! I guessed at the late seventies but . . . She must have a strong constitution!'

'Indeed! And in all likelihood she will need it. If you call in some time tomorrow for the prescriptions I have given you, you may be able to tell me more. If her finances allow I could write at once to the sanatorium and make arrangements for her. She would be very well looked after by devoted staff. The food is also quite excellent and dietary needs are catered for.' He raised his hat, resettled it and without waiting for an answer, hurried back towards his home and his interrupted sleep.

When consulted on the question of Switzerland, Gertrude refused to consider it. Madeline was pleased in one way because she dreaded a solitary existence, but she was also worried that Gertrude's health would suffer a major setback. After consultation with Doctor Forbes it was finally agreed that they would continue as they were for three weeks and see if Gertrude was any better. If she were not, or if she were worse, she would agree to three months at the sanatorium. The doctor decided she was to stay in bed and take the various medicines he had prescribed for her. André wrote at once to say he would be glad to accompany her to Switzerland if it became necessary and if he could take a few days leave from his training.

At the end of two weeks, it was obvious that Gertrude was making no progress. She was still losing weight and her cough grew worse. The doctor's dire warnings of impending tragedy frightened Gertrude into carrying out her promise to go abroad for treatment. Ever faithful, André came hurrying across to England to fetch her and, delighted with his responsibility, escorted Gertrude safely across the Channel and by train to Zurich, cheerfully pushing her in her bath chair wherever necessary.

The specialist medical care, the carefully chosen diet and the wonderful summer weather did seem to have a beneficial effect on Gertrude's health and, to everyone's relief, she slowly began to respond.

On Thursday, the 16th of August, Madeline was still living alone. Soon after ten a.m. she hurried to answer the doorbell and discovered Sarah Gravely standing on the step. For a moment neither spoke.

Sarah broke the silence. 'I heard you were on your own.'

'I am. How did you know?'

'I met Agatha. She told me.'

Madeline groaned inwardly. Agatha would have told her everything. 'Mrs Legrand is in Switzerland,' she said, her throat tight.

'Very ill, I heard.'

'I hope not *too* ill! We have high hopes for the treatment.' Madeline couldn't help staring at her erstwhile housekeeper. Sarah looked older and thinner and her eyes were slightly bloodshot, as though, perhaps, she had been crying. Her familiar grey coat looked shabby and one of her thick lisle stockings was wrinkled at the ankle. Her appearance suggested that she no longer cared; that something was missing from her life and a rush of compassion swept through Madeline. Some part of her mind made a connection with this unhappy looking woman and herself. We all have our trials and tribulations, she thought. We all have a cross to bear. Different crosses but heavy nonetheless.

She said, 'Perhaps you'd like to come in. I'll make a pot of tea.'

Sarah followed her into the kitchen and sat down without removing her hat and coat. Tightly clutching her purse, Sarah glanced round her and Madeline was immediately aware of telltale signs that spoke of her own state of mind. The floor had not been scrubbed for nearly a week and the crockery from breakfast was still on the draining board. After Gertrude had been confined to bed, Madeline had bothered less and less about the housework and, if she were honest, had worried less about herself. She almost apologized for the kitchen but stopped herself in time.

Sarah said, 'Lonely, isn't it? Being on your own.'

'It is. But now you've got Bert.' For some reason her hands shook as she spooned tea into the pot and poured on boiling water. She was now regretting her invitation. Sarah might ask after Louise and she didn't want to talk about it.

The ensuing silence was broken by a frantic scratching at the back door and Sarah smiled faintly. 'That must be Middy!'

'I expect he heard our voices. He loves visitors, as you know.' Madeline let the dog in, thankful for his excitable behaviour which immediately distracted Sarah. While Sarah made a fuss of the dog, she made an effort to control her feelings. Seeing Sarah again had brought back all the unhappy memories.

'So how's Louise getting along?'

Briefly Madeline closed her eyes. Opening them again she

said, 'They didn't stay together. I expect Agatha told you.'

'I heard.'

Madeline hesitated, wondering how to present the truth to best advantage without actually lying. She didn't know exactly when Agatha and Sarah had met or what Agatha had told her. 'Louise has married a very nice man – an American called Robert.' She changed the subject abruptly. 'How's Bert? Did he get the promotion? It was in a warehouse, wasn't it?'

Sarah's eyes darkened and for a moment she fussed with the snap lock of her purse. 'He's back inside. Stole some stuff from the warehouse. Wines and spirits – and got caught red-handed.' Suddenly tears filled her eyes. 'I gave him every chance! I did. I . . . I trusted him and he . . . That's all the thanks I get.'

She brushed at her eyes with the back of her hand. She was on the verge of tears, thought Madeline and wondered what she could say that would not push her over the edge but nothing came to mind.

Sarah rushed on, the words tumbling out. 'Two policemen came to the door, looking for him. I said he was at work and they said no, he'd run off to avoid arrest and if I was . . . if I was harbouring him, I'd be an accessory to the crime. They asked if they could search the house. I said, "Yes, but you won't find anything. He's going straight now." Because I was so sure he was! I believed in him. I was so . . . so *proud* of him.'

Madeline said nothing. Telling Sarah she was sorry would sound trite and meaningless.

Sarah found a handkerchief, blew her nose and went on. 'In the cellar they found bottles of wine and stuff hidden under the coal. I couldn't believe it. I mean, how had he got it all down there without me knowing?' She picked up her teacup and sipped the hot liquid carefully. 'I nearly died of shame, I don't mind telling you! They were very good, the policemen. They could see the shock I'd had, seeing it all there. They said I wasn't involved and wouldn't be prosecuted. They caught Bert three days later and off he went to prison.' She glanced up. ' If only I hadn't loved him. But I did . . . and he broke my heart.'

Madeline said, 'I sometimes think love's a two-edged sword.'

Her smile was a little crooked. 'The more you love someone, the more power they have to hurt you. If you don't care, they can go to the dogs and you don't suffer at all.' In the silence that followed, she realized that she was feeling uncomfortable. And less than honest. Sarah had told her everything about her own troubles and Madeline had told only a carefully edited truth. Perhaps a little honesty was called for. She took a deep breath. 'Louise had a child by Mr Grant. A little boy but . . .'

Sarah gave a wry smile. 'She always said she would give you a boy! Remember?'

Madeline nodded. 'She and Mr Grant were never married but she . . . she married the other man and . . . took little Dan with her.' Now it was her turn to be near to tears. 'She came here once with the boy. He's wonderful.' Her voice cracked suddenly and she whispered, 'I have some photographs. Would you like to see them?'

'Not just now but . . .' She forced a light laugh. 'Well, we are a pair!'

Madeline realized that there was more to say. 'Louise is expecting again. Robert's child.'

Middy, feeling neglected, put his paws on Madeline's lap and she fondled his silky ears.

Sarah said, 'I'm glad you kept Middy.'

'He's a sort of link with Louise. Her room is just the way she left it! Foolish, isn't it?'

'I really came . . . to ask . . .'

'If I need help?' She guessed at once what Sarah wanted and decided not to make her ask. 'Yes, I do, Sarah. Desperately. Would you come back?'

'I'd be glad to.'

To busy herself, Madeline refreshed the tea cups. They discussed terms. Madeline was unable to offer any more money, but Sarah readily agreed and they decided that the previous hours would still suit. When Sarah eventually left, Madeline missed her already.

'But never mind. She'll be back first thing tomorrow,' she consoled herself.

At the end of October, Madeline received a letter from André which took her entirely by surprise. He was putting forward

207

the idea that Gertrude, whose health was continuing to improve slowly, should stay in France.

> We have a small spare room and Victoria is kindly willing for her to live with us in Paris. Gertrude adores Paris and would be happy here. It mean she do not have to make the dreadful sea crossing again. At her age I would be alarmed for her. If her health got worse she could more easy be move back to the sanatorium in Switzerland. Gertrude is more to me like a mother and I want her to spend her last years with us. But I will not suggest this if you are not happy for this to happen . . .

Madeline's first reaction was one of horror. She had been looking forward to Gertrude's return, but the more she thought about André's letter, the more she saw that his suggestion made perfect sense. After a few days during which she tried to think of good reasons for her to return to England, she gave in and wrote back saying that she approved the idea if it was Gertrude's choice. She also insisted, but with some misgiving, that she would find a way to visit occasionally

She steeled herself for his next letter, but it was Gertrude who wrote to tell her that she had accepted the offer made by André and Victoria. Now Madeline realized she would be alone for the rest of her life and the thought saddened her but, refusing to give way to self pity, she accepted it. She asked Sarah to help her pack Gertrude's clothes so that they could be dispatched to Paris in time for Gertrude's homecoming.

A letter from Gertrude at the beginning of January assured her that she was nicely settled in André 's spare room and enjoying his cooking – especially the pastries. She also passed on the news that Victoria was expecting a child.

'For Gertrude it will be like another grandchild,' Madeline told Sarah. 'She and André are so close and his own parents haven't featured in his life for years. Do you think your sons will marry and have children?'

Sarah shrugged. 'Wilfred, perhaps, but not Arnold. He

loves the army and has no time for women.' Sarah eyed Madeline over the silver she was cleaning. 'No letter from Louise?'

'I'm afraid not. Her life is very full, of course. She'll write eventually.' She didn't add that it was Daniel who worried her and it was a letter from him that she most wanted. Did his silence mean that he had given up on his attempt to see Dan. Secretly she feared that he would not succeed and that his life would be embittered if he failed. If so, would he ever find another woman to love him? And if he did, would the loss of Dan haunt him and cast a shadow over his marriage? Only to herself could she admit how hurt she was by the lack of contact. He knew how much she cared about him and young Dan, and understood how much the letters and news meant to her.

She had still not heard from him when, in the middle of February, as snow lay thickly upon the ground, she answered a knock at the door soon after ten o'clock in the morning, to find Daniel standing there, holding a small boy by the hand. But if this were Dan, he was not the Dan from the photographs. Then he had beamed and laughed, obviously as happy as a sandboy! Now he was solemn and anxious.

For a moment she couldn't speak. Then she whispered, 'Daniel! And Dan! Oh, Lord! I thought . . .' Her mouth was dry. 'Come in out of the cold. Oh, this is wonderful! A visit. I never expected . . .' She pulled them inside. 'Oh, listen to me. You must be so cold. Come inside to the fire and warm up.' Shutting the front door, she hustled them into the sitting-room and knelt to gently kiss her grandson. At last! He had grown so much, but he was still eerily like his mother. 'You must both be hungry. I'll make some tea. I have a nice cherry cake and . . . and . . .' She faltered, her mind full of fears. Had Daniel kidnapped his son? Was he in trouble? She couldn't believe that Louise and Robert would allow the boy to travel to England with Daniel in the middle of winter. Chattering helplessly, she tried to brace herself for the worst.

Daniel took off his coat and she hurried into the hall to hang it on the hall stand. Do not panic! she told herself. This may not be as bad as you think. Stay calm. It came to her that so far Daniel had not said a word. So something *was* wrong. Perhaps he was wanted by the American police. Maybe the English police had been alerted. Did that make Daniel a fugitive? She took several breaths and went back into the sitting room. One look at Daniel's face told her the news was bad.

She said, 'Would you like something stronger than tea?'

'Tea's fine. And some warm milk for Dan, please.'

Madeline looked at Dan who looked tired and utterly bewildered and longed to take him in her arms and hug him. But she wondered if he was ready for that. To Dan she was a stranger and the journey from America must have been something of a nightmare for the poor child. Give it time, she thought. Dan has to get to know you. She prayed to God to give them a little time together.

She went into the kitchen to prepare some food. Was Robert in pursuit? The idea made her feel faint. He knew where she lived! If he came to the door she would refuse to let him in and would say she hadn't seen them. If the police came she would lie to them, too. She remembered what Sarah had said about being an accessory to a crime.

'I don't care! I'll do it!' she muttered. But then she thought of Louise and began to fret on her behalf. Louise would be desperate if her son had been stolen and if she found out that her mother had taken them in, Louise would never forgive her. Once again she seemed to be facing a dilemma. If only they had been able to come to some kind of civilized agreement none of this would have happened. How she longed for wise words from Oscar or Gertrude! Minutes later she was back in the sitting room with a tray holding tea, cake and biscuits. Daniel and Dan came downstairs and were soon enjoying the food. Madeline now turned her attention to Daniel and saw that he was haggard and appeared much older than when he had first left England.

She said, 'You look so weary. Whatever it is, it must have been dreadful for you?'

'It's worse than you can imagine, Madeline. When Dan is asleep I'll tell you, but he's had enough to cope with for the moment. It's hard to know just how much he understands. He's beginning to talk, but when he's unhappy he seems unable to make the effort. Perhaps we could talk about something else.'

In an agony of frustration and fear, Madeline searched her mind for a safer topic. 'Gertrude is going to stay in Paris,' she told him. 'André and his wife are going to look after her. It seems she is in her eighties – and of course, she is very frail with the diseased lung. She may not have long to live.'

Daniel sighed heavily. 'Are you quite alone, then?'

'Sarah comes in most mornings though her work is reduced. There's only me and . . .' She smiled faintly. 'I don't generate much mess!' She expected a smile from him in return, but he seemed distracted and she wondered if he was listening for an unwanted knock at the door. 'Her husband is back in prison for stealing from his employers. It's so sad for her. She recently hinted that she would like to work longer hours because she needs the money, but I can't afford to pay any more without Gertrude's contribution.'

Daniel talked for a while about his new gallery which was slowly attracting new clients and promising to do well. While he talked young Dan finally fell asleep on his lap and they laid him on the sofa and covered him with a blanket.

Madeline tried to brace herself for the bad news that she knew was coming and promised herself that however bad it was, she would not let Daniel see her distress. She would be strong.

To her surprise he knelt beside her and took her hands in his. 'It's Louise,' he said softly. 'Three weeks ago she was out riding and the horse threw her off. She landed badly and . . .'

'Louise?' For a moment Madeline was confused. This was about Louise?

'She fell badly and hit her head.'

She clutched his hands. 'Louise is hurt? Oh, I must go to her, Daniel. Can I see her?' Surely Robert would understand her need to see her daughter through such a perilous time, she reasoned. The thought of the long sea crossing leaped into her mind, but she ignored it. She would swim the Atlantic if it were necessary. 'Oh! The new baby? She's expecting Robert's child.'

211

He said, 'What I'm saying is . . . Oh, Madeline, I'm so sorry, but . . .'

Madeline felt a flash of anger. 'Don't say it! They can't keep me away. I'm her *mother*!'

Daniel swallowed. 'There's no point, Madeline. Louise . . .'

A dreadful fear now replaced Madeline's anger. 'She's . . . in a coma? It was her head, you said. She injured her head? She's not paralysed, is she? Oh, God!' She stared at him in dread. 'Is that it?'

'No. I'm desperately sorry, but Louise died of her injuries. She was killed instantly. It was very merciful and quick.'

Madeline's mouth fell open as her eyes searched his for a denial of what she thought she had heard. She clutched her chest with trembling hands. This wasn't possible, she promised herself. It was a mistake.

'And they couldn't save the baby.' Daniel swallowed, trying in vain to hide his own pain. 'She didn't suffer, Madeline, I promise you. Stuart was most definite on that point.'

Madeline moved her hands to cover her ears. 'No! I can't bear it! Don't! *Don't* tell me she's dead.' Tears did not come to her aid and she stared at him dry-eyed as the truth finally dawned.

Daniel put his arms around her as she began to tremble with shock, but she was hardly aware of it. What she *was* aware of was a deep, dark grief rising slowly within her, but for the present her mind was not mercifully confused but clear and sharp.

'Poor Dan!' she whispered. 'Poor little soul! He's lost his mama. Oh, God! No wonder he looked so woebegone,' she said. 'Does he know?'

Daniel nodded.

She thought of the funeral 'Were you there? At Louise's funeral?'

'Yes. Robert was very good about that, at least. He was in rather a state. I think he loved her. He looked gaunt and was openly weeping at the graveside. Dan was there with his nanny. I'm sorry you weren't able to see her laid to rest. A letter is so impersonal. I thought it would be best if I told you in person so I was planning to come back to see you, when Stuart Hine contacted me about . . .' He retreated to his chair and sat forward.

'What did *he* want?' Madeline's voice sounded thin and high and seemed to be coming from someone else. At the back of her mind the words echoed again and again. *Louise is dead.*

Daniel said, 'Stuart thought that since Louise was dead, his son Robert might lose interest in Dan and suggested that I should have him back. He said I should legally adopt him and he would talk to his son and persuade Robert to give Dan up. If there was to be a big change in his life, Stuart thought it should happen sooner rather than later.'

Madeline, still in shock, tried to consider this idea. 'So you haven't . . . kidnapped him? He's with you . . . legally?'

'Kidnapped him? Good heavens, no!' Daniel stared at her in surprise. 'Whatever gave you that idea?'

'I don't know. I knew you were desperate and I thought . . .' She shook her head.

'He's with me with their blessing.'

Madeline closed her eyes, weak with relief. That was something to be thankful for.

'What will you do now,' she asked. 'Will you stay in England?'

'I'm still trying to decide what would be best for Dan. He was happy in New York, but he was leading the sort of life I could never give him. I want him to be happy. I keep wondering what Louise would have wanted for him . . . in the present circumstances. I might . . .'

'I can't believe . . . Poor Louise! If only . . .' She stopped herself abruptly.

'I know what you're thinking. If only we hadn't . . . I should never have taken her to New York, but it seemed such an opportunity. If we'd stayed in England she would never have met Robert Hine . . .'

'And she would never have been riding a dangerous horse. That was her fault, though, Daniel. You mustn't blame yourself for her death. That's too great a burden. She told me herself that Robert thought the horse too strong and spirited for a woman to ride! Maybe if Robert had forbidden it . . . But what's the point in trying to blame someone?

213

Circumstances play a great part, don't they, and one step leads to another. Perhaps there is such a thing as fate.' She glanced towards Dan who was murmuring in his sleep. 'What a beautiful child he is, Daniel. I always wanted a son and Louise promised to give me one. In a way she has. A grandson, anyway.'

'I was thinking that I might start up a gallery in the West Country. It has always been an area that attracts artists. Somewhere like St Ives, perhaps. I've always liked it since we visited the town when I was a child. I'd like Dan to grow up in the country. All I want now is his happiness. He's not yet three, but he's lost his mother, poor little mite. I don't know how I can ever make that up to him.' He watched her carefully. 'I wonder, Madeline, if you'd consider moving to St Ives to be with us. I know you have your own life here but . . .'

Madeline sat up straighter. 'Come with you? How do you mean, exactly?'

'I thought if we found a house that was big enough, we could all live in it. You and me. We could bring Dan up between us. It's just a thought, but if you wanted to be near him it would solve all our problems. Otherwise I need a housekeeper and a nanny, and I'm sure a loving grandmother would be better for Dan.'

Madeline's eyes widened . 'Do you mean it? Oh, it would be perfect! I'd move to the other side of the world to be with him . . . I've worried about you both all the time you've been away. I can assure you, the three of you have been in my thoughts every hour of every day.' She sighed. 'And now it's come to this. You and me and Dan. We could be happy, couldn't we? We could make a life for ourselves.'

'I think we could,' he agreed. 'In fact, I'm counting on it!'

That night Madeline allowed herself the luxury of tears and cried herself to sleep. In the morning she awoke dazed with grief and weary from the emotional turmoil. She couldn't stop thinking about her lovely, willful daughter. Louise had certainly lived her short life to the full. Madeline knew that the ache in her own heart would always be there, but she would carry on for Dan's sake. She would have to write to Gertrude and tell her that Louise was dead and that would be difficult for there was no way to soften the blow. She would, however, point out how much joy Louise had brought into their lives and suggest that the joy cancelled out some of the sorrow. Gertrude had André and he would help her.

She sat up with a new air of purpose and pushed back the bedclothes.

Five years later, seven-year-old Dan waited in the school playground at the end of the afternoon. Children of all ages hurried past him eager to go home. It was Friday and tomorrow, Saturday, was his birthday. He would be eight years old. *Eight!* The word had a powerful magical ring about it for him. When he was eight he would be so much older and cleverer and life would be so much more exciting. Tomorrow he would have a birthday present and Papa would take a day off from his work at the gallery and take him and Grandmama for a ride on the train to St Ives and they would have tea in a real teashop with iced buns and ginger pop.

Mothers of all shapes and sizes appeared in the playground to collect the younger ones while the older children swaggered off on their own, trusted to walk home along the lanes with their friends.

'Waiting for your ma, Dan?' asked Mary. She was in his class at school and had brown eyes, a snub nose, and two short brown plaits, each tied with a red ribbon. She carried a doll with yellow wool for hair.

'Not my ma,' he corrected her patiently. 'My grandmama.'

'Why doesn't your ma come?'

'She's in heaven with the angels.'

'In heaven? She never is!'

'She *is*! She was riding a great big horse with a flying mane and tail and she fell off and died. Papa told me. I've got some photographs of her before she was dead.'

Mary fiddled with her doll's hair. 'Is she in the churchyard then? My Uncle Stan's in a coffin buried in the churchyard and his name's on a big stone thing. Stanley Arthur Morris.'

'My mama's buried in New York in America. I'm going

there one day.' Dan looked up and his face broke into a smile as Madeline approached with Middy. Both children rushed forward to make a fuss of the dog, who, although becoming sober with age, went mad with excitement as Dan leaned down to fuss over him.

Madeline said, 'Hello Dan. Hello Mary. Did you both have a nice day at school?'

Dan said, 'A big boy pushed me over and Miss May made him say sorry.'

'I'm sure he didn't mean it, Dan.' Madeline turned to Mary. 'I told your mother you could walk home with us because she's feeling rather tired.'

Mary eyes brightened. 'Can I hold Middy's lead?'

'Of course you can. You can hold him until we reach your farm and then it will be Dan's turn.' She tucked the doll under her arm and handed over Middy's lead.

Dan said. 'He didn't mean it, the big boy. He said it was an accident.'

Mary regarded Madeline earnestly. 'Is Dan's mother really dead and buried in New York?'

'Yes, she is.'

'My uncle's name is Stanley Arthur Morris and he's dead.'

Dan said, 'My mother's name was Louise.'

Mary cried, 'Stop pulling, Middy! You're not to chase sheep so I can't let you off.' She faced Madeline. 'My Uncle Stan was a fisherman on a trawler and there was a storm. The boat didn't come back and the men were all drowned. Grandmama cried a lot. She says the world is a vale of tears.' She glanced up at Madeline. 'Is it a vale of tears?'

'Sometimes life is sad and sometimes it's happy,' Madeline told her. 'We just have to get over the sad times and carry on.'

They set off along the lane together. The March wind was cool but the hedges were filled with primroses and a scattering of late violets.

Mary said, 'We're going to have a baby brother – or it might be a baby sister.'

Dan said, 'We don't want one, do we, Grandmama, because Papa doesn't want to find another wife because Grandmama looks after us so well?'

216

Madeline rolled her eyes. This was news to her. 'Is that what Papa told you?'

'Yes. He asked me if I minded and I said it was fine. Do *you* mind, Grandmama?'

'Not at all, Dan.'

She had faced the idea that one day Daniel might remarry but when the time came, *if* it came, she promised herself she would deal with the event sensibly. In the meantime she was content. The gallery was doing well and Daniel gave a few private art lessons in the barn they had adapted for the purpose. He adored his son and took great pleasure in watching him grow up. Dan was a sunny child who thrived on country life. The old cottage where they lived had seen better days, but was roomy and comfortable.

They reached Gadden's Farm and Middy was handed over to Dan while Mary reclaimed her doll. They reached Mary's home and she was returned to her mother who was expecting her third child at the end of the week.

When Dan and Madeline arrived at their own home, Madeline was surprised to find Daniel already there.

Dan released Middy and ran to his father who kissed him and tousled his hair affectionately.

Madeline said, 'Don't forget Middy's dinner, Dan.'

This was one of Dan's few tasks and he hurried off importantly to find the bowlful of scraps that had been set aside for the dog.

'I'm starving,' said Daniel. 'Can't wait for the shepherd's pie!'

'How on earth did you guess?' Madeline grinned. Monday, shepherd's pie; Tuesday, meat pasties . . . Daniel, it seemed, liked old-fashioned food.

She said, 'There was a letter from André this morning. Gertrude still survives and sends her love. Nearly ninety years old. She has amazing stamina.'

'I'm planning to do the same!' He grinned. 'Can you bear the thought of having me around for all those years?'

She gave him a quick smile. 'That sounds like a threat.'

'It was meant to be a promise!'

She gave him a quick hug. 'I think I could bear it, Daniel.'

'No plans to run off with the postman?'

Laughing, she shook her head, but then her expression changed. 'I have everything and everyone I need right here in this house,' she told him softly.

As he washed his hands in the sink, she slipped the pie into the oven and then glanced out of the window into the yard where Dan was sprinkling a measure of corn for the hens. With a sigh of contentment she tied on her apron and, collecting knives and forks from the dresser drawer, began to lay the table for supper.